From being a humble shipping clerk in Liverpool who enjoyed inventing toys for his children, to becoming a major toy manufacture in the early years of the 20th Century, Frank Hornby has left a legacy that lives on to this very day.

Frank Hornby first introduced his Mechanics Made Easy, later to be renamed Meccano at the turn of the last century. The success with Meccano led him by listening to public demand to produce, in 1920 his first tinplate locomotive, branding his new venture 'Hornby Trains'. His ability to understand the market and producing what his customers required allowed him, over the following years to significantly expand the Hornby selection of '0' gauge locomotives, rolling stock, buildings and track. His innovative mind created Dinky Toys to complement his Hornby Trains but it was the development of the smaller 'H0' train systems being produced in mainland Europe where he saw potential but sadly died some two years before the launch of Hornby Dublo, in 1938.

The history of Hornby from the its very beginnings has been superbly documented in the new Hornby Book of Trains – The First Hundred Years, which traces the company's development during the last 100 years, highlighting the twists and turns, the successes and the changes that have occurred to Hornby over that time.

During the past 100 years Hornby models have evolved from being large, coarse scale tinplate toy trains to the increasingly refined and accurate '00' scale models of today. However, with the on going developments and refinements associated with their current creations, Hornby still adheres to the original ethos of the company's founder which is to produce quality products for the enjoyment of all. Times change but the simple fact remains that for generation after generation Hornby simply means model railways.

The Era System...

The operation of the railway network in the United Kingdom has evolved greatly since the 1826 Liverpool & Manchester Railway Act, which engendered the 'railway mania' of the pioneering local regional companies in the Victorian era and their eventual consolidation towards the end of the19th century. This was then followed by the emergence of the 'Big Four' railway companies, after which came the nationalisation of the nation's railways in 1948, the sectorisation of British Rail in the 1980s, privatisation of British Rail and finally, the modern day franchising arrangements.

In an effort to clarify these changes for model railway enthusiasts, the model railway industry adopted an 'Era', or 'Epoch' system; the idea being to group models into a defined time bracket so that locomotives, coaching and wagon stock could be reasonably grouped together.

The trouble with such a system is that as model ranges expand and evolve the boundaries between eras become blurred, a situation not helped by the national railway network's own great changes since the system was adopted during the 1990s. Since 1995, motive power and rolling stock investment has increased, leading to new locomotives, coaches and wagons, while new Train Operating Companies have filled the void left by British Rail. Traditional mineral freight has declined in some areas, while in others it has been resurrected, being joined by new types of freight movement such as Biomass. Passenger numbers have increased, leading to new coaching stock being developed, along with new multiple units that have been designed to operate on both diesel and electric power.

As a result, Hornby, in conjunction with partners in the publishing and retail trades, have decided to adjust the era system we use, so that it clearly reflects the time periods covered, especially when taking into account the 'grey' areas that have arisen as one period blurs into the next. The table below provides full details of our system.

Era	Description	Date Range	Example
1	Pioneering	1804-1869	Stephenson's 'Rocket'
2	Pre-Grouping	1870-1922	Peckett W4
3	Grouping	1923-1947	Wainwright H Class
4	Early British Railways	1948-1956	Gresley B17
5	Late British Railways	1956-1968	Standard 4MT
6	British Rail Pre-TOPS	1957-1971	Class 71
7	British Rail TOPS	1971-1986	Class 87
8	BR Sectorisation	1982-1997	Class 50
9	Privatisation	1996-2008	Class 67
10	Network Franchising	2006-2017	Class 60
11	Present Day	2014 on	Hitachi IEP

🔊 **Sound Fitted**
Pre-fitted with 8 Pin TTS Decoder

NEW Q4
New tooling, or livery & date due

💡 **Directional/Interior Lights**
Locomotives and coaches fitted with either directional lighting or interior lighting

Due Q4
Deferred item from 2019 range & date due

NEM **NEM Couplings**
Fitted with NEM pockets

3

Train Sets, Train Packs, Locomotives, Diecast Vehicles & Memorabilia

Ideas, like human beings, start small, then grow.

Very few brand names become synonymous with the items that they produce, yet just like many other household names Hornby has become far more than just a brand name, it has become a byword for model railways, a name burned deep into the consciousness of adults and children through the generations. In 2020 we rightly celebrate the centenary of Hornby, as the following pages will illustrate, but how we arrived here today, from those first steps taken into the model railway business in 1920, is a story that is still being told.

When Frank Hornby produced 'The Hornby Clockwork Train' toy railway system in 1920, it was an extension of his Meccano range, a 'Meccano model of an altogether new and delightful type' that could be assembled, and dismantled, from components that adhered to the principles of the company. New parts could be purchased and fitted by the owner, as Hornby positively encouraged customers to 'take them all to pieces and refashion them' and each set contained an engine and tender in one of originally three colours, one truck and a set of rails that included a circle and two straights. The price was 27/6, which at the time was around four days' wages for a skilled tradesman but today would equate to around £39.95 (Source: The National Archives Currency Convertor 1270-2017).

THE HORNBY Electric Train

1920

With the Great War over and German toy trains not being imported due to the bitterness towards the vanquished, Frank Hornby saw an opportunity to expand his manufacturing business into the production of toy trains and consequently in 1920 he launched Hornby Trains.

Frank Hornby's first British made Hornby '0' gauge locomotives were produced in tinplate and assembled using nuts and bolts at the Meccano Ltd. factory situated in Binns Road, Liverpool. The first locomotive design of this construction was a simple generic style 0-4-0 locomotive using a clockwork mechanism and connected to a simple 4 wheel tender.

The No.1 0-4-0 Hornby '0' Gauge locomotive design featured cylinders and connecting rods, plus brass handrail knobs. Also, all variants were fitted with cylinders with the bodies having an enamelled finish.

Inspired by the railway companies of the day, the first four tinplate '0' gauge Hornby Trains locomotives produced respectively in 1920 were liveried in Midland Railway (MR) Maroon, London North Western Railway (LNWR) Black, Caledonian Railway (CR) Blue and Great Northern (GN) Green. These locomotives continued to be produced until 1923.

The four liveried Hornby Train replicas, using where possible the original Frank Hornby design have been produced as close to the original model specifications as possible but in place of a clockwork mechanism a 12vDC electric motor has been fitted allowing for three rail operation.

100 of these highly collectable but functioning limited edition models have been exclusively produced in four liveries, reminiscent of the originals with each model authenticated by an individually signed and numbered certificate.

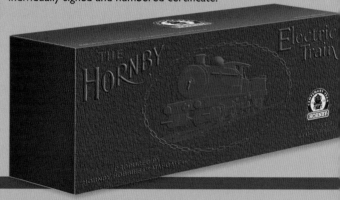

1930

By the 1930s Frank Hornby's '0' Gauge train system had grown considerably both in the large number of items available and in popularity but new houses were by that time being built smaller than they had been previously and consequently limiting the space available for amongst other things an '0' Gauge train layout. Consequently, such restriction on space had an influence on the sales of Hornby's '0' Gauge trains.

In mainline Europe a smaller gauge was being developed which was half the size of '0'. This new scale was aptly classified as 'H0' as it was half the size of the '0' Gauge models.

Faced with this potential competition, the Meccano Board in 1937 decided to introduce their own system but due to scale versus mechanical size restrictions they could not quite produce an 'H0' system but opted for a slightly larger scale which was given the name 'Dublo' by Meccano's Commercial Director. The Hornby Dublo scale used more or less the same wheel back to back measurements of the 'H0' system but generally speaking all other dimensions were increased by 0.5mm.

By 1938 the first adverts started to appear promoting the new Hornby Dublo system. Two locomotives were initially produced one of which was a generic 0-6-2 freight model and available with GWR, LNER, LMS or SR markings while the other featured the LNER Class A4, 'Sir Nigel Gresley'. These two locomotives were available with either a clockwork mechanism or a 12vDC motor and both featured in individual train sets where they shared a common pack.

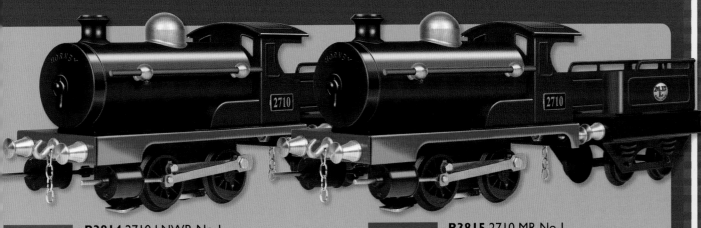

NEW Q1	**R3814** 2710 LNWR No.1, Centenary Year Limited Edition
NEW Q2	**R3815** 2710 MR No.1, Centenary Year Limited Edition

NEW Q3	**R3816** 2710 CR No.1, Centenary Year Limited Edition
NEW Q4	**R3817** 2710 GN No.1, Centenary Year Limited Edition

HORNBY-DUBLO

This celebratory set goes some way to replicating the first Hornby Dublo 1938 passenger train set. The stunning and heavily detailed LNER Class A4, 'Sir Nigel Gresley' illustrates how the design and scale integrity of model production has developed over the years. Similarly, the Gresley teak effect coaches that are of a different type to those produced in 1938 show the amazing advances in model production since the launch of Hornby Dublo's 1938 train sets.

This limited edition of 1000 Hornby Dublo 'Sir Nigel Gresley' train set forms part of the Hornby Trains Centenary group of products and celebrates the 1930s decade by using artwork inspired by the Hornby Dublo packaging style of that period. Included with each set and as authentication is a numbered certificate confirming the quantity of limited edition sets produced.

NEW Q3	**R1252M** LNER 'Sir Nigel Gresley' Train Set, Centenary Year Limited Edition

SET CONTENTS

ROLLING STOCK

LNER A4 Class 4-6-2 4498 'Sir Nigel Gresley'
LNER 61' 6" Gresley Corridor Third, 1434
LNER 61' 6" Gresley Corridor Composite Brake, 58700

TRACK & ACCESSORIES

3rd Radius Oval,
Train Controller (R7229),
Wall Plug Transformer (P9000W),
Power Connecting Track (R8206),
Rerailer.

DCC READY | 8 PIN CONNECTION

1100mm
1070mm

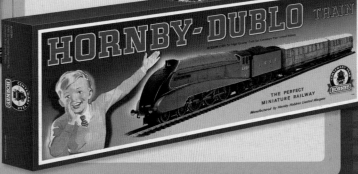

Although there had been some development at the Meccano factory after the end of hostilities in 1945, it was not until 1948 that the Meccano factory resumed full production.

1948 saw business as usual with models designed prior to the Second World War starting to appear.

The Hornby Dublo 'Duchess' was first designed in January 1939 but it was not until Spring 1948 that the 'Duchess of Atholl' appeared in LMS Maroon. The locomotive was fitted with a metal body while the tender top was produced in moulded plastic. The launch of the 'Duchess of Atholl' in 1948 was a major milestone for Hornby Dublo and it is therefore appropriate in this, Hornby's Centennial Year that the same named locomotive be made available once again with a metal locomotive body and a moulded tender top.

NEW Q2

R7241 MG TC, Centenary Year Limited Edition

R7242 Morris J Van, Centenary Year Limited Edition

R7243 Austin K8 Van, Margate Hotel & Boarding Association, Centenary Year Limited Edition

R7249 Scammell Mechanical Horse Van Trailer, Centenary Year Limited Edition

R7248 VW T2 Van, Centenary Year Limited Edition

R7247 Fordson Tractor, Centenary Year Limited Edition

This limited edition Hornby Dublo 'Duchess of Atholl' has been specially produced as part of the Hornby Centenary Collection and celebrates the 1940s decade by not only reproducing a metal bodied locomotive for the first time in many years but by also using artwork inspired by the Hornby Dublo packaging style of that period.

Included with this Limited Edition model is a numbered certificate confirming that the model is just one of 500 produced.

NEW Q2 **R3819** LMS 6231 'Duchess of Atholl', Centenary Year Limited Edition

Gauge 00   2 RAIL

HORNBY DUBLO

R3819 LOCOMOTIVE AND TENDER L.M.S.

"DUCHESS of ATHOLL"

In late 1957 the first of the Dinky Dublo diecast models were released.

Along with the models release was an advertising campaign advising that the new range of vehicles, produced in '00' scale, would be excellent models to collect or play with while at the same time the advert promoted that the new range of vehicles were suitable to adorn a model railway layout.

Even though the life of the Dinky Dublo series of models was relatively short, nonetheless it can be argued that the Development and Marketing teams associated with the Hornby Dublo brand of the 1950s were decades ahead of their time when comparisons are made to the large number of accurately scaled models available to the current railway modeller of today. As a tribute to the first 'Dublo' scale models of that period and as part of the Hornby Centenary Collection a new range of carefully selected limited edition vehicles have been specially commissioned, reflecting the character of 'Dublo' diecast models of the 1950s.

The six models chosen incorporate where possible the spirit of the 1950s and include vehicles similar to those of the original 'Dublo' range, together with one fitting model calling out the various holiday destinations around Margate, the seaside town where Hornby now resides.

There are only 2000 each of these six limited edition 'Dublo Diecast' models available, with each presented in the packaging style reminiscent of the 1950s period.

Although small in number, this 'Dublo Diecast' selection of vehicles forms an important part of the Hornby Centenary Collection.

DUBLO DIECAST

'The 'Rocket', built by Mr. Robert Stephenson of Newcastle in 1825, drew a load equivalent to three times its own weight at a speed of 12.5 m.p.h. With a full passenger carriage it did 24 m.p.h. and the cost of fuel was approximately 1½d. per mile. In doing so the locomotive won a premium of £500, offered by the directors of the Liverpool & Manchester Railway, for the most improved locomotive of its time. Rocket's success was one definitely that the steam locomotive was suitable as a means of general railway haulage and that speeds previously approached could be maintained'.

So ran the copy of the advertising sheet that announced in 1963 Tri-ang Railways 'Rocket'.

The original model was sold without coaches but in 1964 a coach was added but later in 1968 a further two coaches were included with the locomotive, a format which remained until the following year.

1982 saw the reintroduction of Stephenson's 'Rocket' presented as a limited edition in a brown, gold and sepia 5th face pack which this time was branded Hornby Railways. This model like the previous one was manufactured at Hornby's Margate factory but so difficult was the assembly that a special team of factory workers were put together who had been involved with the original build in 1963.

This latest model from Hornby employs the very finest of design, tooling and assembly technology with the result that the model is as true a scale model of Stephenson's masterpiece that is currently possible.

This 1500 piece limited edition of Stephenson's 'Rocket' and three 1st Class coaches, being 'Times', 'Despatch' and 'Experience' forms part of the Hornby Trains Centenary Year group of products and celebrates by using the 1960s packaging style of that decade.

The Class 9F was in many respects Robert Riddles ultimate development of his BR Standard classes with the 2-10-0 wheel arrangement, a major influence from the success he had achieved with the WD 2-10-0 built during the Second World War. Initially designed as a freight locomotive, it was soon found that they were ideally suited for passenger train service as well.

National Railway Museum
The National Railway Museum is the largest railway museum in the world with exhibitions and collections illustrating over 300 years of British railway history.
Produced under licence for SCMG Enterprises Ltd. © SCMGE. Every purchase supports our museums. www.nrm.org.uk

No 92220 BUILT AT SWINDON
MARCH 1960
THE LAST STEAM LOCOMOTIVE FOR BRITISH RAILWAYS.
NAMED AT SWINDON ON MARCH 18TH 1960 BY
K.W.C. GRAND ESQ.
MEMBER OF THE BRITISH TRANSPORT COMMISSION

Tri-ang RAILWAYS

OO HO GAUGE

NEW Q1   **R3809** Stephenson's Rocket Train Pack, Centenary Year Limited Edition

The 'Evening Star', which is now part of the National Collection was not only the last of the class but also the last steam locomotive to be built by British Railways, leaving the Swindon Locomotive Works in March 1960. Attached to each of the locomotive's smoke deflectors are special commemorative plates situated just below each nameplate highlighting that it was the last steam locomotive built at Swindon and that 'Evening Star' was named by K. W. C. Grand, a member of the British Transport Commission.

The Tri-ang Hornby model of 'Evening Star' was announced at the British Toy Fair in 1971. The model was the first locomotive produced by the company with a Ringfield motor installed in the tender. Similar motors used in models produced by European manufacturers had no doubt inspired the Tri-ang Hornby Ringfield motor design. Branded as part of their 'Silver Seal' range, the model was released into the UK market towards the end of 1971 and was the last totally new locomotive to be released carrying the brand name Tri-ang Hornby.

Since its first release the model has undergone several modifications, the most important of which was the removal of the Ringfield motor from the tender and with a more conventional 5 pole motor being installed in the locomotive itself.

The Tri-ang Hornby Class 9F 'Evening Star' forms an important part of Hornby's history, which is why it has been included in the Hornby Centenary Collection and celebrates the 1970s decade by using pack artwork inspired by the Tri-ang Hornby packaging style of that period.

Not only is the model supplied with a numbered certificate confirming that the model is one of a limited production run of 1000 but also included is a cast resin miniature replica of the commemorative plate denoting that 'Evening Star' was the last steam locomotive to be built at the British Railways Swindon Locomotive Works.

NEW Q3   **R3821** BR 92220 'Evening Star', Centenary Year Limited Edition

11

'Smokey Joe'

Released in 1980, the original Hornby Class 0F 'Pug' was first included in a train set but later became available as a solo model liveried in Caledonian Blue as well as a red engine named 'Desmond'.

These models included metal hand and cab rails, however in 1983 there was a demand for a low cost solo locomotive that could also be included in a train set, the 'Industrial Freight'.

The train set locomotive now devoid of handrails and cab railings was painted in maroon and carried the company name of 'Stewarts & Lloyds', while the solo model similarly lacking in metal parts was painted black and given simple cab lining and the running number of '56025', all based on an actual locomotive.

When this particular model was shown to a Scottish customer he explained that it reminded him of a locomotive he used to see in the shunting yards of Glasgow and that it had been unofficially marked in chalk on both sides of the boiler, with the name 'Smokey Joe'. Immediately the artwork for '56025' was changed and the model was released carrying the name 'Smokey Joe' and has been part of the Hornby range ever since.

Due to its length of time in the Hornby range and the many thousands produced it is only fitting that as part of the Hornby Centenary celebrations a special limited edition 'Smokey Joe' should be produced and as such the model has been fitted with metal hand and cab rails as well as an enhanced BR livery.

The Hornby Class 0F 'Smokey Joe' has and continues to be an important part of Hornby's history which is why the model has been included in the Hornby Centenary Collection and celebrates the 1980s decade by using box artwork inspired by the Hornby Railways packaging style of that period.

This very special and enhanced collectable model of 'Smokey Joe' is supplied with a numbered certificate confirming that it is one of 2000 limited edition examples produced.

'Merton'

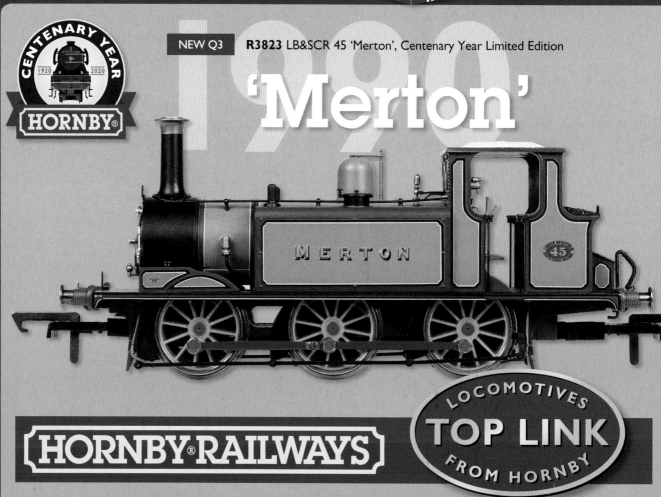

HORNBY RAILWAYS

LOCOMOTIVES **TOP LINK** FROM HORNBY

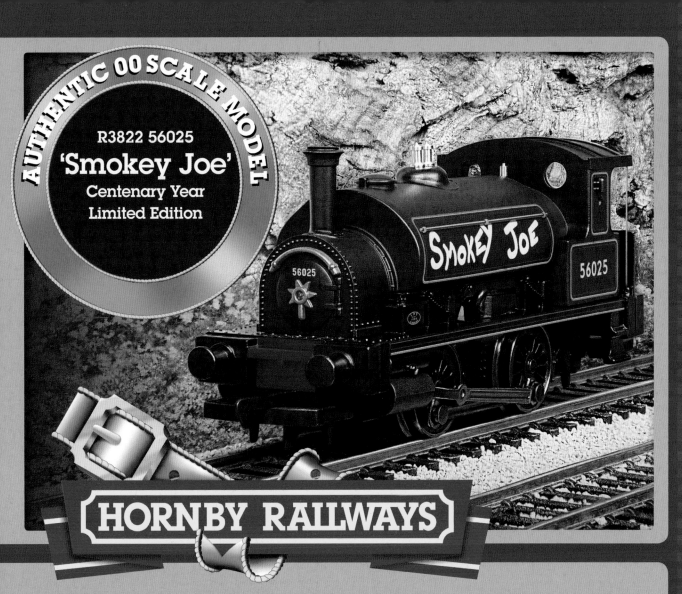

HORNBY RAILWAYS

Hornby's lack of investment in new tooling from the mid 1980s until 1997 began to weaken the brand and had it not been for a change at Board level, the prospects were far from favourable for the Hornby model railway brand.

However, with a new Board and in particular a new Chairman, a positive wind began to blow through Hornby and with it a desire to produce high quality detailed models but such developments took time and what Hornby really needed was something that they could introduce almost immediately.

While Hornby were keen to develop new products, other manufacturers were eager to move away from the industry and focus their attention on other markets. In 1997 Hornby were offered and purchased tooling for a number of locomotives and rolling stock.

There was much to do in such a short space of time but the newly purchased tooling was refurbished and improved with the result that in 1998 Hornby were able to release a selection of 'new' models giving the Hornby team time to focus on future major developments.

One of the 'new' 1998 models was the SR 0-6-0T Terrier locomotive, 'Freshwater'. This model was the first of many variants of the Terrier that were produced by Hornby over the subsequent years and because of its diminutive appearance and subsequent charm proved a great favourite with modellers and collectors alike.

Eventually it became necessary to replace the ageing tooling and in 2019 a totally new 'Terrier' model was introduced into the range, incorporating many of the tooling changes that would allow Hornby to produce the numerous detail variations that the full size locomotives had evolved during their many years in service.

Without the influx in 1998 of the 'new' tooling it could be argued that Hornby's revival may have taken much longer to achieve.

The 'Terrier' was instrumental in that recovery which is why the LBSC Terrier 'Merton' has been included as part of the Hornby Centenary Collection and symbolises the great changes that occurred to Hornby in the 1990s.

To commemorate this particular period in Hornby's history the box artwork accompanying 'Merton' replicates elements of the packaging style from that period.

This very special and enhanced collectable model of 'Merton', using the 2019 tooling is supplied with a numbered certificate confirming that it is one from a limited edition of 1000.

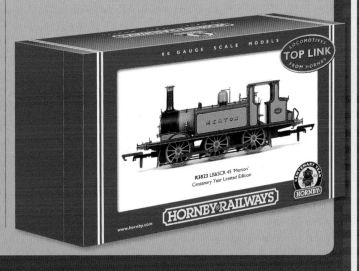

Although the introduction of new locomotives and rolling stock provided by the purchase of tooling in 1997 from an external source had been extremely useful, Hornby desperately needed to introduce a totally new locomotive and one in demand by the railway modellers.

After much research it was abundantly clear that the model most in need of introduction was the rebuilt Merchant Navy.

Hornby's rebuilt Merchant Navy was released in 2000 and was the first Hornby model to be designed in the UK but developed and manufactured in China. The body and chassis detail were like nothing else that Hornby had ever produced. A totally new power drive was developed which utilised a large 5 pole, skew wound motor that provided ultra smooth and low speed running,

while the gearing and weight of the model offered immense tractive effort. In short it was by far the most advanced locomotive that Hornby had ever produced.

The first model released was the rebuilt Merchant Navy 'Clan Line' and heralded Hornby's desire to produce high quality, detailed model locomotives. Since then Hornby has continued to develop new and ground-breaking models but the success and development of such items stems back to the launch of 'Clan Line' in 2000.

Over the years there had been very little demand for industrial locomotives, which was why Hornby had not even considered producing such models, opting only for locomotives that had operated on the UK national rail network.

Over the years Hornby had introduced several pseudo industrial locomotives but these were using models from their standard range.

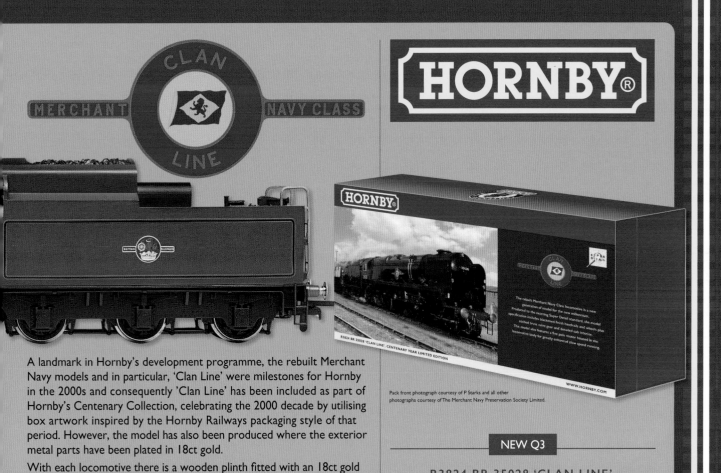

A landmark in Hornby's development programme, the rebuilt Merchant Navy models and in particular, 'Clan Line' were milestones for Hornby in the 2000s and consequently 'Clan Line' has been included as part of Hornby's Centenary Collection, celebrating the 2000 decade by utilising box artwork inspired by the Hornby Railways packaging style of that period. However, the model has also been produced where the exterior metal parts have been plated in 18ct gold.

With each locomotive there is a wooden plinth fitted with an 18ct gold track piece, plus a numbered certificate authenticating that the model is just one of 1000 models produced.

Pack front photograph courtesy of P Starks and all other photographs courtesy of The Merchant Navy Preservation Society Limited.

NEW Q3

R3824 BR 35028 'CLAN LINE', CENTENARY YEAR LIMITED EDITION

On a dull and rainy day while the Hornby development team were visiting a heritage railway with the intention of measuring and photographing a wagon, they chanced upon a 4wDM 0-4-0 Sentinel industrial locomotive and decided, as they had time that they would measure and photograph the locomotive. Returning to Hornby it was suggested that a model of the diesel shunter would make an excellent addition to the range. After some deliberation it was agreed to produce the model which consequently appeared in the 2013 Hornby range. So successful was the Sentinel it was decided that the next Industrial locomotive to be produced would be of a more traditional type and the one chosen was the charming Peckett W4 Class.

When Hornby announced in October 2015 that they were to produce a model of the Peckett W4 the news was received with great enthusiasm. During 2016 the development of the model was followed closely with a further announcement stating that there were to be three variants of the elegantly proportioned Peckett and by the end of that year all had been sold in advance of release.

By the time the three Pecketts arrived in the Summer of 2017, Hornby had already announced further releases and once again sales for those models were very quickly presold. In 2018 and again in 2019 Hornby revealed additional variants and as with previous releases all were presold long before they reached the retailers' shelves.

The Hornby Peckett W4 is both elegant in style, graceful in performance and is arguably one of Hornby's success stories of the years, making up the 2010 decade. As such, this special limited edition Peckett W4 model in Works photographic grey has been produced as part of Hornby's Centenary Collection and is presented in a special limited edition commemorative pack which includes a resin miniature maker's plate. Supplied complete with a certificate which states that the model is from a production run of just 2000.

NEW Q3

R3825 PECKETT 614, CENTENARY YEAR LIMITED EDITION

15

Rovex Plastics Ltd was formed in 1946 by Alexandra Gregory Vanetzian who had quickly, after the end of the Second World War mastered the technique of moulding plastic into brightly coloured miniature cars that he supplied under contract to Marks & Spencer.

Centenary Year Collectables

NEW Q1

GS62617
Centenary Year Collectables, Hornby Pen
Only available from Hornby Direct or through the Hornby Collector Club

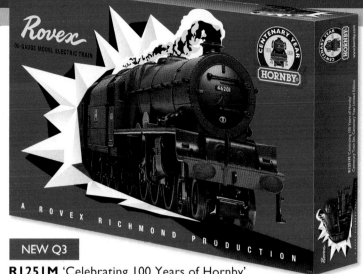

Unfortunately, Vanetzian had to cease production of his cars as the name Rovex conflicted with the already registered Rover Car Company name and he consequently had to undertake not to manufacture any more cars, miniature or otherwise.

So impressed had Marks & Spencer been with the toy car Vanetzian had supplied that they asked him in 1948 to produce an inexpensive battery powered train set. Vanetzian accepted the challenge and in 1950, just in time for Christmas, the first train sets started to appear in the Marks & Spencer stores.

The first Rovex set consisted of an oval of track, a battery box controller, two coaches and a black Princess locomotive, 'Princess Elizabeth'. However the task of completing the huge order for Marks & Spencer was not a smooth one and weighed down with financial issues Alexandra Vanetzian sold Rovex Plastics Ltd. to Lines Bros in October 1951 and in 1952 Tri-ang Railways was formed.

The current Hornby range of train sets can trace their lineage to the very first set produced by Rovex Plastics Ltd., which contained a black Princess Coronation Class locomotive, 'Princess Elizabeth'. With the twin celebrations of not only the Hornby Trains 100th Anniversary but also the 70th anniversary of the first Rovex, later to become Tri-ang Railways, there can only be one locomotive suitable to be included in a set celebrating these two momentous anniversaries and that is the 'Princess Elizabeth'.

This set features the 21st century equivalents of not only the locomotive but also the coaches that replicate as closely as possible the very first Rovex train set. As part of the Hornby Trains Centenary group of products, this set represents the coming together of the latest highly detailed models of 2020 with the pack artwork inspired by that of the very first set produced in 1950 by Rovex Plastics Ltd.

This special limited edition train set contains an authenticating certificate confirming that it is just one of a production quantity of 1000 sets.

NEW Q3

R1251M 'Celebrating 100 Years of Hornby' Train Set, Centenary Year Limited Edition

SET CONTENTS
ROLLING STOCK
BR A4 Princess Royal Class 4-6-2, 46201 'Princess Elizabeth'
LMS Period III Corridor First, 7573
LMS Period III Corridor Third, 27424

TRACK & ACCESSORIES
3rd Radius Large Oval,
Train Controller (R7229),
Wall Plug Transformer (P9000W),
Power Connecting Track (R8206),
Rerailer.

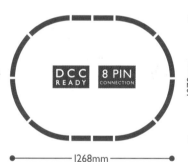

DCC READY | 8 PIN CONNECTION

1070mm
1268mm

NEW Q1 **GS62616**
Centenary Year Collectables, Hornby Centenary Mug

NEW Q1 **GS62615**
Centenary Year Collectables, Gold Plated Centenary Badge

The Hornby

CENTENARY YEAR
1920 2020
HORNBY®

THE HORNBY
BOOK OF TRAINS
THE FIRST ONE HUNDRED YEARS

PAT HAMMOND

CONTENTS

The perfect table railway

About this Book

Frank Hornby and Meccano Ltd.

Meccano Magazine

HORNBY DUBLO – PRE-WAR
1938 A Table Railway

1920
THE FIRST TRAIN SETS

HORNBY 0 GAUGE TRAINS

Hornby 0 gauge trains were initially a development of the Meccano system. It is said that the idea developed out of a new piece of Meccano, a corner bracket called an 'architrave', which could be used to form cab sides when building a locomotive out of Meccano. This had been produced during the First World War and a small model locomotive was made up with it in the factory.

Whether or not this was what inspired the Hornby trains, the first train sets were put on the market in 1920 and the models were advertised as being 'constructional', i.e. being held together with nuts and bolts so that they could be taken apart like Meccano. This, no doubt, was what Frank Hornby was referring to in Meccano Magazine as 'designed on Meccano principle'. The steel pressings, which formed the parts, were purpose made to look like real railway engines and rolling stock, when assembled, and not something built out of Meccano. They came with paint and were in strong cardboard boxes.

Binns Road factory in 1920 were cheap copies of a pre-war German sets by Bing, and were in fact made in tinplate and not the enamelled pressed steel, which would be used for the main products. Arriving in the shops in June 1920, the cheap tinplate sets came in a choice of three liveries. A 0-4-0 tender locomotive could be in lined black livery (LNWR) and named George the Fifth or green & red (GNR) or maroon (MR); the last two being un-named. The locomotives had an under-size tender and each came with two very short 4-wheel coaches appropriately liveried.

It is not known how well those tinplate sets sold, as the main attention was focused on the enamelled sets which, if the reports in Meccano Magazine are to be believed, the public were clamouring to get their hands

SUMMARY –

RETURN O
AND THE

1993
COLOURFUL BATTERY POWER

Hornby Railways toy range was StationMaster, which consisted range in bright colours. A train standard track, a Class D tank wagons, a four-wheel coach, a roof car park). By clever design, ped together to form a carrying and coach were available solo, 'Monobloc' tank wagon, LMS nd signal, island platform, t. The colours were red, combinations.

to Flying Scotsman in 1993,

with four versions of the locomotive covering different periods in its life. For 1924–28 the model was an A1 with the number on the tender and the coat-of-arms on the cab-side. For the period 1928–36 it was still an A1, but with the number on the cab sides. For 1961–63 the model was an A3 in late BR green with German smoke deflectors. The fourth version, for 1966–73, caused the most excitement as it was a model of the locomotive in Alan Pegler's ownership, with two tenders and an LNER green livery.

2018
UNDER NE
MANAGEME

The end of year Annual Report for March 2018 revealed how serious the position was for the company, showing further slumps in revenue down to £35.7 million and a widening pre-tax loss of £7.6 million.

There were four new locomotives and two of them were new subjects. One was the 0-6-0 North British Railway Class C, which in 1923 became LNER Class J36, and the other was the Hitachi Class 800/0 IEP. The other two new locomotives were a fourth version of the 'Coronation' design and a new super-detailed West Coast Main Line Class 87 electric locomotive, replacing the former Lima model with a high-quality alternative. There was also a new toy train set from new tooling and called the 'Junior Express'.

Book of Trains...

The First One Hundred Years

NEW Q1

R8158 The Hornby Book of Trains - The First One Hundred Years - by Pat Hammond

Frank Hornby, the founder of Meccano Ltd, situated in Binns Road, Liverpool, launched Hornby Trains as a brand in 1920. Since then the product and the company has gone through many changes.

The original scale of 7mm to the foot commonly known at '0' gauge was joined and eventually superseded by the smaller and almost half sized '00' scale system branded creatively as Hornby Dublo in 1938.

After the Second World War manufacturing of the Hornby Dublo system recommenced and soon became the dominant scale but new materials and cheaper prices quickly brought major competition to Hornby in the form of Rovex Industries, which eventually became Tri-ang Railways. Over time Tri-ang obtained the Meccano company and rebranded their railway system Tri-ang Hornby. Eventually, after one more takeover the name Tri-ang was removed and the system simply became Hornby Railways.

By the turn of the last century Hornby Railways had become just Hornby and with it a new evolution with manufacturing moving from the Margate factory where it had been since 1954 to the Far East where modern manufacturing techniques lifted the Hornby products from being pseudo toys to exquisite models demanded by today's selective modeller.

This Hornby Book of Trains – The First Hundred Years, has been researched and written by renowned author, editor and model railway historian, Pat Hammond who using his amazing archive traces the one hundred year history of Hornby with facts, features and an abundance of images, supported by historical information explaining the twists and turns of this much loved and respected model railway brand. With over 448 fact packed pages, plus in excess of 800 images this book is an amazing historical adventure taking the reader on a 100 year model railway journey that is Hornby. (Book dimensions: 245 x 170mm).

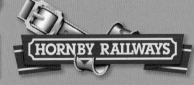

TRAIN SETS

Analogue & Digital

Just as a key opens up a door, a Hornby train set is the first step into an adventure that can span a lifetime, creating treasured memories along the way.

Every one of the train sets featured in this year's catalogue range has been carefully selected to fulfil a specific requirement of experience or space constraint; from the battery powered Hornby Junior Paddington set with its self-assembly cardboard buildings, to a small analogue controlled 0-4-0 locomotive hauling a coach and wagon around a simple oval of track. Then there are the impressive Eurostar sets with their extended track layouts and for those looking to explore digital layout operation, there is the Mixed Traffic set with multiple locomotives to operate. There is even the option of having a set that has been especially designed to fit around the base of a Christmas Tree!

For the budding rail enthusiast, a new GWR themed freight set has been introduced this year, featuring an 0-6-0 Pannier Tank and a working crane, as well as a second Eurostar set that features the stunning 'Yellow Submarine' artwork. For those who like a touch of magic, the Harry Potter Train set continues to charm adults and children alike. Featuring the 'correct' Hall class Hogwarts Castle locomotive with its operating headlight, the set is supported by a range of plastic and resin buildings available to buy separately.

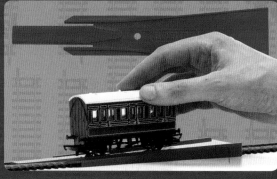

At Hornby, we realise that it is not always easy to place locomotives and rolling stock onto your new layout at the first attempt, especially as the excitement of wanting to operate it for the first time takes hold.

For most of our sets, we have included an item to make life easier for the operator; the Hornby Re-Railer. Simply place the Re-Railer onto a straight piece of track, place the locomotive, coach or wagon onto the Re-Railer and guide it gently down the slope and onto the track for a perfect placement.

20

PADDINGTON™

R1247M

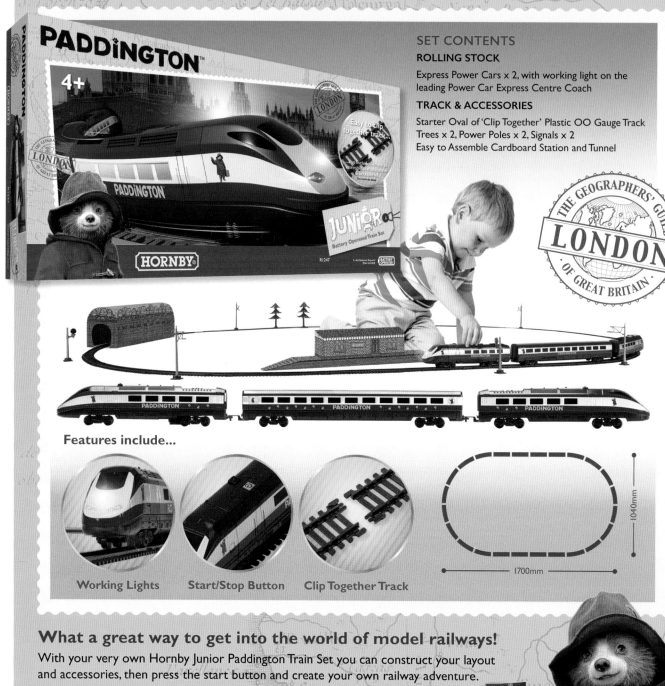

SET CONTENTS

ROLLING STOCK

Express Power Cars x 2, with working light on the leading Power Car Express Centre Coach

TRACK & ACCESSORIES

Starter Oval of 'Clip Together' Plastic OO Gauge Track
Trees x 2, Power Poles x 2, Signals x 2
Easy to Assemble Cardboard Station and Tunnel

THE GEOGRAPHERS' GUILD
LONDON
OF GREAT BRITAIN

Features include...

Working Lights   **Start/Stop Button**   **Clip Together Track**

1040mm

1700mm

What a great way to get into the world of model railways!

With your very own Hornby Junior Paddington Train Set you can construct your layout and accessories, then press the start button and create your own railway adventure.

Battery Controlled - 2 x 1.5V AA Batteries (not included)
© P&Co. Ltd./SC 2020

CENTENARY YEAR
1920 2020
HORNBY®

R1248 Santa's Express Analogue Train Set

Analogue

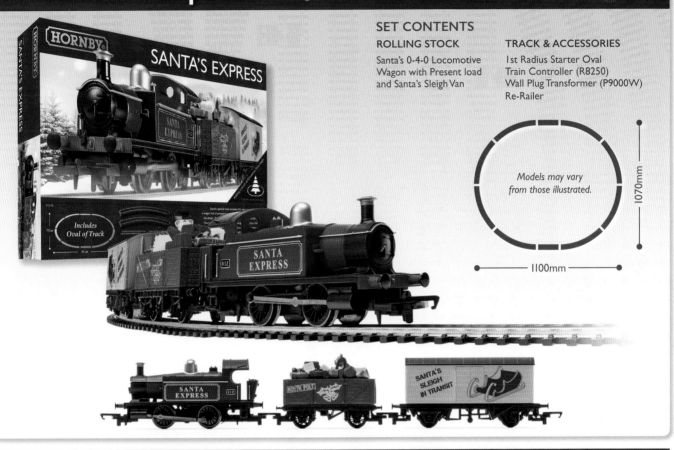

SET CONTENTS

ROLLING STOCK

Santa's 0-4-0 Locomotive
Wagon with Present load
and Santa's Sleigh Van

TRACK & ACCESSORIES

1st Radius Starter Oval
Train Controller (R8250)
Wall Plug Transformer (P9000W)
Re-Railer

*Models may vary
from those illustrated.*

1070mm

1100mm

R1233 Coca-Cola Christmas Analogue Train Set

Analogue

SET CONTENTS

ROLLING STOCK

0-4-0 Diesel Shunter
Locomotive, Coca Cola®
Closed Box Van, Coca Cola®
Container Wagon,
Coca Cola®

TRACK & ACCESSORIES

1st Radius Starter Oval
Train Controller (R8250)
Wall Plug Transformer (P9000W)
Re-Railer

*Models may vary
from those illustrated.*

1070mm

1100mm

R1220 Highland Rambler Analogue Train Set

Analogue

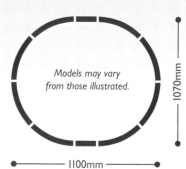

SET CONTENTS

ROLLING STOCK

HR 0-4-0 Locomotive
Four-wheel coach
Open wagon

TRACK & ACCESSORIES

3rd Radius Starter Oval
Train Controller (R8250)
Wall Plug Transformer (P9000W)
Power Connecting Track (R8206)
Hornby MidiMat (1600 x 1180mm)

*Models may vary
from those illustrated.*

1070mm
1100mm

R1228 Industrial Freight Analogue Train Set

Analogue

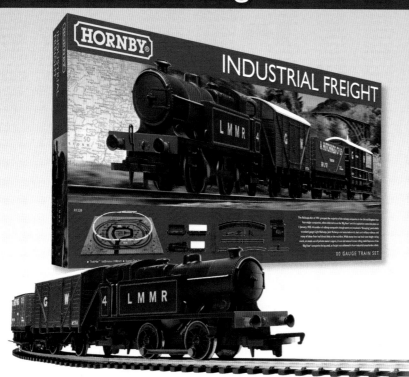

SET CONTENTS

ROLLING STOCK

LMMR 0-4-0 Locomotive
GWR Box Van
Private Owner 7 Plank Wagon
GWR Toad Brake Van

TRACK & ACCESSORIES

3rd Radius Starter Oval, with Track Pack A
(includes point and buffer)
Train Controller (R7229)
Wall Plug Transformer (P9000W)
Power Connecting Track (R8206)
Hornby MidiMat (1600 x 1180mm)
Re-Railer

*Models may vary
from those illustrated.*

1130mm
1550mm

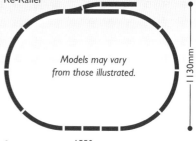

CENTENARY YEAR
1920 2020

HORNBY®

To place an order contact Hornby Customer Services on: **01843 233512** or visit your local stockist.

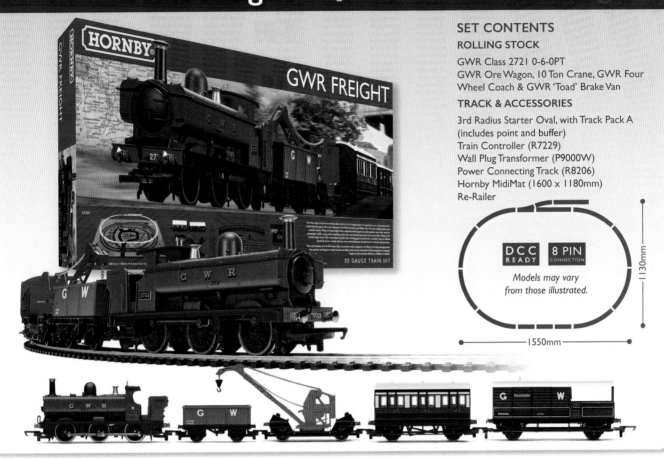

NEW Q2 R1254M **GWR Freight** Analogue Train Set

Analogue

SET CONTENTS

ROLLING STOCK

GWR Class 2721 0-6-0PT
GWR Ore Wagon, 10 Ton Crane, GWR Four Wheel Coach & GWR 'Toad' Brake Van

TRACK & ACCESSORIES

3rd Radius Starter Oval, with Track Pack A (includes point and buffer)
Train Controller (R7229)
Wall Plug Transformer (P9000W)
Power Connecting Track (R8206)
Hornby MidiMat (1600 x 1180mm)
Re-Railer

DCC READY 8 PIN CONNECTION

Models may vary from those illustrated.

1130mm
1550mm

R1214 **East Coast Express** Analogue Train Set

Analogue

SET CONTENTS

ROLLING STOCK

BR Class B17 'West Ham United'
BR MK1 Corridor Composite Coach
BR MK1 Brake 2nd Class Coach

TRACK & ACCESSORIES

3rd Radius Starter Oval
Train Controller (R8250)
Wall Plug Transformer (P9000W)
Power Connecting Track (R8206)
Hornby MidiMat (1600 x 1180mm)

DCC READY 8 PIN CONNECTION

Models may vary from those illustrated.

1070mm
1100mm

25

NEW Q2   R1255M   The Flying Scotsman Analogue Train Set

Analogue

SET CONTENTS

ROLLING STOCK

LNER Class A1 4-6-2 'Flying Scotsman'
Two LNER composite coaches
LNER brake coach

TRACK & ACCESSORIES

3rd Radius Starter Oval, with Track Pack A
(includes point and buffer)
Train Controller (R7229)
Wall Plug Transformer (P9000W)
Power Connecting Track (R8206)
Hornby MidiMat (1600 x 1180mm)

FLYING SCOTSMAN

Produced under licence
for SCMG Enterprises Ltd.
© SCMGE.
Every purchase supports
the museum.

DCC READY   8 PIN CONNECTION

*Models may vary
from those illustrated.*

1130mm

1550mm

CENTENARY YEAR 1920 2020

HORNBY®

To place an order contact Hornby Customer Services on: **01843 233512** or visit your local stockist.

R1202 The Mallard Pullman Analogue Train Set

Analogue

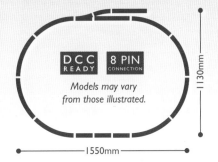

SET CONTENTS

ROLLING STOCK

LNER Class A4 4-6-2 Pacific 4468 'Mallard'
Pullman Parlour Car
Pullman Brake Car

TRACK & ACCESSORIES

3rd Radius Starter Oval, with Track Pack A
(includes point and buffer)
Train Controller (R8250)
Wall Plug Transformer (P9000W)
Power Connecting Track (R8206)
Hornby MidiMat (1600 x 1180mm)

RAILWAY MUSEUM

Produced under licence
for SCMG Enterprises Ltd.
© SCMGE.
Every purchase supports
the museum.

DCC READY | 8 PIN CONNECTION

*Models may vary
from those illustrated.*

1130mm

1550mm

R1230M GWR HST Analogue Train Set

Analogue

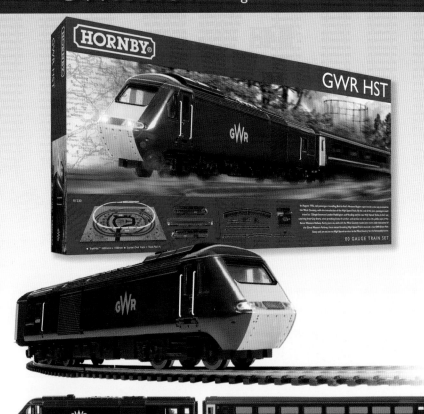

SET CONTENTS

ROLLING STOCK

GWR Class 43 HST Power Car
GWR Class 43 HST Dummy Power Car
GWR Mk3 TSO Coach

TRACK & ACCESSORIES

3rd Radius Starter Oval, with Track Pack A
(includes point and buffer)
Train Controller (R7229)
Wall Plug Transformer (P9000W)
Power Connecting Track (R8206)
Hornby MidiMat (1600 x 1180mm)
Re-Railer

DCC READY | 8 PIN CONNECTION

*Models may vary
from those illustrated.*

1130mm

1550mm

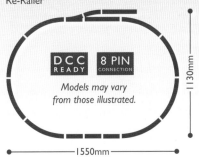

NEW Q3 | R1253M | Analogue Train Set

EUROSTAR

The Beatles Yellow Submarine

Decoration as shown on side 1

Decoration as shown on side 2

Eurostar's first use of the Class 373 for an external agency marketing campaign took place in September 1999 when the Sets 3005/3006 were transformed with a vinyl wrap that recreated scenes from The Beatles' film 'Yellow Submarine'. This was just one of the promotional events that marked the release of the remixed music track that Autumn.

Along with the remastered version of the film that was released in cinemas and on video, the film which had not been available for over a decade included scenes that were edited out of the original, while the album featured new mixes of songs, such as 'With A Little Help From My Friends' and 'Lucy In The Sky With Diamonds', the first such time a Beatles album had ever been remixed.

SET CONTENTS

ROLLING STOCK

Eurostar, Class 373 Power Driving Car + Eurostar, Class 373 Dummy Driving Car, 2 x Eurostar, Class 373 Passenger Saloons, with non-working pantographs

TRACK & ACCESSORIES

3rd Radius Starter Oval, with Track Pack A (includes point and buffer)
Train Controller (R8250), Wall Plug Transformer (P9000W), Power Connecting Track (R8206), Re-Railer
Hornby MidiMat (1600 x 1180mm)

Note: The designs featured on this model and on the two centre cars availble separately are acurate representation of the graphics that were applied to the eighteen passenger cars of Sets 3005/3006 but are not intended to accurately portray the whole livery that was in service.

DCC READY | 8 PIN CONNECTION

Models may vary from those illustrated.

1130mm

1550mm

NEW Q2 | Additional coaches available:

R40001 | Eurostar, Class 373/1 'Yellow Submarine' Divisible Centre Saloons Coach Pack - Era 9

CENTENARY YEAR 1920 2020 HORNBY

R1176 Eurostar Analogue Train Set

Analogue

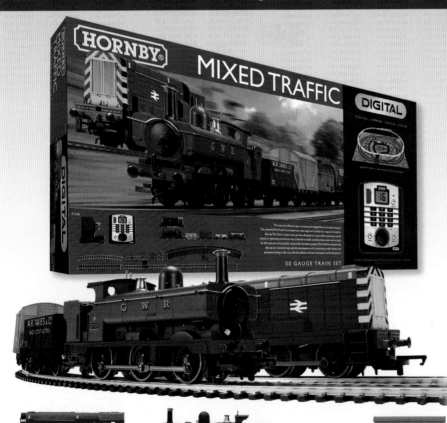

SET CONTENTS

ROLLING STOCK

Eurostar e300 Power Driving Car
Eurostar e300 Dummy Driving Car
2 x Eurostar e300 Passenger Saloons, with non-working pantographs

TRACK & ACCESSORIES

3rd Radius Starter Oval, with Track Pack A (includes point and buffer)
Train Controller (R8250)
Wall Plug Transformer (P9000W)
Power Connecting Track (R8206)
Hornby MidiMat (1600 x 1180mm)
Re-Railer

Aditional coaches available:
R4580 Eurostar, Class 373/1 e300
Divisible Centre Saloons Coach Pack

DCC READY **8 PIN CONNECTION**

Models may vary from those illustrated.

1130mm
1550mm

R1236 Mixed Traffic Digital Train Set

DIGITAL

SET CONTENTS

ROLLING STOCK

BR 0-6-0 Class 08 Diesel Shunter
GWR 0-6-0PT Class 2721
Private Owner 7 plank wagon
BR 12 ton Box Van
Iron Ore wagon
Private Owner Tanker wagon

TRACK & ACCESSORIES

3rd Radius Starter Oval, with Track Pack A (includes point and buffer)
Select DCC Controller (R8213)
1 Amp Wall Mounted Transformer (P9000W)
Power Connecting Track (R8241)
Hornby MidiMat (1600 x 1180mm)
Re-Railer

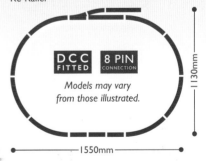

DCC FITTED **8 PIN CONNECTION**

Models may vary from those illustrated.

1130mm
1550mm

29

Harry Potter™

HOGWARTS EXPRESS
5972

WIZARDING WORLD™

Harry Potter
HOGWARTS EXPRESS | Electric Train Set
HORNBY
WIZARDING WORLD

Harry Potter
HOGWARTS EXPRESS
5972
HOGWARTS EXPRESS | Electric Train Set
HORNBY

WIZARDING WORLD

To place an order contact Hornby Customer Services on: **01843 233512** or visit your local stockist.

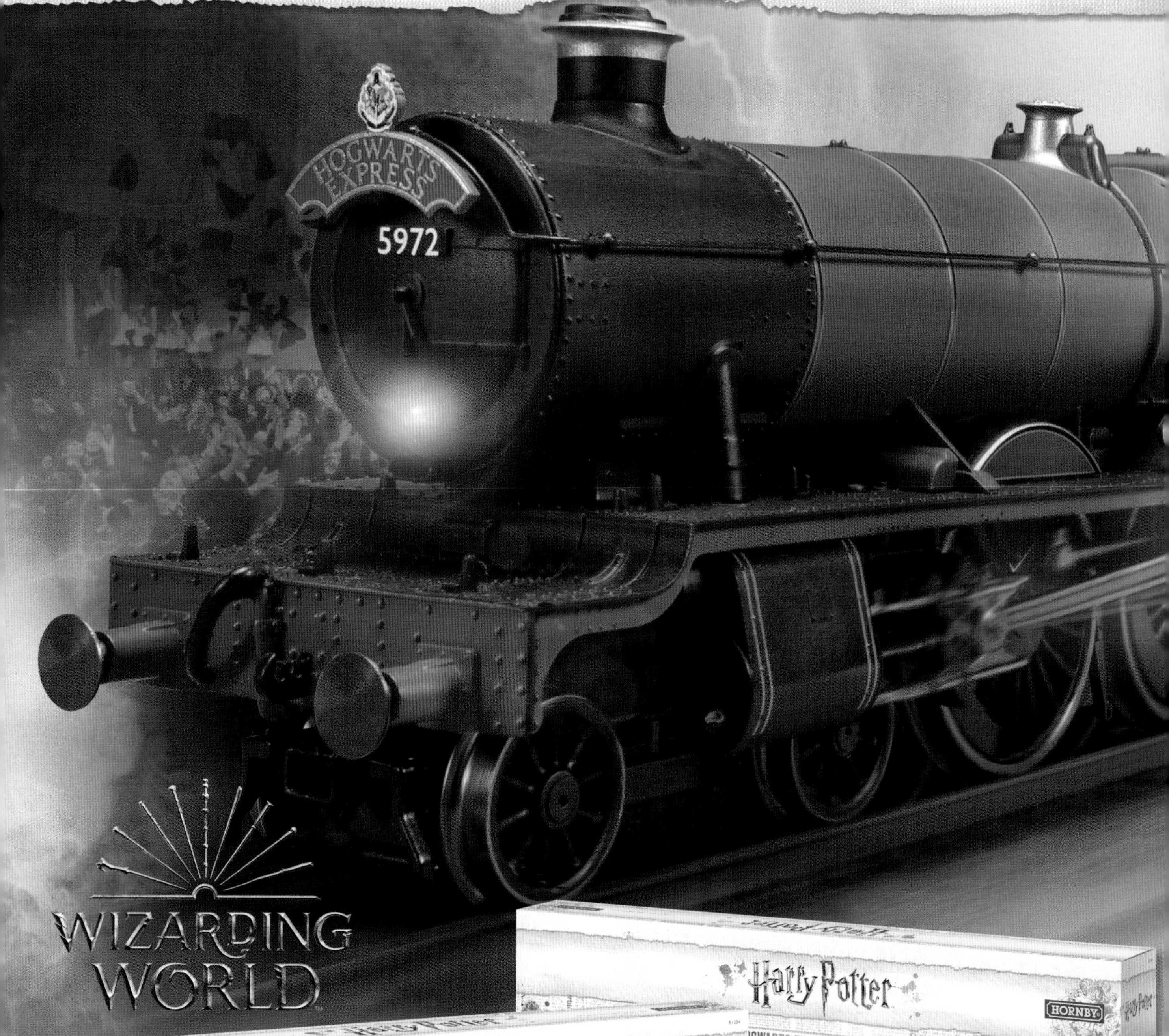

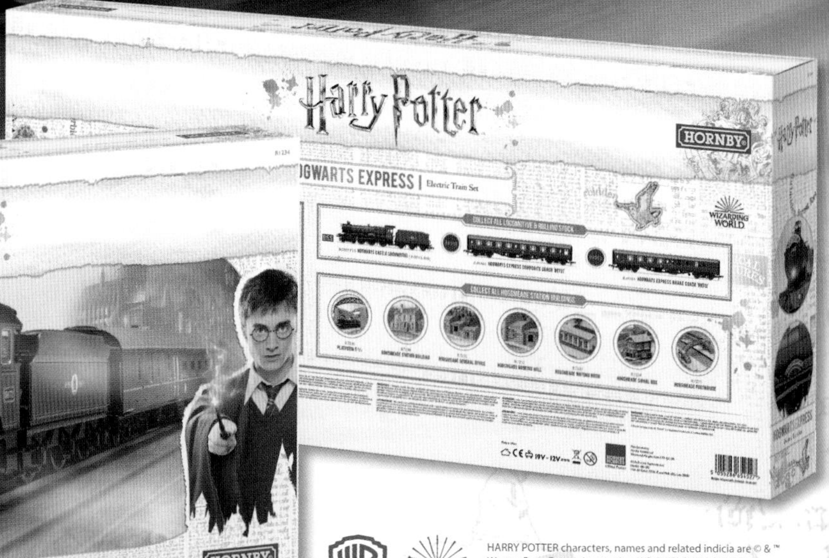

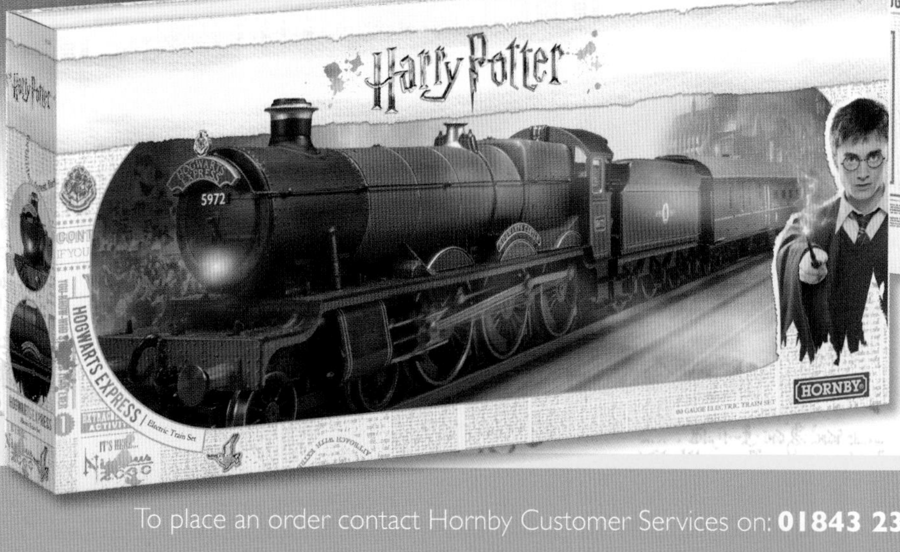

From the superb Harry Potter 'Hogwarts Express' Train Set, to locomotives, rolling stock, buildings and accessories, Hornby are delighted to welcome you to the world of Harry Potter!

R1234M 'Hogwarts Express' Train Set

DCC READY | 8 PIN CONNECTION

Designer: Ottaline Gambol, Minister for Magic	Period: 1827-1835	Motor: 3 Pole and Fly Wheel. Loco Drive	Curved Track: Hornby 2nd Radius + / 438mm+
Locomotive: 5972 'Hogwarts Castle', with working headlight	Coaches: Hogwarts, Mk1 SK, 99716 Hogwarts, Mk1 BSK, 99723	Livery: Hogwarts Red	Operating Area/Route: London Kings Cross - Hogsmede 11:00 September 1st (annually), then as required

31

R3804	5972 'Hogwarts Castle', with Working Headlight				DCC READY	8 PIN CONNECTION
	Designer: Ottaline Gambol, Minister of Magic	Entered Service: 1827-1835	Length: 254mm	Motor: 3 Pole and Fly Wheel Loco Drive	Curved Track: Hornby 2nd Radius + / 438mm+	

R4934/A	Hogwarts, Mk1 SK Nos. 99716/99721
Livery Hogwarts Red	Length: 265mm

R4935/A	Hogwarts, Mk1 BSK Nos. 99723/99312
Livery Hogwarts Red	Length: 265mm

For added realism, 5972 'Hogwarts Castle' locomotive with sound and working headlight!

R3803TTS	5972 'Hogwarts Castle', with Sound and Working Headlightight				DCC FITTED	8 PIN CONNECTION
	Designer: Ottaline Gambol, Minister of Magic	Entered Service: 1827-1835	Length: 254mm	Motor: 3 Pole and Fly Wheel Loco Drive	Curved Track: Hornby 2nd Radius + / 438mm+	

Hogsmeade resin and plastic buildings.

| R7230 | Hogsmeade Station, Station Building | R7232 | Hogsmeade Station, Booking Hall | R7231 | Hogsmeade Station, General Office |

| R7235 | Hogsmeade Station, Footbridge | R7233 | Hogsmeade Station, Waiting Room | R7234 | Hogsmeade Station, Signal Box |

| R7236 | Platform 9¾ | Platform Length: 594mm | R7238 | Hogsmeade Station, Platform Pack |

Resin platform arches, with plastic slot together canopy, footbridge and platform sections

33

RAILROAD
Locomotives & Rolling Stock

Whether you are adding to your first train set, buying a present for the younger, or older, enthusiast, or developing modelling techniques, the Hornby RailRoad range is the ideal introduction to railway modelling.

From locomotives fitted with Hornby's own Twin Track Sound (TTS) chips, to a basic long wheelbase open wagon, the RailRoad system is fully compatible with the standard Hornby main range. With easily damaged fine detail parts being omitted from the models they are more suitable for less gentle handling or, at the other end of the scale, are a solid base for detailing or conversion projects. Liveries are accurate renditions of the full size prototypes but again lack the finer details that are a standard feature of Hornby's main range items. This allows the beginner or enthusiast to add decals, change running numbers, experiment with weathering techniques or even go 'full on' with a complete livery change.

Prices of the RailRoad range are tailored to suit the average wallet, allowing collections to be built up from the contents of a basic train set, or to populate large layouts or 'backscenes'. With the range covering everything from freelance private owner type locomotives, to icons of steam and diesel traction, right through to the stalwarts of diesel freight and passenger haulage. The Hornby RailRoad range is there to suit most pockets and abilities. Rolling stock reflecting coaches from the era of the 'Big Four' to the introduction of air-conditioned British Rail standard coaches, as well as wagons that cover the same wide time period.

There is a strong GBRf presence in the 2020 RailRoad range, reflecting the widespread popularity of the blue and yellow locomotives, with a welcome return for the Class 20 and Class 73 locomotives, as well as additional GBRf liveries for the Class 47. The Class 37 also makes a welcome return to the range for 2020, modelled in its popular yellow Network Rail livery.

RAILROAD

COCK O' THE NORTH

LNER 8482

N° 200

RUF 324

RAILROAD Steam Locomotives

R3359 Rothery Industries, Ex-GWR 101 Class, 0-4-0T, 391 - Era 4/5

| Designer: James Holden | Livery: Private Owner | Entered Service: 1901 |
| Length: 108mm | Motor: RM | Curved Track: Hornby 1st Radius + / 371mm+ |

R3752 S. Wilson Paper Mills, 0-4-0T, No. 2112 - Era 2/3

| Designer: Freelance | Livery: Private Owner | Entered Service: NA |
| Length: 108mm | Motor: RM | Curved Track: Hornby 1st Radius + / 371mm+ |

R3584 Godfrey & Mitchell Coal Merchants, 0-4-0T, No. 9 - Era 3/4

| Designer: George Robson | Livery: Private Owner | Entered Service: 1912 |
| Length: 108mm | Motor: RM | Curved Track: Hornby 1st Radius + / 371mm+ |

R3754 Blundell King Timber Merchants, 0-4-0T, No. 7 - Era 3/4

| Designer: George Robson | Livery: Private Owner | Entered Service: 1912 |
| Length: 108mm | Motor: RM | Curved Track: Hornby 1st Radius + / 371mm+ |

R3064 BR, Class 0F 'Pug', 0-4-0ST, 56025 'Smokey Joe' - Era 4/5

| Designer: Dugald Drummond | Livery: BR Lined Black | Entered Service: 1960 |
| Length: 108mm | Motor: RM | Curved Track: Hornby 1st Radius + / 371mm+ |

R3753 Beggs Tooling, Class 0F 'Pug', 0-4-0ST, 854 - Era 2/3

| Designer: Dugald Drummond | Livery: Private Owner | Entered Service: 1890 |
| Length: 108mm | Motor: RM | Curved Track: Hornby 1st Radius + / 371mm+ |

R3668 LNER, Class J83, 0-6-0T, 8472 - Era 3

| Designer: Matthew Holme | Livery: LNER Green | Entered Service: 1924/5 |
| Length: 108mm | Motor: Type 7 | Curved Track: Hornby 1st Radius + / 371mm+ |

R3759 | GWR, Class 3031 'Dean Single', 4-2-2, 'Achilles' - Era 2 | DCC READY | 8 PIN CONNECTION

| Designer: William Dean Livery: GWR Green | Entered Service: 1894 | Length: 232mm | Motor: 3 Pole and fly wheel. Loco Drive | Curved Track: Hornby 2nd Radius + / 438mm+ |

R3276 | LMS, Class 4P Compound, 4-4-0, 1072 - Era 3 | DCC READY | 8 PIN CONNECTION

| Designer: Henry Fowler Livery: LMS Black | Entered Service: 1924 | Length: 237mm | Motor: 3 Pole and fly wheel. Loco Drive | Curved Track: Hornby 2nd Radius + / 438mm+ |

R3586 | BR, V 'Schools' Class, 4-4-0, 30935 'Sevenoaks' - Era 4 | DCC READY | 8 PIN CONNECTION

| Designer: Richard Maunsell Livery: BR Lined Green | Entered Service: 1934 | Length: 239mm | Motor: 3 Pole and fly wheel. Loco Drive | Curved Track: Hornby 2nd Radius + / 438mm+ |

R3588 | LNER, Class B17, 4-6-0, 2864 'Liverpool' - Era 3 | DCC READY | 8 PIN CONNECTION

| Designer: Sir Nigel Gresley Livery: LNER Apple Green | Entered Service: 1937 | Length: 249mm | Motor: 3 Pole and fly wheel. Loco Drive | Curved Track: Hornby 2nd Radius + / 438mm+ |

R3060 | British Railways, Peppercorn Class A1, 4-6-2, 60103 'Tornado' - Era 11 | DCC READY | 8 PIN CONNECTION

| Designer: A1 Steam Locomotive Trust Livery: LNER Apple Green | Entered Service: 2008 | Length: 293mm | Motor: 3 Pole and fly wheel. Loco Drive | Curved Track: Hornby 2nd Radius + / 438mm+ |

37

R3171 | LNER, Class P2, 2-8-2, 2001 'Cock 'O The North' - Era 3 | DCC READY | 8 PIN CONNECTION

Designer: Sir Nigel Gresley | Entered Service: 1934 | Length: 296mm | Motor: 3 Pole and fly wheel. | Curved Track: Hornby 2nd Radius +
Livery: LNER Apple Green | | | Loco Drive | / 438mm+

Produced under licence for SCMG Enterprises Ltd. © SCMGE. *Every purchase supports the museum.*

R3086 | LNER, Class A1, 4-6-2, 4472 'Flying Scotsman' - Era 3 90th ANNIVERSARY OF APPEARING IN THE FIRST BRITISH 'TALKING' FILM | DCC READY | 8 PIN CONNECTION

Designer: Sir Nigel Gresley | Entered Service: 1923 | Length: 293mm | Motor: 3 Pole and fly wheel. | Curved Track: Hornby 2nd Radius +
Livery: LNER Apple Green | | | Loco Drive | / 438mm+

Produced under licence for SCMG Enterprises Ltd. © SCMGE. *Every purchase supports the museum.*

R3371 | LNER, Class A4, 4-6-2, 4468 'Mallard' - Era 3 | DCC READY | 8 PIN CONNECTION

Designer: Sir Nigel Gresley | Entered Service: 1938 | Length: 291mm | Motor: 3 Pole and fly wheel. | Curved Track: Hornby 2nd Radius +
Livery: LNER Garter Blue | | | Loco Drive | / 438mm+

R3942 | BR, Class 9F, 2-10-0, 92219 - Era 5 | DCC READY | 8 PIN CONNECTION

NEW Q4 | Designer: Robert Riddles | Entered Service: 1960 | Length: 266mm | Motor: 5 Pole Skew Wound, | Curved Track: Hornby 2nd Radius +
| | | Loco Drive | / 438mm+

R3756 | BR (Heavily Weathered), Crosti Boiler Class 9F, 2-10-0, 92028 - Era 4 | DCC READY | 8 PIN CONNECTION

Designer: R.A Riddles | Entered Service: 1955 | Length: 266mm | Motor: 5 Pole Skew Wound. | Curved Track: Hornby 2nd Radius +
Livery: BR Black | | | Loco Drive | / 438mm+

To place an order contact Hornby Customer Services on: **01843 233512** or visit your local stockist.

RAILROAD
Locomotives with sound

Produced under licence for SCMG Enterprises Ltd. © SCMGE. *Every purchase supports the museum.*

R3284TTS | LNER, Class A1, 4-6-2, 4472 'Flying Scotsman' - Era 3 90th ANNIVERSARY OF APPEARING IN THE FIRST BRITISH 'TALKING' FILM | DCC FITTED | 8 PIN CONNECTION

Designer: Sir Nigel Gresley
Livery: LNER Apple Green | Entered Service: 1923 | Length: 293mm | Motor: 3 Pole and fly wheel. Loco Drive | Curved Track: Hornby 2nd Radius + / 438mm+

Produced under licence for SCMG Enterprises Ltd. © SCMGE. *Every purchase supports the museum.*

R3395TTS | LNER, Class A4, 4-6-2, 4468 'Mallard' - Era 3 | DCC FITTED | 8 PIN CONNECTION

Designer: Sir Nigel Gresley
Livery: LNER Garter Blue | Entered Service: 1938 | Length: 291mm | Motor: 3 Pole and fly wheel. Loco Drive | Curved Track: Hornby 2nd Radius + / 438mm+

R3663TTS | British Railways, Peppercorn Class A1, 4-6-2, 60103 'Tornado' - Era 11 | DCC FITTED | 8 PIN CONNECTION

Designer: A1 Steam Locomotive Trust
Livery: LNER Apple Green | Entered Service: 2008 | Length: 293mm | Motor: 3 Pole and fly wheel. Loco Drive | Curved Track: Hornby 2nd Radius + / 438mm+

RAILROAD Diesel Locomotives

R3755 | BR, Bagnall 0-4-0DH, D9706 - Era 6

Designer: W.G Bagnall | Livery: BR Green | Entered Service: 1960

Length: 110mm | Motor: RM | Curved Track: Hornby 1st Radius + / 371mm+

39

R3757 | EWS, Class 47/7, Co-Co, 47798 'Prince William' - Era 9 | DCC READY | 8 PIN CONNECTION

Designer: Brush Traction | Entered Service: 1965 | Length: 251mm | Motor: 5 Pole Skew Wound | Curved Track: Hornby 2nd Radius +
Livery: EWS Royal Claret | | | | / 438mm+

R3758 | EWS, Class 47/7, Co-Co, 47799 'Prince Henry' - Era 9 | DCC READY | 8 PIN CONNECTION

Designer: Brush Traction | Entered Service: 1965 | Length: 251mm | Motor: 5 Pole Skew Wound | Curved Track: Hornby 2nd Radius +
Livery: EWS Royal Claret | | | | / 438mm+

R3666 | Yeoman Aggregates, Class 59, Co-Co, 59004 'Paul A. Hammond' - Era 8 | DCC READY | 8 PIN CONNECTION

Designer: Electro-Motive Diesel | Entered Service: 1985 | Length: 280mm | Motor: 5 Pole Skew Wound | Curved Track: Hornby 2nd Radius +
Livery: Yeoman Aggregates | | | | / 438mm+

R3608 | BR InterCity, Class 43 HST Pack, Power Cars W43002 and W43003 - Era 7 | DCC READY | 8 PIN CONNECTION

Designer: Sir Kenneth Grange | Entered Service: 1978 | Length: 235mm | Motor: 5 Pole Skew Wound | Curved Track: Hornby 2nd Radius +
Livery: BR InterCity | | Each Unit | | / 438mm+

R3760	GBRf, Class 59, Co-Co, 59003 - Era 10				DCC READY	8 PIN CONNECTION
	Designer: Electro-Motive Diesel Livery: GBRf Blue/Yellow	Entered Service: 1985	Length: 280mm	Motor: 5 Pole Skew Wound	Curved Track: Hornby 2nd Radius + / 438mm+	

R3585	BR, Class 90, Bo-Bo, 90135 - Era 6				DCC READY	8 PIN CONNECTION
	Designer: British Rail Livery: BR InterCity	Entered Service: 1987	Length: 245mm	Motor: 5 Pole Skew Wound	Curved Track: Hornby 2nd Radius + / 438mm+	

RAILROAD PLUS
—New enhanced livery for 2020—

R3912	GBRf, Class 20/9, Bo-Bo, 20901 - Era 10				DCC READY	8 PIN CONNECTION
NEW Q3	Designer: English Electric	Entered Service: 1959	Length: 188mm	Motor: 5 Pole Skew Wound	Curved Track: Hornby 2nd Radius + / 438mm+	

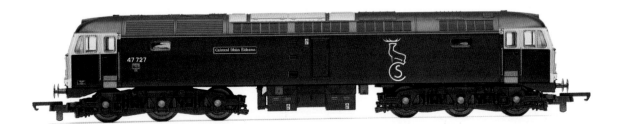

R3905	GBRf, Class 47/7, Co-Co, 47727 'Caisteal Dhùn Èideann' (Includes etched nameplates) - Era 11				DCC READY	8 PIN CONNECTION
NEW Q3	Designer: Brush Traction	Entered Service: 1964	Length: 251mm	Motor: 5 Pole Skew Wound	Curved Track: Hornby 2nd Radius + / 438mm+	

RAILROAD PLUS
New enhanced livery for 2020

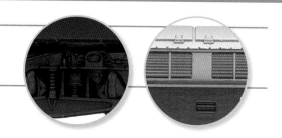

R3906
GBRf, Class 47/7, Co-Co, 47739 - Era 11

DCC READY | 8 PIN CONNECTION

NEW Q3

| Designer: Brush Traction | Entered Service: 1964 | Length: 251mm | Motor: 5 Pole Skew Wound | Curved Track: Hornby 2nd Radius + / 438mm+ |

R3907
GBRf, Class 47/7, Co-Co, 47749 'City of Truro' (Includes etched nameplates) - Era 11

DCC READY | 8 PIN CONNECTION

NEW Q3

| Designer: Brush Traction | Entered Service: 1965 | Length: 251mm | Motor: 5 Pole Skew Wound | Curved Track: Hornby 2nd Radius + / 438mm+ |

R3910
GBRf, Class 73, Bo-Bo, 73964 'Jeanette' (Includes etched nameplates) - Era 11

DCC READY | 8 PIN CONNECTION

NEW Q3

| Designer: EE/BREL | Entered Service: 1966 | Length: 215mm | Motor: 3 Pole | Curved Track: Hornby 2nd Radius + / 438mm+ |

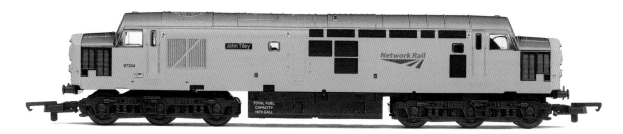

R3914
Network Rail Class 37 '97304' 'John Tiley' (Includes etched nameplates) - Era 11

DCC READY | 8 PIN CONNECTION

NEW Q3

| Designer: English Electric | Entered Service: 1964 | Length: 252mm | Motor: 5 Pole Skew Wound | Curved Track: Hornby 2nd Radius + / 438mm+ |

RAILROAD Rolling Stock

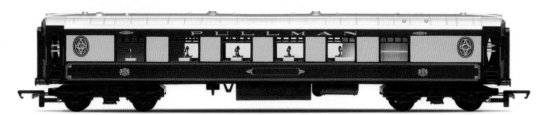

R4312	Pullman, Parlour Car - Era 3	
	Livery: Umber and Cream	Length: 263mm

R4313	Pullman, Brake Parlour Car - Era 3	
	Livery: Umber and Cream	Length: 263mm

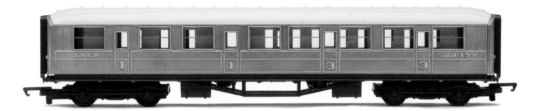

R4332	LNER, Composite Coach - Era 3	
	Livery: Teak	Length: 242mm

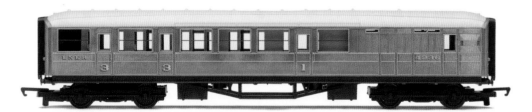

R4333	LNER, Brake Composite Coach - Era 3	
	Livery: Teak	Length: 242mm

R4388	LMS, Composite Coach - Era 3	
	Livery: LMS Crimson	Length: 242mm

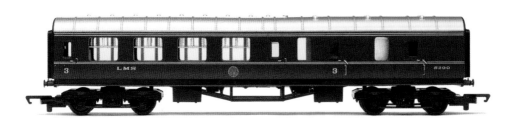

R4389	LMS, Brake Third Coach - Era 3

Livery: LMS Crimson | Length: 242mm

R4523	GWR, Composite Coach - Era 3

Livery: GWR Chocolate & Cream | Length: 242mm

R4525	GWR, Restaurant Coach - Era 3

Livery: GWR Chocolate & Cream | Length: 242mm

R4524	GWR, Brake Third Coach - Era 3

Livery: GWR Chocolate & Cream | Length: 242mm

R4353	BR, Mk1 Corridor Composite Coach - Era 4

Livery: BR Chocolate & Cream | Length: 270mm

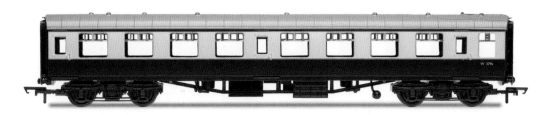

R4630   BR, Mk1 Tourist Second Open Coach - Era 4

Livery: BR Chocolate & Cream   Length: 270mm

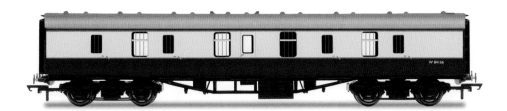

R4626   BR, Mk1 Parcels Coach - Era 4

Livery: BR Chocolate & Cream   Length: 238mm

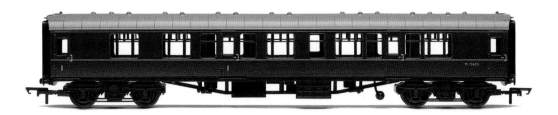

R4350   BR, Mk1 Corridor Composite Coach - Era 5

Livery: BR Maroon   Length: 270mm

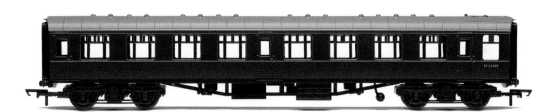

R4351   BR, Mk1 Corridor Second Coach - Era 5

Livery: BR Maroon   Length: 270mm

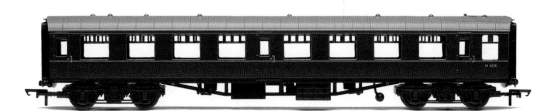

R4627   BR, Mk1 Tourist Second Open Coach - Era 5

Livery: BR Maroon   Length: 270mm

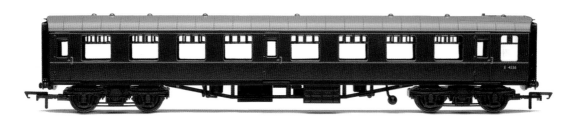

R4629 | BR, Mk1 Tourist Second Open Coach - Era 5

Livery: BR Maroon | Length: 270mm

R4625 | BR, Mk1 Parcels Coach - Era 5

Livery: BR Maroon | Length: 238mm

R4352 | BR, Mk1 Corridor Brake Second Coach - Era 5

Livery: BR Maroon | Length: 270mm

R4628 | BR, Mk1 Tourist Second Open Coach - Era 4

Livery: BR Crimson & Cream | Length: 270mm

R4743 | SR, Composite Coach - Era 3

Livery: SR Green | Length: 242mm

R4622 BR Intercity, Mk2 Second Open Coach - Era 7

Livery: BR Blue & Grey | Length: 270mm

R4671 LMS, Four-wheel Coach - Era 3

Livery: LMS Lined Crimson | Length: 100mm

R4672 GWR, Four-wheel Coach - Era 3

Livery: GWR Chocolate & Cream | Length: 100mm

R4673 SR, Four-wheel Coach - Era 3

Livery: SR Lined Green | Length: 100mm

R4674 LNER, Four-wheel Coach - Era 3

Livery: LNER Teak | Length: 100mm

R296 Track Cleaning Coach - Era 7

Livery: Track Maintenance Department | Length: 100mm

R6370 LWB Open Wagon, Tredegar - Era 3

Livery: Private Owner | Length: 88mm

R6422 North Eastern, Box Van - Era 3

Livery: NE | Length: 88mm

R6423 BR, Car Transport Bogie Wagon - Era 7

Livery: BR | Length: 265mm

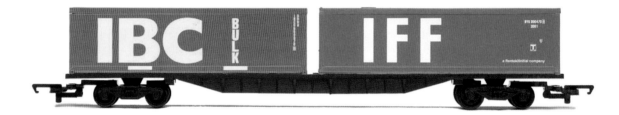

R6425 BR, FFA Container Wagon, with two 30' containers - Era 7

Livery: BR | Length: 250mm

R6881 Breakdown Crane - Era 5

Livery: BR | Length: 250mm

R6368 BR, 20T Brake Van - Era 4/5

Livery: BR | Length: 98mm

R6930	Open Wagons, three pack, Various - Era 2/3	
	Livery: Private Owner	Length: 3 x 88mm

R6836	Box Vans, three pack, Various - Era 3	
	Livery: LMS	Length: 3 x 88mm

R6891	Petrol Tankers, three pack, Various - Era 2/3	
	Livery: Private Owner	Length: 3 x 114mm

49

TRAIN PACKS

Hornby's selection of Train Packs during 2020 covers the lifespan of passenger railways in the United Kingdom, from Stephenson's Rocket to LNER's new Azuma sets and provide the railway modeller with a chance to match locomotives with suitable rolling stock, or to complete entire trains.

A Hornby Train Pack represents a snapshot in time, drawn from research archives that can mark an anniversary of a particular locomotive, train or event, an unusual livery combination, a specific pairing of locomotive and rolling stock, or to simply represent a common train type in service.

Several newly tooled models appear in this year's range, starting with George Stephenson's Rocket, which is combined with three First Class coaches in a train pack that is representative of the Rocket's condition during the L&MR's Rainhill Trials. Building on the experience gained from designing the diminutive Peckett W4 and Ruston 48DS, this new model of the Rocket is a world away from the original Tri-ang model in terms of detail and fidelity and is, quite simply, a piece of modelling history. The second totally new model is as far removed from the Rocket as could possible be, features British Rail's ill-fated Class 370 Advanced Passenger Train, a design that would eventually lead to the development of GEC/BR's Class 91 and Mk.4 sets on the ECML and GEC/Alsthom's Pendolino on the WCML. Two train packs are available; the five-car pack forming the basis upon which a full fourteen-car set can be built and the seven-car pack, which represents a prototypical set appearing late on in the APT's timeline, during the APT-U testing phase.

Other train packs in the 2020 range include several stunning liveries, from the Pullman inspired 'Northern Belle', to the Inter7City ScotRail HSTs plus LNER's graceful Azuma and TransPennine's striking Nova 1 AT300 bi-mode sets and Northern Rail's inspired 'Spirit of the Royal Air Force' Class 156. The highlight of the new liveries though, has to be that which appears on the Eurostar Class 373 'Yellow Submarine' train pack; a striking representation of Eurostar's first vinyl wrap.

To place an order contact Hornby Customer Services on: **01843 233512** or visit your local stockist.

LIVERPOOL & MANCHESTER RAILWAY

Rocket was designed and built as a direct response to the invitation to the Rainhill Trials issued by the Directors of the Liverpool and Manchester Railway on April 25, 1829 for, 'a Locomotive Engine, which shall be a decided improvement on any hitherto constructed, subject to certain stipulations and conditions.'

Initially known as the Premium Locomotive Engine, design and development work on the locomotive took place at Robert Stephenson & Co's Newcastle factory and while George Stephenson is acknowledged as the engineer responsible for Rocket, much of the work was carried out by his son Robert, in conjunction with the company's draftsman George Phipps and Works Manager William Hutchinson. Rocket was completed to Robert Stephenson's satisfaction on September 2, 1829 and was transported to Killingworth Colliery for steam and load haul testing prior to the Rainhill Trials. Rocket's livery of yellow and black, with a white chimney, mirrored that of the L&MR's existing first class coaches which, in turn, copied that of the fastest road coaches at the time and was chosen by George Stephenson in 1828 to suggest speed and reliability to a new class of travelling public. The outcome of the Rainhill Trials established Rocket as the clear winner and the L&MR Board awarded Robert Stephenson and Co. the contract to produce four further 'Rocket' type locomotives, all of which were to incorporate improvements highlighted by the Rainhill Trials.

Over the next three years, 'Rocket' itself was gradually improved, until February 1833 when the locomotive was relegated to secondary and standby duties. 'Rocket' was purchased by Thompson & Sons of Kirkhouse for operating mineral trains on the Brampton Railway, but could not cope with the heavy trains and was withdrawn from service in 1840. In 1850 'Rocket' was moved to the Newcastle works of Robert Stephenson & Co. and in 1862 was donated to the Patent Museum, the forerunner of the Science Museum, by the Thompson family.

| R3810 | L&MR, Stephenson's Rocket Train Pack - Era 1 | | | DCC READY | 8 PIN CONNECTION |

NEW Q2

| Designer: George Stephenson | Period: 1829 Rainhill Trials | Motor: 5 Pole Skew Wound | Curved Track: Hornby 1st Radius + / 371mm+ |
| Locomotive: Stephenson 0-2-2 'Rocket' type | Coaches: L&MR Three Compartment First Class | Locomotive Livery: L&MR, Yellow | Coaches Livery: L&MR, Yellow | Operating Area/Route: Liverpool & Manchester Railway |

RAILWAY MUSEUM
National Railway Museum
The National Railway Museum is the largest railway museum in the world with exhibitions and collections illustrating over 300 years of British railway history.
Produced under licence for SCMG Enterprises Ltd. © SCMGE
Every purchase supports our museums. www.nrm.org.uk

Limited Availability

| R3670 | BR, Class 72xx Freight Pack - Era 5 | | | DCC READY | 8 PIN CONNECTION |

| Designer: Charles Collett | Period: 1950s | Motor: 3 Pole | Curved Track: Hornby 2nd Radius + / 438mm+ |
| Locomotive: BR Class 72xx, 2-8-2T '7224' | Wagons: Private Owner 4 Plank Wagon No. 337 'Granomac', Private Owner 6 Plank Wagon No. 3262 'Cory Brothers', Private Owner 6 plank Wagon No. 106 'Corker & Bevan' | Locomotive Livery: BR Black | Wagons Livery: Private Owner | Operating Area/Route: South/Mid Wales |

HORNBY®

To place an order contact Hornby Customer Services on: **01843 233512** or visit your local stockist.

R3398	BR, The Lyme Regis Branch Line Train Pack - Era 4				DCC READY	8 PIN CONNECTION

Designer: William Adams	Period: Late 1940s/ Early 1950s	Motor: 5 Pole Skew Wound,	Curved Track: Hornby 2nd Radius + / 438mm+	
Locomotive: BR Adams 415 Class, 4-4-2 '30583'	Coaches: Maunsell (ex-LSWR) Brake Third 'S2636S' and Brake Composite 'S6401S' forming Set 42	Locomotive Livery: Early BR, Lined Black	Coaches Livery: BR Maroon	Operating Area/Route: Dorset/Devon Boarder

R3397	LMS, Suburban Train Pack - Era 3				DCC READY	8 PIN CONNECTION

Designer: Sir Henry Fowler	Period: 1930s	Motor: 5 Pole Skew Wound	Curved Track: Hornby 2nd Radius + / 438mm+	
Locomotive: LMS Fowler 4P 2-6-4T '2328'	Coaches: Stanier 57' Non-Corridor Brake Third No. 20768, Non-Corridor Brake Third No. 20769, Non-Corridor Composite No. 16592	Locomotive Livery: LMS, Lined Black	Coaches Livery: LMS Maroon	Operating Area/Route: Suburban areas of London, the Midlands and Scotland

R3828	BR (The Aberdonian) Tornado Train Pack - Era 11				DCC READY	8 PIN CONNECTION

NEW Q4	Designer: A1 Steam Locomotive Trust	Period: 2019	Motor: 3 Pole and Fly Wheel	Curved Track: Hornby 2nd Radius + / 438mm+	
	Locomotive: Peppercorn A2 4-6-2 60163 'Tornado'	Coaches: BR Mk1 BSK 35185, TSO 4856, FO 3096	Locomotive Livery: Transitional BR, Apple Green	Coaches Livery: BR Maroon	Operating Area/Route: Edinburgh -- Aberdeen

53

The Sir Nigel Gresley Locomotive Trust Ltd is the owner and operator of the A4 Pacific locomotive 4498 / 60007 Sir Nigel Gresley, the post war steam speed record holder. www.sirnigelgresley.org.uk

R3402 — LNER, The Queen of Scots Train Pack - Era 3

DCC READY | 8 PIN CONNECTION

Designer: Sir Nigel Gresley	**Period:** 1930s	**Motor:** 5 Pole Skew Wound, Loco Drive	**Curved Track:** Hornby 2nd Radius + / 438mm+	
Locomotive: Gresley Class A4 4-6-2 No. 4500 'Garganey'	**Coaches:** Pullman First Class Kitchen Car, 'Thelma' Pullman First Class Parlour Car 'Sheila' Pullman Third Class Brake Car No.77	**Locomotive Livery:** LNER Garter Blue	**Coaches Livery:** Pullman Umber and Cream, Early Crest	**Operating Area/Route:** East Coast Main Line: London - Glasgow - London

R3606 — Pullman, 5-BEL 'Brighton Belle' Train Pack - Era 6

DCC READY | 8 PIN CONNECTION

Designer: Metropolitan Cammell	**Period:** 1967 to 1969	**Motor:** 5 Pole Skew Wound	**Length:** 279mm Each Unit	**Curved Track:** Hornby 2nd Radius + / 438mm+

Contents: Pullman, 5-BEL 'Brighton Belle' Unit No. 3053, Driving Motor Brake Parlour Third, Car No. 92 and No. 93

The inaugural trip of the new 'Southern Belle' service took place on 1 January, 1933, headed by Unit 2051 with the train becoming an immediate success, despite the season.

On 29 June, 1934, to coincide with the opening of the 'Swimming Stadium' in Brighton, the Southern Railway renamed the service as the 'Brighton Belle'. Designated initially as 5-PUL, the new electric Pullman cars were built in three sets of five by Metropolitan Cammell in Birmingham, each set consisting of a Driving Motor Brake Parlour Third (DMBPT) at either end, with two Trailer Parlour First with Kitchen cars (TPFK) and a Trailer Parlour Third (TPT) in between.

The introduction of the 5-PUL Pullman cars in 1933 marked a departure in the naming convention of the First Class cars, with the classical female names of the Royal family giving way to short spelled, popular female names of the late 1920s/1930s.

Third Class cars were still numbered from the last two digits of their Pullman schedule numbers but the Unit numbers provided were assigned according to the needs of the Southern Railway. The 5-BEL designation that the Sets are now known came into effect sometime after 1935.

Eventually, faced with competition on all fronts, the loss of the luxury reputation during the late 1960s/early 1970s under BR's blue and grey livery scheme, as well as the gradual deterioration of the units, the last ever 'Brighton Belle' departed for Victoria on April 30, 1972. All five cars from Unit 3053 have survived into preservation, four being stored by Venice-Simplon Orient Express with the fifth, Car No. 85, currently being restored by the 5-BEL Trust (www.brightonbelle.com), their intention being to return a four-car unit to mainline running.

| R3607 | BR, The 15 Guinea Special Train Pack - Era 5 | | | DCC READY | 8 PIN CONNECTION |

Designer: Robert Riddles	Period: August 1968	Motor: 5 Pole Skew Wound, Loco Drive	Curved Track: Hornby 2nd Radius + / 438mm+
Locomotive: BR Standard 7 'Britannia' Class 4-6-2 '70013' 'Oliver Cromwell'	Coaches: BR Mk1 BSO 'E9223' BR Mk1 TSO 'M4995' BR Mk1 TSO 'M4933'	Locomotive Livery: BR Lined Brunswick Green	Coaches Livery: BR Maroon, BR Blue and Grey	Operating Area/Route: 1T57 Liverpool - Manchester - Carlisle - Manchester - Liverpool

| R3700 | SR 2-BIL Train Pack - Era 3 | | | | DCC READY | 8 PIN CONNECTION |

Designer: Richard Maunsell	Period: 1937	Motor: 5 Pole Skew Wound	Length: 264mm Each Unit	Curved Track: Hornby 2nd Radius + / 438mm+

Contents: SR, 2-BIL, Unit 2152; DMBT(L) No. 10718 and DTC(L) No. 12185

A modified design from the first of the 2-BIL units, unit 2152 was the last in the series and was delivered in November 1938 for use on the London Waterloo to Reading Route.

Unit 2152 was finally withdrawn from British Rail service on 4 April, 1970 and following withdrawal it was initially stored at Lancing, before being moved to Selhurst for stripping out.

| R3699 | BR 2-HIL Train Pack - Era 5 | | | | DCC READY | 8 PIN CONNECTION |

Designer: O.V.S Bulleid	Period: 1939	Motor: 5 Pole Skew Wound	Length: 264mm Each Unit	Curved Track: Hornby 2nd Radius + / 438mm+

Contents: BR 2-HIL Unit 2611; (HAL) DMBT No. 10729 and (BIL) DTC(L) No. 12146

Designed for the 1939 London to Maidstone and Gillingham electrification scheme, Unit 2611 was one of the first 2-HAL units to be built at Eastleigh, entering service in February 1939. Unit 2611 was damaged by enemy action while at London Victoria Station on 9 October, 1940, but was repaired and

sent back to service. Involved in a collision with a 2-BIL in late 1959, the undamaged vehicles from each set were paired as a '2-HIL' until March 1961, when 2611 reverted to being a 2-HAL unit.

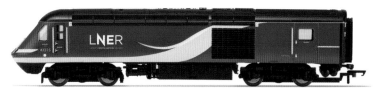

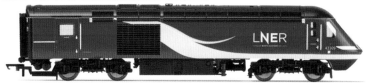

R3802	**LNER, Class 43 HST Train Pack - Era 11**				**DCC READY** **8 PIN CONNECTION**

Designer: Sir Kenneth Grange	**Period:** Late 1970s onwards	**Motor:** 5 Pole Skew Wound	**Length:** 235mm Each Unit	**Curved Track:** Hornby 2nd Radius + / 438mm+

Contents: LNER, Class 43 HST, Power cars 43315 and 43309

Both units were built at Crewe, being delivered in early 1979; 43309 on 20 January and 43315 on 10 March, but initially the vehicles were formed into different sets and numbered 43109 and 43115 respectively.

Both have shared similar naming conventions, as 'Yorkshire Evening Press' and 'Yorkshire Cricket Academy', then as 'Scone Palace' and 'Aberdeenshire', but both are currently unnamed in LNER service.

R3944	**BR, Class 43 HST Train Pack - Era 8**				**DCC READY** **8 PIN CONNECTION**

NEW Q4

Designer: Sir Kenneth Grange	**Period:** 1978	**Motor:** 5 Pole Skew Wound	**Length:** 235mm Each Unit	**Curved Track:** Hornby 2nd Radius + / 438mm+

Contents: BR InterCity (Swallow) 'City of Edinburgh', Class 43 HST, Power Cars 43123 and 43065

43123 was delivered into service on 14 April 1979 and 43065 on 15 October 1977 and both power cars have had their operational life extended by the fitting of MTU power units at Brush Traction, 43123 being the last of the Valenta engine HSTs. Both cars are easily identified by virtue of the buffers that were fitted during the 'surrogate' DVT period and by the fact that they were redesignated as Class 43/4

following their conversion to MTU power. 43123 was renumbered as 43423 on 31 January 2011 and given the name 'VALENTA 1972-2010' on 15 May 2011, while 43065 was renumbered 43465 on 31 December 2010, retaining the name 'City of Edinburgh' that it had first received on 25 February 1996.

R3808	**Cross Country, Class 43 HST Train Pack - Era 10**				**DCC READY** **8 PIN CONNECTION**

Due Q2

Designer: Sir Kenneth Grange	**Period:** 1978	**Motor:** 5 Pole Skew Wound	**Length:** 235mm Each Unit	**Curved Track:** Hornby 2nd Radius + / 438mm+

Contents: Cross Country Class 43 HST, Power Cars 43285 and 43304

Originally numbered as 43085 and 43104 respectively, 43285 was delivered into service on 25 March 1978 and 43304 on 14 October 1978. Operational life was extended by Brush Traction when MTU

Power Units were fitted, 43285 being so fitted between November 2007 and 13 August 2008, with 43304 following it by entering Brush's Works the next day and being returned on 12 December 2008.

To place an order contact Hornby Customer Services on: **01843 233512** or visit your local stockist.

| **R3685** | GWR, Class 43 HST Train Pack - Era 10 | | | | **DCC READY** | **8 PIN CONNECTION** |

| | **Designer:** Sir Kenneth Grange | **Period:** 1978 | **Motor:** 5 Pole Skew Wound | **Length:** 235mm Each Unit | **Curved Track:** Hornby 2nd Radius + / 438mm+ |

Contents: GWR, Class 43 HST, Power Cars 43041 'Meningitis Trust Support for Life' and 43005

43041 was built at Crewe and entered traffic on 28 February, 1977, while 43005 entered traffic on 30 September, 1976. 43041 carried the name 'City of Discovery' between 27 June, 1990 and 30 June, 2011, before being renamed as 'Meningitis Trust Support for Life' on 1 July, 2011, while 43005 has remained unnamed.

| **R3903** | ScotRail, Class 43 HST Train Pack - Era 10 | | | | **DCC READY** | **8 PIN CONNECTION** |

| **NEW Q3** | **Designer:** Sir Kenneth Grange | **Period:** 1978 | **Motor:** 5 Pole Skew Wound | **Length:** 235mm Each Unit | **Curved Track:** Hornby 2nd Radius + / 438mm+ |

Contents: ScotRail, Class 43 HST, 'A New Era' 43021 and 43132

43021 was delivered into service on 9 July 1976 and 43132 on 21 July 1979. Operational life was extended by Brush Traction when MTU power units were fitted, 43021 being fitted between 9 October 2006 and 21 December 2006, with 43132 going into Brush's Works between 18 July 2007 and 20 September 2007. On 31 August 2017 both units were taken off lease from First Great Western to be transferred to ScotRail, running as a 2+4 set to Craigentinny on 1st September, along with Mk.3 coaches 40207, 42047, 42207 and 44015, where they were rebranded with vinyls proclaiming 'A New Era' on the power cars and 'We're building the best railway Scotland's ever had' on the central two coaches.

| **R3770** | GWR, Class 43 HST Train Pack - Era 11 | | | | **DCC READY** | **8 PIN CONNECTION** |

| **NEW Q2** | **Designer:** Sir Kenneth Grange | **Period:** 1976/1982 | **Motor:** 5 Pole Skew Wound | **Length:** 235mm Each Unit | **Curved Track:** Hornby 2nd Radius + / 438mm+ |

Contents: GWR, Class 43 HST, Power Cars 43002 'Sir Kenneth Grange' and 43198

The first and last production HST Power Cars into traffic, 43002 was delivered into service on 18 February 1976 and 43198 on 13 August 1982. Operational life was extended by Brush Traction when MTU power units were fitted, 43002 being fitted between 4 January 2008 and 6 March 2008, with 43132 going into Brush's Works between 19 January 2006 and 26 September 2008. On 18 May 2019, the Great Western Railway ran their last HST services out of London Paddington, with 43002 'Sir Kenneth Grange' and 43198 working the very last diagram, the 18:30 London Paddington to Exeter St. Davids.

57

R3769	Network Rail, Class 43 HST Train Pack - Era 11			DCC READY	8 PIN CONNECTION

NEW Q2

Designer: Sir Kenneth Grange	Period: 1976	Motor: 5 Pole Skew Wound	Length: 235mm Each Unit	Curved Track: Hornby 2nd Radius + / 438mm+

Contents: Network Rail, Class 43 HST, Power Cars 43013 'Mark Carne CBE' and 43014 'The Railway Observer'

Both 43013 'Mark Carne CBE' and 43014 'The Railway Observer' entered traffic on the Western Region in May 1976, although they were not paired together in a set, but with 43012 and 43015 respectively. Having been absorbed into the Virgin fleet following privatisation, in October 2002 both power cars were released to Network Rail by Virgin, along with 43062, for use on their High Speed National Measurement Train (NMT). During mid-2009, both 43013 and 43014 were fitted with MTU engine units by Brush Traction, replacing the original Paxman units. On June 14, 2014, 43014 was named 'The Railway Observer' at Derby RTC by the Vice-President of the RCTS, Eric Palmer, while 43013 was named 'Mark Carne CBE' in a ceremony at Paddington Station on July 12, 2018.

R3697	'Northern Belle' Train Pack - Era 10			DCC READY	8 PIN CONNECTION

Designer: Brush Traction	Period: Early 2000s	Motor: 5 Pole Skew Wound	Curved Track: Hornby 2nd Radius + / 438mm+	

Locomotive: WCR Class 57 57601 'Windsor Castle'	Coaches: Northern Belle Mk2D: FO 'Chatsworth' FO 'Warick' BFK '17167'	Locomotive Livery: Northern Belle Umber & Cream	Coaches Livery: Northern Belle Umber & Cream	Operating Area/Route: Across the UK rail network

R3750	Belmond, 'British Pullman' Train Pack - Era 11			DCC READY	8 PIN CONNECTION

Designer: Alstom	Period: 2017 onwards	Motor: 5 Pole Skew Wound,	Curved Track: Hornby 2nd Radius + / 438mm+	

Locomotive: DB Cargo UK Class 67 '67021'	Coaches: Pullman First Class Kitchen car 'Ibis', Pullman First Class Kitchen car 'Ione', Pullman first class Parlour car 'Minerva',	Locomotive Livery: Belmond Pullman Umber & Cream	Coaches Livery: Belmond Pullman Umber & Cream	Operating Area/Route: Across the UK rail network

R3399 | **EWS, Class 67 Freight Train Pack - Era 9** | DCC READY | 8 PIN CONNECTION

| Designer: Alstom | Period: Late 1990s onwards | Motor: 5 Pole Skew Wound, | Curved Track: Hornby 2nd Radius + / 438mm+ |
| Locomotive: EWS Class 67 '67003' | Coaches: MHA Wagons Nos. '394652', '394653' and '394654', | Locomotive Livery: EWS Maroon and Gold | Wagons Livery: EWS Maroon and Gold | Operating Area/Route: Across the UK rail network |

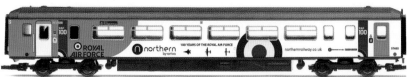

R3772 | **Northern Rail, Class 156 'Spirit of the Royal Air Force' Train Pack - Era 11** | DCC READY | 8 PIN CONNECTION

| Designer: Metro-Cammell | Period: 1989 | Motor: 5 Pole Skew Wound | Length: 310mm Each Unit | Curved Track: Hornby 2nd Radius + / 438mm+ |

Contents: Northern Rail, Class 156, Set 156480, DMS No. 57480 and DMSL No. 52480, 'Spirit of the Royal Air Force'

The Provincial Services sector of British Rail was formed in 1982 and was responsible for a diverse range of routes across the United Kingdom, many of which were heavily subsidised and operated by either elderly first-generation Diesel Multiple Units, or cascaded locomotive hauled coaching stock. With this in mind, rather than refurbish or overhaul existing stock, it was felt that investment in a new fleet of DMUs was more cost effective, compared to loco-hauled trains.

Consequently, a modern DMU was cheaper to operate, caused less wear to the track and could reduce journey times, leading to a higher frequency service. Low cost, lightweight railbus 'Pacer' DMUs were seen as the solution for the short distance and lightly used routes, while for inter-urban routes, medium-weight 'Sprinter' DMU's of a more traditional design would be used. The Class 156 two-car sets formed part of the second generation of medium-weight DMUs, being designed to feel more

like locomotive hauled stock, or an express coach, with end doors and 2+2 seating fitted with arm rests and tables. To differentiate them from the first generation 'Sprinters', the class came to be known as 'Super Sprinters', along with their Class 155 stablemates and between 1987-1989, Metro-Cammell of Birmingham built 114 of the two-car Class 156 sets, numbered in the series 156401-156514. Each set was formed from a Driving Motor Standard (DMS), which contained an area for storing wheelchairs, bicycles and bulky luggage, and a Driving Motor Standard Lavatory (DMSL).

Two-car set 156480, comprising DMS No. 57480 and DMSL No. 52480, was built in February 1989 and entered traffic at Neville Hill. Currently operating with Northern Rail, on 23 June, 2018 at a ceremony at Newcastle Central station, the unit was unveiled in a special RAF100 livery wrap that it will carry for the next three years.

R3773 | **BR Provincial, Class 156 Train Pack - Era 8** | DCC READY | 8 PIN CONNECTION

| Designer: Metro-Cammell | Period: 1982 - 1997 | Motor: 5 Pole Skew Wound | Length: 310mm Each Unit | Curved Track: Hornby 2nd Radius + / 438mm+ |

Contents: BR Provincial, Class 156, Set 156401, DMS No. 57401 and DMSL No. 52401

Two-car set 156401, comprising DMS No. 57401 and DMSL No. 52401, was the first of the class to enter service, being built in November 1987 and was sent to the RTC at Derby in December for type testing and evaluation. Wearing the Provincial Sector mid-blue and grey livery with 'Sprinter' branding, 156401 entered revenue earning service at Norwich Crown Point, working on East Anglia to North West express services.

Between 1989-91, 'Super Sprinter' branding replaced 'Sprinter' but the Provincial base livery was carried long into privatisation under Central Trains, with 156401 not receiving the 'Barmouth to Yarmouth Railway' two-tone green until 2004/05. Once Central Trains was disbanded in November 2007, 156401 passed into East Midlands Train service and can currently still be seen working under East Midlands Railway operations.

By the end of 1970 the British Rail Board began considering how best to practically incorporate the technology of the APT-E into a prototype that would lead to full production Advanced Passenger Trains on the West Coast Main Line.

From the outset the pre-production APT project, or APT-P, was considered to be nothing more than a proving prototype for evaluation, prior to the finalised Advance Passenger Train design being authorised for squadron service as the APT-S. Commencement of services was set for 1977 and the Chief Mechanical and Electrical Engineers' Department (CM&EE) design engineers began work in October 1973. Due to the unsuitability of the OHP wires in place on the WCML at that time, the design had to be compromised by arranging the two power cars in the middle of the train, rather than at the ends and this created two 1+6 formations of DTS, TS, TRBS, TU, TF, TBF and NDM (Non-Driving Motor).

The NDM was completed for testing in June 1977 and in mid-1978 was joined by the rest of the first half set for testing on the WCML, being unveiled to the Press on June 7th. Hampered by industrial action, it was February 1979 before the full train was marshalled for testing but by the end of the year, on December 20, 1979, a new rail speed record of 162.2mph was achieved and in March 1980 all three APT-P trains were delivered and ready for mileage accumulation on the WCML.

A demonstration run on 18 April 1980 with a 1+9 set was ended with a derailment caused by a faulty articulated bogie, signalling the beginning of the APT 'jinx' and the postponement of passenger introduction. Mainline testing resumed in Spring 1981 but media and public opinion was turning against the project, with some individuals in Government and within the British Railways Board expressing their discontent as well. Entering public service on December 7, 1981, cold weather braking problems resulted in the APT being taken out of traffic once more, this time until the Summer of 1982. At the beginning of 1982, the CM&EE considered that development problems with the ATP-P project would mean that the introduction of APT-S, scheduled for 1988, would not happen because APT-P still required at least six more years to achieve an acceptable degree of reliability and given this situation, a meeting of the BRB Railway Executive Group on 23 June 1982 looked at options for the commercial introduction of APT as part an overall InterCity traction strategy. The quickest solution was a tilting but non-articulated, option of two power cars, one at either end of the train and ten passenger cars that formed the APT-U. Exceeding its budget, APT-P had now reached the end of its development programme and from March 1983 the fleet was reduced, with parts being cannibalised to keep the remaining vehicles running. At the end of May 1985, the APT-P was withdrawn from service, with the Intercity Development Train (APT-D) continuing until December 1986.

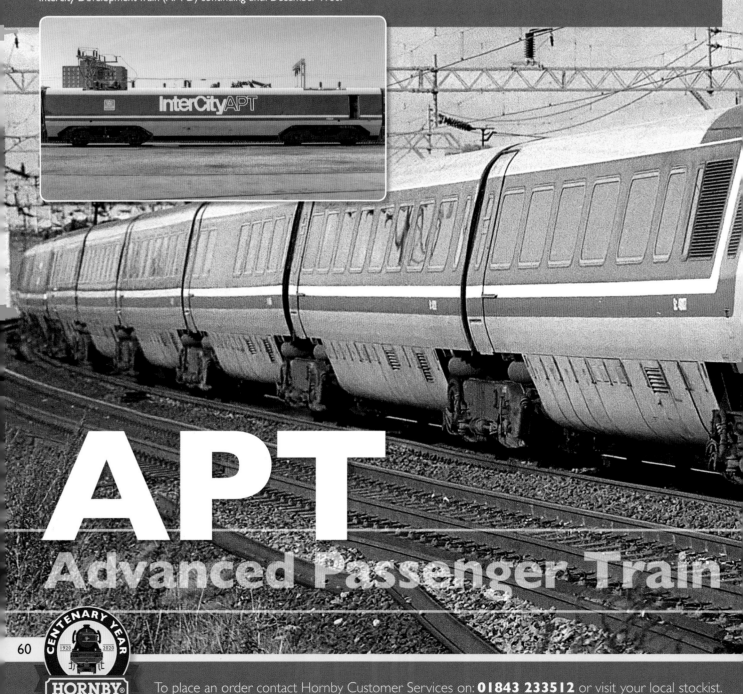

APT
Advanced Passenger Train

CENTENARY YEAR 1920 2020 HORNBY®

NEW Q4 All models shown are 'NEW Q4'.

APT 5-Car Train Pack:

R3873	BR, Class 370 Advanced Passenger Train, Sets 370 003 and 370 004, 5-car pack - Era 7	DCC READY	8 PIN CONNECTION

Designer: BREL | Livery: BR Intercity, Intercity Executive | Motor: 5 Pole Skew Wound

Curved Track: Hornby 2nd Radius + / 438mm+

APT 7-Car Train Pack:

R3874	BR, Class 370 Advanced Passenger Train, Set 370 001 and 370 002, 7-car pack - Era 7	DCC READY	8 PIN CONNECTION

Designer: BREL | Livery: BR Intercity, Intercity Executive | Motor: 5 Pole Skew Wound

Curved Track: Hornby 2nd Radius + / 438mm+

Non-Driving Motor Unit:

R3948	BR InterCity Non-Driving Motor (NDM), 49004 - Era 7	DCC READY	8 PIN CONNECTION

Designer: BREL | Livery: BR Intercity, Intercity Executive | Motor: 5 Pole Skew Wound

Curved Track: Hornby 2nd Radius + / 438mm+

Aditional coaches available:

R4970	BR, InterCity APT-U Ex-TS Development Vehicle, Sc48204/977527 - Era 7

Designer: BREL | Livery: BR Intercity, Intercity Executive | Length: 276mm

Curved Track: Hornby 2nd Radius + / 438mm+

R40011/A	BR, Class 370 Advanced Passenger Train 2-car TS Coach Pack, 48203 + 48204 / 48201 + 48202 - Era 7

Designer: BREL | Livery: BR Intercity, Intercity Executive | Length: 276mm

Curved Track: Hornby 2nd Radius + / 438mm+

R40011 This coach pack includes the two TS coaches required in part to complete R3873 5-car Pack (Sets 370 003 and 370 004).
R40011A This coach pack includes the two TS coaches required in part to complete R3874 7-car Pack (Sets 370 001 and 370 002).

R40012/A	BR, Class 370 Advanced Passenger Train 2-car TRBS Coach Pack, 48403 + 48404 / 48401 + 48402 - Era 7

Designer: BREL | Livery: BR Intercity, Intercity Executive | Length: 276mm

Curved Track: Hornby 2nd Radius + / 438mm+

R40012 This coach pack includes the two TRBS coaches required in part to complete R3873 5-car Pack (Sets 370 003 and 370 004).
R40012A This coach pack includes the two TRBS coaches required in part to complete R3874 7-car Pack (Sets 370 001 and 370 002).

R40013/A	BR, Class 370 Advanced Passenger Train 2-car TU Coach Pack, 48303 + 48304 / 48301 + 48302 - Era 7

Designer: BREL | Livery: BR Intercity, Intercity Executive | Length: 276mm

Curved Track: Hornby 2nd Radius + / 438mm+

R40013 This coach pack includes the two TU coaches required in part to complete R3873 5-car Pack (Sets 370 003 and 370 004).
R40013A This coach pack includes the two TU coaches required in part to complete R3874 7-car Pack (Sets 370 001 and 370 002).

R40014/A	BR, Class 370 Advanced Passenger Train 2-car TF Coach Pack, 48503 + 48504 / 48501 + 48502 - Era 7

Designer: BREL | Livery: BR Intercity, Intercity Executive | Length: 276mm

Curved Track: Hornby 2nd Radius + / 438mm+

R40014 This coach pack includes the two TF coaches required in part to complete R3873 5-car Pack (Sets 370 003 and 370 004).
R40014A This coach pack includes the two TF coaches required in part to complete R3874 7-car Pack (Sets 370 001 and 370 002).

InterCity APT

370 007

HORNBY®

R3952	Avanti West Coast, Class 390 Pendolino Train Pack - Era 11			DCC READY	8 PIN CONNECTION

NEW Q4

Designer: Alstom	Period: 2019	Motor: 3 Pole	Curved Track: Hornby 2nd Radius + / 438mm+
Locomotive and Coaches: Avanti West Coast Black/Blue	Locomotive Livery: Avanti West Coast Black/Blue	Coaches Livery: Avanti West Coast Black/Blue	Operating Area/Route: West Coast Main Line

The Pendolino, named after Fiat Ferroviaria's tilting train Pendolino technology and built by Alstom, is one of the fastest domestic electric multiple units operating in Britain, setting a new speed record for the southbound West Coast Main Line of three hours, fifty-five minutes in September 2006. The first Class 390 Pendolino launched into passenger service on 23 July 2002 and following this, train sets numbered up to 390 034 were initially delivered as eight-car units, with the TS coaches being added during 2004-5 to make nine-car sets. Thirty-one sets were then increased to eleven-car capacity between 2010 and 2012, with four additional eleven-car sets being delivered from Italy, these all being identified in the 390 1xx range. This model is in the latest identity for these trains, Avanti West Coast which took over operation of the West Coast Main Line services in December 2019.
© Copyright FTWCR 2019 manufactured by Hornby under license from FTWCR.

Additional coaches and further information regarding the Avanti West Coast, Class 390 Pendolino can be found on p175 of this catalogue.

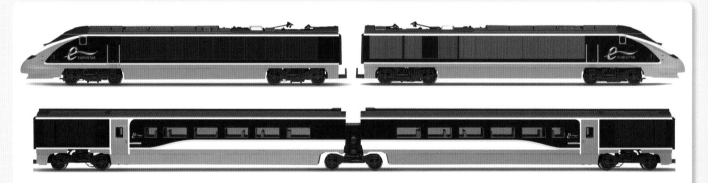

R3215	Eurostar, Class 373/1 e300 Train Pack - Era 10			DCC READY	8 PIN CONNECTION

Designer: GEC-Alstom	Period: 2015 onwards	Motor: 3 Pole, Loco Drive	Curved Track: Hornby 2nd Radius + / 438mm+
Locomotive: Eurostar e300 Power Cars 3015, 3016	Coaches: Eurostar e300 Standard Class Cars, 93 70 373015 1-5 GB EIL 93 70 373016 1-4 GB EIL	Locomotive Livery: Eurotunnel e300 Blue/ Yellow Grey	Coaches Livery: Eurotunnel e300 Blue/ Yellow Grey	Operating Area/Route: London - Paris - London London - Brussels - London

Nothing can beat the performance and sheer awesome elegance of the 300kph Eurostar train as it hurtles through the Kent countryside heading for the Channel Tunnel and then on from there to Paris or Brussels.

However, the old grey and yellow livery has given way to the more modern and striking colour scheme of steel blue and grey with yellow banding which now clearly illustrates the current and dynamic Eurostar corporate colours.

Additional coaches available:

R4580	Eurostar, Class 373/1 e300 Divisible Centre Saloons Coach Pack - Era 10

Designer: GEC-Alstom	Livery: Eurotunnel e300 Blue/Yellow/Grey	Length: 290mm Each

R3827 — LNER, Hitachi Class 800/1, 'Azuma' Set 800 104 'Celebrating Scotland' Train Pack - Era 11

DCC READY | 8 PIN CONNECTION

NEW Q3

Designer: Hitachi Rail	Period: 2019	Motor: 5 Pole Skew Wound, Loco Drive	Curved Track: Hornby 2nd Radius + / 438mm+

Locomotive and Coaches: Set No. 800 104 'Celebrating Scotland', comprising PDTS 811 104, MS 813 104, MS 815 104, MF 818 104 and PDTRBF 819 104	Locomotive Livery: LNER, Azuma/LNER Tartan	Coaches Livery: LNER, Azuma/LNER Tartan	Operating Area/Route: ECML

Set 800 104 was chosen for the launch of the flagship 05.40 Flying Scotsman service from Edinburgh to London King's Cross on August 1 2019, along with the 17.30 return working, and for the occasion a new livery 'Celebrating Scotland' was designed, featuring a newly created LNER tartan.

Designed by Ken MacDonald, of Houston Kiltmakers in Paisley, the tartan colours combine blue for Scotland, red for England, white for the Yorkshire rose, purple for the heather of Scotland, green for the rolling hills and landscape along the ECML and silver grey to represent the tracks of the railway.

R3813 — SouthEastern Class 395 'Hornby Visitor Centre' - Era 11

DCC READY | 8 PIN CONNECTION

Designer: Hitachi Rail	Period: 2019	Motor: 5 Pole Skew Wound, Loco Drive	Curved Track: Hornby 2nd Radius + / 438mm+

Locomotive and Coaches: Set 395 013 'Hornby Visitor Centre' comprising PDTSO 39131, MSO 39132, MSO 39133 and PDTSO 39136	Locomotive Livery: South Eastern Highspeed Blue	Coaches Livery: South Eastern Highspeed Blue	Operating Area/Route: CTRL/HS1

The first completed train, 395 001, arrived at Southampton Docks on 23 August 2007 and was moved to Hitachi's new £53 million maintenance facility at Ashford on 30th August where testing commenced on local lines during October.

On 1st November test running commenced on the CTRL, with homologation testing being undertaken by Serco and SNCF International assisting with the testing of signalling systems. By March 2008, 395 001 had been joined by three further sets, with shipping of the main production batch beginning in December 2008. The ORR performance acceptance tests of 4,000 miles fault-free running were achieved six months ahead of schedule, allowing a 'preview' service between London St. Pancras, Ebbsfleet International and Ashford International stations to

commence on 29 June 2009. The final three trains arrived in the UK during August 2009, with the final train being delivered to Southeastern on 11 December 2009, just ahead of the official launch of HS1 services on 14th December.

Almost ten years to the day after Class 395 001 preview services commenced, a ceremony at Southeastern's Ramsgate Engineering Depot Open Day on Saturday 8 June officially named Set 395 013 as 'Hornby Visitor Centre', recognising the value to tourism in Thanet that the attraction provides, as well as marking the return to Margate by the manufacturer after an absence of four years.

Additional coaches available:

R4999 — South Eastern, Class 395 Highspeed Train 2-car Coach Pack, MSO 39134 and MSO 39135 - Era 11

NEW Q1

Designer: Hitachi Rail	Livery: South Eastern, Blue	Length: 263mm

Train Packs

Once upon a time...

3005

The Beatles
Yellow Submarine

Side 1

Side 2

Eurostar's first use of the Class 373 for an external agency marketing campaign took place in September 1999 when the Sets 3005/3006 were transformed with a vinyl wrap that recreated scenes from The Beatles' film 'Yellow Submarine'.

The Eurostar vinyl wrap was just one of the promotional events that marked the release of the remixed album that Autumn, along with the remastered version of the film that was released in cinemas and on video. At the time, the film had been unavailable for over a decade and the relaunched version included scenes that were edited out of the original version, while the album featured remixes of songs, such as 'With A Little Help From My Friends' and 'Lucy In The Sky With Diamonds'; the first such time a Beatles album had ever been remixed.

Costing in excess of £100,000 the artwork was the result of four months intensive work with the finishes vinyl artwork taking two weeks to print and a further six days to apply to the train. At over 400 metres in length, each carriage portrayed a different design, telling a different part of the Yellow Submarine story. On Wednesday 8 September, accompanied by a Jazz band playing 'Yellow Submarine', Sets 3005/3006 departed Waterloo on the official launch, much to the surprise of passengers booked on the service, which was a normal departure rather than a dedicated press charter. Industrial action at the time resulted in the roll-out being a lower key event than may otherwise have been planned, but the train still retained the graphics for the next three months, operating between London, Paris and Brussels.

R3829	Eurostar, Class 373/1, Set 3005/3006 'Yellow Submarine' Train Pack - Era 9			DCC READY	8 PIN CONNECTION
NEW Q3	Designer: GEC-Alstom	Period: 1999	Motor: 3 Pole, Loco Drive	Curved Track: Hornby 2nd Radius + / 438mm+	

CENTENARY YEAR
1920 2020
HORNBY®

Additional coaches available - Side 1 and Side 2 are shown below

R40001	Eurostar, Class 373/1 'Yellow Submarine' Divisible Centre Saloons Coach Pack - Era 9

| NEW Q2 | Designer: GEC-Alstom | Livery: Eurostar, Beatles imagery | Length: 288mm Each |

65

DCC SOUND
& Accessories

Locomotive sounds add an extra layer of atmosphere to a layout, but the costs associated with third party sound chips can often negate the pleasure that this brings.

To counteract this, Hornby's engineers developed their own in-house system of sound chip, the Hornby Twin Track Sound (TTS) decoder, that not only provides superior DCC control over the regular R7274, R7150 and R8249 decoders but also provides a number of realistic sound functions. Hornby models equipped with TTS have a minimum of sixteen sound functions, some though have more and many are specific to the chosen model, including whistles, horns, start up, idling and in-motion sounds, as well as other relevant sounds.

This digital sound system is not just limited to main range items either, as three RailRoad level models, covering the best known steam locomotives in the United Kingdom, also come equipped with TTS; proving an ideal introduction to sound for those starting out in the hobby. As well as being fitted in locomotives, Hornby have produced two TTS Vent Vans that bring ambient railway sounds to the model railway layout, the content based on feedback received across Hornby's social media, the Engine Shed blog and the various exhibitions that Hornby have attended during the last couple of years.

In addition to TTS fitted locomotives and the TTS Vent Vans, Hornby continue to offer TTS Decoders as solo items, allowing enthusiasts to match their non-TTS fitted locomotives against a range of specific locomotive sounds, with new sound files being worked on by Hornby's Development team for future introduction. All of Honby's newer locomotive models, whether they be steam, diesel or electric, are designed to be 'sound ready', making the process of fitting decoder and speaker more straightforward but the engineers are constantly looking at ways to improve sound quality in the Hornby models and are beginning to fit alternative speaker fitting options into the newly tooled models in the 2020 range, such as the Thompson A2, BR Standard 2MT and Gresley W1. The design of the Class 91 model will also introduce a new speaker configuration and application for Hornby, taking TTS forward in its development.

R3898TTS | BR, Class 08, 0-6-0, 3817 - Era 6 | **DCC FITTED** | **8 PIN CONNECTION**

NEW Q3

Designer: BREL	Entered Service: 1959	Length: 124mm	Motor: 5 Pole Skew Wound	Curved Track: Hornby 1st Radius + / 371mm+

R3605TTS | DB Schenker, Class 60, Co-Co, 60044 'Dowlow' - Era 10 | **DCC FITTED** | **8 PIN CONNECTION**

Designer: British Rail	Entered Service: 1991	Length: 280mm	Motor: 5 Pole Skew Wound	Curved Track: Hornby 2nd Radius + / 438mm+

R3383TTS | BR, Castle Class, 4-6-0, 5050 'Earl of St. Germans' - Era 4 | **DCC FITTED** | **8 PIN CONNECTION**

Designer: Charles Collett	Entered Service: 1936	Length: 265mm	Motor: 5 Pole Skew Wound, Loco Drive	Curved Track: Hornby 2nd Radius + / 438mm+

Locomotive TTS Sound Decoders

R8110	TTS Sound Decoders - 'Castle' Class	8 PIN
	Speaker: 28mm Round	
R7141	TTS Sound Decoders - Merchant Navy (Rebuilt)	8 PIN
	Speaker: 28mm Round	
R7142	TTS Sound Decoders - Class P2	8 PIN
	Speaker: 28mm Round	
R7143	TTS Sound Decoders - 'Britannia' Class	8 PIN
	Speaker: 28mm Round	
R7147	TTS Sound Decoders - Princess Royal Class	8 PIN
	Speaker: 28mm Round	
R7239	TTS Sound Decoders - J36 Class	8 PIN
	Speaker: 28mm Round	
R8108	TTS Sound Decoders - Class A1	8 PIN
	Speaker: 28mm Round	
R8106	TTS Sound Decoders - Class A1/A3	8 PIN
	Speaker: 40 x 20mm Rectangular	
R8107	TTS Sound Decoders - Class A4	8 PIN
	Speaker: 28mm Round	

R8114	TTS Sound Decoders - 'Black 5'	8 PIN
	Speaker: 28mm Round	
R8115	TTS Sound Decoders - Merchant Navy	8 PIN
	Speaker: 28mm Round	
R8117	TTS Sound Decoders - Princess Coronation	8 PIN
	Speaker: 28mm Round	
R8102	TTS Sound Decoders - Class 37	8 PIN
	Speaker: 40 x 20mm Rectangular	
R8119	TTS Sound Decoders - Class 40	8 PIN
	Speaker: 28mm Round	
R7140	TTS Sound Decoders - Class 43 HST (Valenta)	8 PIN
	Speaker: 40 x 20mm Rectangular - Supplied as a twin pack	
R8120	TTS Sound Decoders - Class 43 HST (MTU)	8 PIN
	Speaker: 40 x 20mm Rectangular - Supplied as a twin pack	
R8103	TTS Sound Decoders - Class 47	8 PIN
	Speaker: 28mm Round	
R8123	TTS Sound Decoders - Class 50	8 PIN
	Speaker: 40 x 20mm Rectangular	
R8121	TTS Sound Decoders - Class 66	8 PIN
	Speaker: 40 x 20mm Rectangular	

Rolling Stock with Digital TTS Sound...

The sounds on the current R6925TTS Vent Van have been divided into four groups keeping related sounds together; the Railway Station, Around the Farm, the Town (or Village) and Emergency Services.

Any of these sounds can be played in conjunction with each other, up to the limit of three sounds at any one time, which will encourage enthusiasts to experiment by mixing different sounds together, creating 'soundscapes' that represent different scenarios and applications. This version of the TTS Vent Van adds another twenty-nine sounds and can easily be used in conjunction with the previous model.

The first group of sounds listed are all related to everyday railway sounds of the 1950s/1960s. Enable the 'Main Railway Station' scene by pressing F0 or Function 0 and the continuous random looped sound of a large busy railway station will play. Trains will arrive, doors will slam, announcements will be made, and passengers will walk about the platform.

F1, F2 and F3 relate to an EMU and add arriving, passing and departing sounds, however for a quieter station, just play the sounds individually. Nearby, in a siding, steam locomotives are taking on coal and water, added by F4 and F5. Passing flat wagons (F6) squeal by, adding to the overall scene, while further down the line there might be a level crossing (F7) with a signal box (F8) operating.

At the local bus stop, an AEC RT bus stops, the conductor rings the bell and the bus moves off again (F9), while overhead, a Douglas Dakota DC3 flies by (F10).

The second group of sounds takes place around the farm. A sheep and cattle auction is taking place (F11) which can be overlaid with extra sheep (F12) and cattle (F13) sounds.

In the distance, a tractor is working (F14), while some way off, a shepherd is working his sheep dog (F15).

The third group of sounds moves on to a small town or village, where many familiar sounds can be heard. Bin men are working on a collection (F16) and a milkman plies his trade, either working with a horse and cart (F18) or an electric milk float (F17). In the distance, an ice cream van plays a familiar tune (F19) and a full peal of church bells marks a wedding celebration (F20).

The final group of sounds covers the emergency services and incidents that may happen in a city, town or village with a range of emergency vehicle sounds covering three different periods (F26, F27 and F28) from the 1920s through to the modern day.

These vehicles could be responding to various incidents; possibly it's the speeding car (F21) that crashes (F22), or maybe there is a break-in, as a glass window is broken (F23) and the burglar alarm sounds (F24 or F25).

R6925TTS	Vent Van with Sound - Era 3/4/5	DCC FITTED	8 PIN CONNECTION
	Livery: Non-specific	Length: 80mm	

...Create sounds to bring layouts alive!

DETAILS

A Different perspective

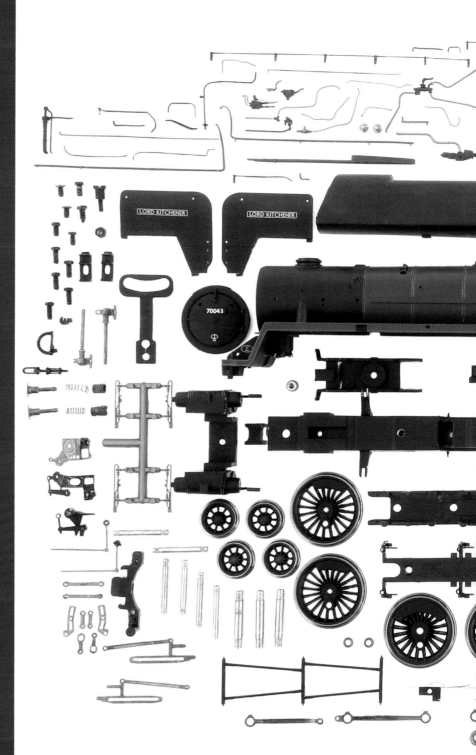

The devil, it is said, lies in the detail and that is a particularly apt statement to make when one considers the wealth of detail that goes into producing Hornby's main range of locomotive, coach and rolling stock models.

The BR Standard 7 'Britannia' class has long been a flagship of Hornby's steam locomotive models and the disassembly of one such model, R3294, 70043 Lord Kitchener, for a press briefing provided an opportunity to lay out each separate item as an example of just how many parts go into making a high end 'ready-to-run' model.

Having produced the individual components, they are then mask sprayed or Tampo printed before being assembled. Once the main body is sprayed and dried it is time for the fine details to be applied and this is done using a process called Tampo printing, which applies 2D designs to 3D surfaces using a silicone pad to stamp a design on to a surface. This simple process belies the fact that lettering might have a number of different colours within it to create effects such as shadowing, or that woodgrain patterns need to be built up. The Tampo printer is indexed to move automatically each time a new colour is required, sometimes only by a matter of tenths of millimetres to allow the colours to be built up.

Each separate item then needs to be assembled and this is not undertaken by automation but by hand on multiple production lines. Each item has to be carefully assembled by hand, passing through the various stages needed to build up each item, whether they be mechanical, or body related. This process includes jobs such as fitting metal etchings, handrails, intakes, panels, body detailing and glazing to bodyshells or the even more complex area of making the chassis, with a number of sub-assemblies coming together that will include wheels, axles, gearboxes and printed circuit boards. It is a massive operation that will use a number of jigs and fixtures to complete, as well as workstations for soldering electrics, assembling and testing motors. Some items will be push fit, some will need gluing, while other components will be secured by rivets, fixed by screws or clamped in place behind other assemblies.

R3294 Lord Kitchener is no longer part of our range but turn to page 109 and you will find R3643, 70046 ANZAC in this year's range of steam locomotives.

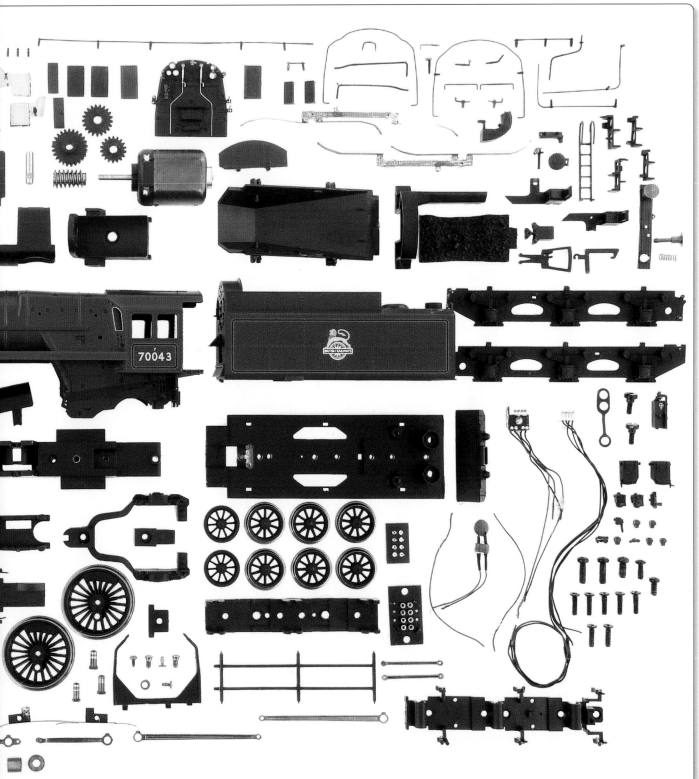

71

STEAM

Locomotives

Ever since the Rainhill Trials in 1829 introduced the general public to the passenger steam locomotive, the 'romance of steam' has enthralled generations and continues to do so today, both in real life and model form.

The Rainhill Trials presented the general public with their first introduction to the glamour and potential of steam travel by rail, fuelling an expansion of the rail network in Britain that was to change the nation's landscape, population centres and social mobility. Even with the demise of steam on the mainline in 1968, industrial use, preservation societies and enthusiastic individuals kept some steam locomotives in use, directly leading to some of the magnificent mainline steam 'specials' and charters that we can see running today. Building on this lineside support, an increasing number of new build projects and major restorations are also encouraging young engineers, through apprenticeships and placements, to bring steam locomotives back to life.

The first of this year's three newly tooled solo steam locomotive classes is the British Railways Standard 2MT 2-6-0, Robert Riddles' workhorse locomotive class that served across much of Britain's railway network in the 1950s and 1960s and examples of which continue to give sterling service in preservation, with 78022 working on the Keighley & Worth Valley Railway and the Great Central Railway hosting 78018 and 78019. Fate was less kind to our next two new model classes, Edward Thompson's rebuilt A2/2 class and his A2/3 class Pacifics, with all twenty-one locomotives across the two classes being scrapped between 1959 and 1965 due to an excess of Pacific type locomotives being available to British Railways' Eastern Region.

The East Coast Main Line was also home to our third newly tooled class of locomotive, although whether a single experimental locomotive can be considered a 'class' is subject to some discussion. Sir Nigel Gresley's 4-6-4HP Baltic, the high-pressure water tube boilered Class W1 'Engine No. 10000', was ordered in February 1928 and made its first track appearance in December 1929, before entering service in June 1930. Five years of hard testing followed, with more time spent in the workshops of the LNER than on the ECML, eventually leading to the locomotive being rebuilt with a traditional steam boiler and an appearance very similar to Gresley's flagship A4 class.

72

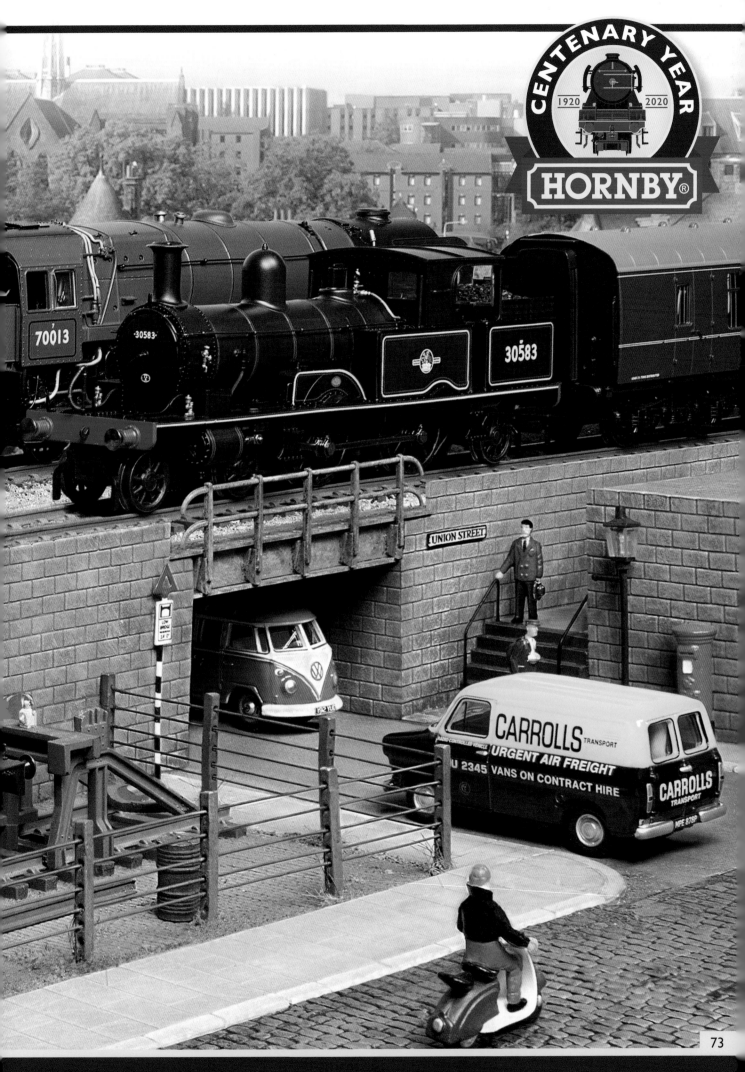

70013

-30583-

30583

UNION STREET

LOW BRIDGE

CARROLLS TRANSPORT
URGENT AIR FREIGHT
U 2345 VANS ON CONTRACT HIRE
CARROLLS TRANSPORT

R3727	LMS, Class B7 'Pug', 0-4-0ST, 11244 - Era 3

Designer: Sir John Aspinall	Entered Service: 1910
Length: 85mm	Motor: 3 Pole Type 7	Curved Track: Hornby 1st Radius + / 371mm+

No. 11244 started life as L&YR No. 28, being built at Horwich in May 1910 and seemingly spent most of its life in and around the dock railway system at Goole. Having spent nearly fifty-two years in traffic, 11244 was withdrawn on 6 March, 1962 and scrapped very shortly after.

R3728	BR, Class B7 'Pug', 0-4-0ST, 51207 - Era 4

Designer: Sir John Aspinall	Entered Service: 1893
Length: 85mm	Motor: 3 Pole Type 7	Curved Track: Hornby 1st Radius + / 371mm+

No. 51207 started life as L&YR No. 504 and was built at Horwich in December 1893, the first locomotive of the second batch built by Aspinall. Having spent over sixty-eight years in traffic, much of it spent around Goole, 51207 was withdrawn in March 1962.

NEW Q3

R3765	Bloxham & Whiston Ironstone Co. Ltd, Peckett B2 Class, 0-6-0ST, 1456/1918 - Era 2	DCC READY	4 PIN CONNECTION

Designer: Peckett & Sons	Entered Service: 1918
Length: 97mm	Motor: 3 Pole	Curved Track: Hornby 1st Radius + / 371mm+

Peckett 1456 was built in 1918 for the Bloxham & Whiston Ironstone Co. Ltd, a firm started by the Whiston Ironstone Co. Ltd in 1914, becoming B&WI Co. Ltd from 22 December 1917. Following the First World War, ironstone was exploited as a resource and in 1918 the B&WI Co. Ltd were in possession of 191 acres of land in and around Bloxham. The workings were short lived though, being abandoned by 1921 and 1456 was sold onto Stewarts & Lloyds Minerals Ltd, working the Harringworth Ironstone Quarries between 1923 and 1952, when the locomotive was scrapped.

NEW Q3

R3766	NCB, Peckett B2 Class, 0-6-0ST, 1426/1916 - Era 6	DCC READY	4 PIN CONNECTION

Designer: Peckett & Sons	Entered Service: 1916
Length: 97mm	Motor: 3 Pole	Curved Track: Hornby 1st Radius + / 371mm+

Peckett 1426 was built in 1916 for the Glasbrook Bros. at their Garngoch Colliery No.3, which employed 468 men at that time. In 1947, as the coal mines were nationalised, Garngoch came under the NCB's South West Division, Area No. 1, No. 2 Group, which covered Morlais, Mountain and Brynlliw collieries, but by 1965 the colliery was uneconomical and the men and locomotives were transferred to Brynlliw, which had reopened in 1961 having received a £4.8 million redevelopment. 1426 remained at Brynlliw until closure in 1982, using spares from Peckett 1187 to keep running and was eventually placed in the care of the Swansea Museum, where it is currently in open storage at the Landore Reserve Collection site.

CENTENARY YEAR 1920 2020 **HORNBY®**

NEW Q1

R3868	Crawshay Brothers, Peckett W4 Class, 0-4-0ST, 490/1890 - Era 2	DCC READY	4 PIN CONNECTION

Designer: Peckett & Sons		Entered Service: 1890

Length: 84mm	Motor: 3 Pole	Curved Track: Hornby 1st Radius + / 371mm+

Peckett Works No. 490/1890 was built for the Crawshay Brothers at Cyfarthfa Ironworks, which had been reopened in 1879 after five years of closure. Unfortunately, Cyfartha had been slow to changeover to steel production and despite an investment of £150,000 by William Thompson Crawshay, the reopening in 1882 as a steel production plant came too late to change the factory's fortunes and it closed again in 1910. In 1915 Cyfarthfa reopened to produce pig iron and shell steel during the First World War but Cyfarthfa finally closed forever in 1919, with dismantling commencing in 1928.

R3702	PO, Tytherington Stone Co, Peckett W4 Class, 0-4-0ST, 'Daphne' - Era 2	DCC READY	4 PIN CONNECTION

Designer: Peckett & Sons		Entered Service: 1899

Length: 84mm	Motor: 3 Pole	Curved Track: Hornby 1st Radius + / 371mm+

Peckett Works No. 737/1899 'Daphne' was purchased new by Howell Lloyd Hardwicke, trading as the Tytherington Stone Co. to shunt at Church Quarry, replacing a road traction engine that had been converted to a 4-2-0 railway locomotive. 'Daphne' was replaced at Church Quarry sometime after 1919 and in 1923 was sold on to Pilkington Bros. of St. Helen's in Lancashire. Now preserved, 'Daphne' can be found at the Ribble Steam Railway Museum in Preston.

R3640	PO, Willans and Robinson, Peckett W4 Class, 0-4-0ST, 882 'Niclausse' - Era 2	DCC READY	4 PIN CONNECTION

Designer: Peckett & Sons Ltd		Entered Service: 1902

Length: 84mm	Motor: 3 Pole	Curved Track: Hornby 1st Radius + / 371mm+

Peckett Works No. 882/1902 Niclausse was built for Willans and Robinson of Queensferry, Flintshire, who were manufacturers of water tube boilers and special steels. The locomotive was named after a type of French designed field tube boiler used in some of the last pre-dreadnought battleships.

NEW Q1

R3869	Dowlais Ironworks, Peckett W4 Class, 0-4-0ST, 33 'Lady Cornelia' - Era 2	DCC READY	4 PIN CONNECTION

Designer: Peckett & Sons		Entered Service: 1900

Length: 84mm	Motor: 3 Pole	Curved Track: Hornby 1st Radius + / 371mm+

Peckett Works No. 834/1900 was built new for the Dowlais Ironworks, which had been sold to Arthur Keen the previous year. With the Dowlais running number of 33 and bearing the name Lady Cornelia, the locomotive operated over the extensive railway system associated with the works which, unlike Cyfartha, had made an early conversion to steel production, enabling its survival into the late 1930s.

75

R3405 | **LNER, J50 Class, 0-6-0T, 585 - Era 3** | DCC READY | 8 PIN CONNECTION

Designer: Sir Nigel Gresley | **Entered Service:** 1939 | **Length:** 152mm | **Motor:** 5 Pole Skew Wound | **Curved Track:** Hornby 2nd Radius + / 438mm+

Locomotive 585 was one of the Gorton built 'Part 4' engines, being built during May 1939 and entering traffic on 29 July, 1939, allocated to Doncaster Shed. Shortly after, 585 was transferred to Sheffield Shed where it stayed until 1952, having been renumbered twice, as 8990 in 1946 and 68990 in 1949. 19 October, 1952 saw the locomotive allocated to Hornsey, where it stayed until April 21, 1961 when it was condemned.

R3406 | **BR, J50 Class, 0-6-0T, No. 14 - Era 5** | DCC READY | 8 PIN CONNECTION

Designer: Sir Nigel Gresley | **Entered Service:** 1926 | **Length:** 152mm | **Motor:** 5 Pole Skew Wound | **Curved Track:** Hornby 2nd Radius + / 438mm+

Entering traffic as LNER No.1658 on 29 November, 1926, at Bradford Shed, then renumbered to 8961 in 1946. On 16 April, 1950, the locomotive was finally renumbered as BR No. 68961 and a move to Hornsey on 28 September, 1952 followed. Spells at New England and Doncaster then followed, before the locomotive was withdrawn on 16 September, 1962, moving to Departmental use at Doncaster Works as No.14.

R3407 | **BR, J50 Class, 0-6-0T, 68959 - Era 4** | DCC READY | 8 PIN CONNECTION

Designer: Sir Nigel Gresley | **Entered Service:** 1926 | **Length:** 152mm | **Motor:** 5 Pole Skew Wound | **Curved Track:** Hornby 2nd Radius + / 438mm+

Locomotive 68959 entered traffic at Bradford Shed on 16 November, 1926 as LNER No. 1037 and it was not until 6 October, 1957 that it moved, to Ardsley Shed, having been renumbered 8959 and 68959 in the meantime. Before being withdrawn from service on 31 August, 1961, 68959 spent spells at Darlington, West Auckland, Wakefield and Low Moor Sheds, finally being cut up at Doncaster Works.

CENTENARY YEAR 1920 2020 HORNBY®

| **R3466** | United Steel Company, Hunslett 'Austerity' Class, 0-6-0ST, 22 - Era 11 | DCC READY | 8 PIN CONNECTION |

| **Designer:** Edgar Alcock | **Entered Service:** 1956 | **Length:** 123mm | **Motor:** 3 Pole Type 7 | **Curved Track:** Hornby 2nd Radius + / 438mm+ |

In 1956, 3846, was allocated to the Graig Merthyr Colliery. Being required urgently, locomotive 3844 was more complete than 3846, so Hunslet simply changed the plates to allow 3846 to be delivered instead.

3846, with no NCB identity, worked until June 1978 when the colliery closed. Eventually rescued in 1997, when she was bought for use at the Appleby-Frodingham Railway Preservation Society, the error was discovered and rectified.

| **R3533** | Preservation, Hunslett 'Austerity' Class, 0-6-0ST, 'Lord Phil' - Era 11 | DCC READY | 8 PIN CONNECTION |

| **Designer:** Edgar Alcock | **Entered Service:** 1943 | **Length:** 123mm | **Motor:** 3 Pole Type 7 | **Curved Track:** Hornby 2nd Radius + / 438mm+ |

Originally built as Hunslet 2868 in 1943 for the War Department and numbered WD 168. In 1963 it was given a new lease of life and rebuilt as Hunslet 3883 as a trial for the Hunslet underfeed stoker and gas producer combustion system (GPCS).

This equipment was removed after purchase from the Rutland Railway Museum in 2008 and prior to service at Peak Rail in 2011, where the locomotive, now owned by Mike Thomas, operates.

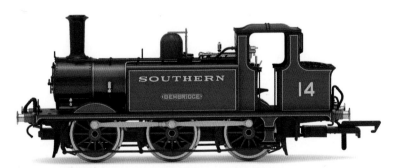

		DCC FITTED	R3847X
R3847/X	SR, 'Terrier', 0-6-0T, W14 'Bembridge' - Era 3	DCC READY	8 PIN CONNECTION
NEW Q3			

| **Designer:** William Stroudley | **Entered Service:** 1880 | **Length:** 105mm | **Motor:** 3 Pole | **Curved Track:** Hornby 1st Radius + / 371mm+ |

Entering service with the LB&SCR as No. 78 'Knowle', the locomotive was moved into storage by the Southern Railway in September 1935, but when the Isle of Wight Railway found itself with a shortage of light engines, 'Knowle' was overhauled, fitted with an extended bunker and shipped to the island in May 1929, taking the number W4 and the name 'Bembridge'.

Push-pull equipment was fitted and the Terrier worked the lighter lines out of Newport, being renumbered as W14 in April 1932. The opening of a bigger 26ft turntable at Bembridge in 1936 allowed heavier 4-4-2T O2 locomotives to work the smaller lines and W14 'Bembridge' became surplus to requirements, being returned to the mainland in May that year.

77

Limited Availability

R3781	K&ESR, 'Terrier', 0-6-0T, No. 5 'Rolvenden' - Era 2	**DCC READY**	**6 PIN CONNECTION**

Designer: William Stroudley		**Entered Service:** 1890
Length: 105mm	**Motor:** 3 Pole	**Curved Track:** Hornby 1st Radius + / 371mm+

Having entered service as No. 71 Wapping, in June 1901 the locomotive was relegated to the L&BSCR 'duplicate list' as 671, during which time it was hired to a contractor, W. Rigby, for construction work on the Sheppey Light Railway. At the beginning of 1905, 671 was sold to the K&ESR, and the locomotive was renamed as No. 5 Rolvenden. Having been worked hard, Rolvenden was withdrawn in 1932, its parts being stripped to maintain No. 3 Bodiam.

R3780	LB&SCR, 'Terrier', 0-6-0T, 655 'Stepney' - Era 2	**DCC READY**	**6 PIN CONNECTION**

Designer: William Stroudley		**Entered Service:** 1890
Length: 105mm	**Motor:** 3 Pole	**Curved Track:** Hornby 1st Radius + / 371mm+

Surplus to requirements as more Stroudley D1s came into service, No. 55 Stepney was renumbered to 655 when placed on the LB&SCR's 'duplicate list' in June 1901, after twenty-six years' service at New Cross. Motor-train services led to the re-introduction of the Terrier fleet, with Stepney being used on pseudo single coach 'motor-trains', until 1907, when 655 was fully converted for motor-train use. A1X re-boilering followed in 1912 and by 1923, 655 was at Fratton.

Terrier 0-6-0T
Locomotives

CENTENARY YEAR 1920 2020

HORNBY®

NEW Q3   DCC FITTED R3845X

| R3845/X | LB&SCR, 'Terrier', 0-6-0T, 40 'Brighton' - Era 2 | DCC READY | 6 PIN CONNECTION |

Designer: William Stroudley | **Entered Service:** 1878

Length: 105mm | **Motor:** 3 Pole | **Curved Track:** Hornby 1st Radius + / 371mm+

No. 40 Brighton was the LB&SCR's celebrity 'locomotive', having been selected by the company's General Manager, J.P Knight, to represent the LB&SCR at the Paris International Exhibition. Setting sail for Dieppe on 30 March 1878, the locomotive was exhibited in the Exhibition's Machinery Hall between May and November, gaining a Gold Medal in the process. On its return to England, a commemorative panel was added to the side tanks and aside from its normal duties, Brighton was also used for a number of Stroudley's experimental fittings, right up until its sale to the IWCR in January 1902.

Limited Availability

| R3811 | LB&SCR, Terrier, 0-6-0T, 48 'Leadenhall', - Era 2 | DCC READY | 6 PIN CONNECTION |

Designer: William Stroudley | **Entered Service:** 1876

Length: 105mm | **Motor:** 3 Pole | **Curved Track:** Hornby 1st Radius + / 371mm+

Built at Brighton Works during December 1876 at a cost of around £1,875.00, 48 Leadenhall was allocated to New Cross from 9 December 1876, but when the Great Eastern, Metropolitan and District railways took greater control of running East London line services during the mid 1880s, the locomotive was transferred to Eastbourne for the Hailsham and Lewes local services. Moved on to Portsmouth in 1890, 48 Leadenhall worked the East Southsea and Hayling Island branch line services until August 1901, when the locomotive was relegated to the LB&SCR Duplicate List.

Limited Availability

| R3782 | SE&CR, 'Terrier', 0-6-0T, 751 - Era 2 | DCC READY | 6 PIN CONNECTION |

Designer: William Stroudley | **Entered Service:** 1890

Length: 105mm | **Motor:** 3 Pole | **Curved Track:** Hornby 1st Radius + / 371mm+

L&BSCR duplicate listed in 1900 as No. 654 Waddon, the locomotive somehow escaped being disposed of and was sold to the SE&CR on 26 August, 1904 for £670. Repainted at Ashford Works in Wainwright Green and renumbered as 751, the locomotive was put to work on the Sheppey Light Railway, commencing services in February 1905. During WW1, 751 worked at Folkestone and Richborough, returning to Folkestone post-war.

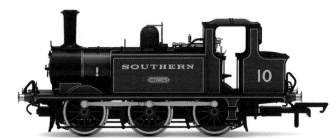

Limited Availability

| R3812 | SR, 'Terrier', 0-6-0T, W10 'Cowes' - Era 3 | DCC READY | 6 PIN CONNECTION |

Designer: William Stroudley | **Entered Service:** 1900

Length: 105mm | **Motor:** 3 Pole | **Curved Track:** Hornby 1st Radius + / 371mm+

Numbered as 69 and named 'Peckham', the Isle of Wight Central Railway (IWCR) took possession of the locomotive on 18 April 1900 and it retained this combination until 1925, two years after being taken into Southern Railway stock. Repainted into Maunsell Green and given the running number of W10, in October 1928 the locomotive received the name 'Cowes' which it retained until May 1936 when it was recalled to the mainland to be stored, then robbed for parts, before finally being scrapped in March 1949.

NEW Q3   DCC FITTED R3848X

| R3848/X | Transitional BR, 'Terrier', 0-6-0T, 13 'Carisbrooke' - Era 4 | DCC READY | 6 PIN CONNECTION |

Designer: William Stroudley | **Entered Service:** 1880

Length: 105mm | **Motor:** 3 Pole | **Curved Track:** Hornby 1st Radius + / 371mm+

When the Isle of Wight Railway relinquished Terriers W9, W10, W12 and W14 back to the mainland, W13 'Carisbrooke' continued as one of three Terriers left on the Island and was fitted with motor gear to operate on Merstone to Ventnor West services, until war was declared in 1939. By November 1945 the locomotive had resumed Ventnor West services, passing into British Railways stock on 1 January 1948. Ryde Works carried out their own relivery on the engine, hand painting shaded 'British Railways' lettering over the base Malachite Green and 'Carisbrooke' remained in this condition until Autumn 1952, by which point it had left the Island and was operating on the Hayling Island Branch, numbered 32677.

NEW Q3   DCC FITTED R3746X

| R3846/X | LSWR, 'Terrier', 0-6-0T, 735 - Era 2 | DCC READY | 6 PIN CONNECTION |

Designer: William Stroudley | **Entered Service:** 1903

Length: 105mm | **Motor:** 3 Pole | **Curved Track:** Hornby 1st Radius + / 371mm+

Entering service with the LB&SCR as No. 68 'Clapham', the locomotive was sold to LSWR in March 1903 for use on the new Lyme Regis branch, receiving the number 735. Unfortunately, the Terrier was not suited to the sharply curved and steeply graded line and 735 was moved to light shunting and other branch line duties until late 1911, when the locomotive was reboilered. Re-entering traffic the following Summer, minus condensing gear and exhaust steam pipes, 735 was engaged on the Chard branch until it was fitted with motor-train gear for use on the Lee-on-Solent Light Railway.

79

R3731	BR, H Class, 0-4-4T, 31177 - Era 4	DCC READY	8 PIN CONNECTION

NEW Q3

Designer: Harry Wainwright	Entered Service: 1909	Length: 132mm	Motor: 5 Pole Skew Wound	Curved Track: Hornby 2nd Radius + / 438mm+

Built at Ashford Works in March 1909, SE&CR No. 177 entered traffic at Bricklayers Arms and following Grouping, in 1924 the locomotive was renumbered as A177. Between January 1943 and August 1944, 1177 went on loan with the LMS, based at Forfar, working Arbroath local traffic. In May 1953, now numbered 31177, the locomotive received a push-pull motor, keeping it until withdrawal in October 1961.

R3631	BR, H Class, 0-4-4T, 31265 - Era 4	DCC READY	8 PIN CONNECTION

Designer: Harry Wainwright	Entered Service: 1905	Length: 132mm	Motor: 5 Pole Skew Wound	Curved Track: Hornby 2nd Radius + / 438mm+

Built at Ashford works in May 1905, the locomotive entered traffic as SE&CR 265 and was equipped with an early type rod and pulley motor fitting for Push/Pull working between late 1912 and early 1914. Renumbered as 1265 for Southern Railway, then 31265 under British Railways, the locomotive was based at Ramsgate Shed from 30 November, 1946, moving on to Tonbridge and Stewarts Lane before withdrawal in August 1960.

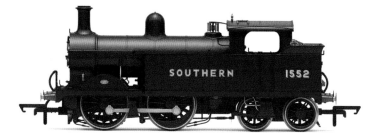

R3763	Southern Railway 'H' Class 0-4-4 - Era 3	DCC READY	8 PIN CONNECTION

NEW Q1

Designer: Harry Wainwright	Entered Service: 1905	Length: 132mm	Motor: 5 Pole Skew Wound	Curved Track: Hornby 2nd Radius + / 438mm+

Built at Ashford Works in January 1905, SE&CR No. 552 entered traffic at Maidstone West. Following Grouping, the locomotive was renumbered to A552, then as 1552 in the July 1931 renumbering scheme whilst allocated to Bricklayers Arms. Following Nationalisation, the locomotive spent some time in storage, briefly being reinstated for two months in early 1953, before re-entering traffic properly at Tonbridge in October 1953, now numbered as 31552 and briefly fitted with a push-pull motor for just two months. In November 1961, 31552 was withdrawn whilst allocated to Ashford.

R3531	BR, M7 Class, 0-4-4T, 30129 - Era 5	DCC READY	8 PIN CONNECTION

Designer: Dugald Drummond	Entered Service: 1911	Length: 139mm	Motor: 5 Pole Skew Wound	Curved Track: Hornby 2nd Radius + / 438mm+

30129 was built at Eastleigh and entered traffic as LSWR No.129 in November 1911. During its lifetime, the locomotive worked across the Southern region, from Yeovil to Faversham Sheds and was finally withdrawn from service in November 1963, while allocated to Bournemouth Shed.

CENTENARY YEAR 1920 2020 HORNBY®

R3422	**SR, Adams Class 415, 4-4-2T, 3125 - Era 3**				DCC READY	8 PIN CONNECTION

Designer: William Adams | **Entered Service:** 1885 | **Length:** 155mm | **Motor:** 5 Pole Skew Wound | **Curved Track:** Hornby 2nd Radius + / 438mm+

3125 was built at Robert Stephenson & Hawthorn in Darlington, during September 1885 and entered service as LSWR 125. The locomotive changed number several times, becoming 0125 in July 1911, E0123 in July 1926 and 3125 in November 1933 but was not immediately renumbered following Nationalisation in 1948. Renumbered 30582 in April 1949, the locomotive remained on the Lyme Regis branch until its final withdrawal in July 1961.

R3423	**BR, Adams Class 415, 4-4-2T, 30583 - Era 5**				DCC READY	8 PIN CONNECTION

Designer: William Adams | **Entered Service:** 1885 | **Length:** 155mm | **Motor:** 5 Pole Skew Wound | **Curved Track:** Hornby 2nd Radius + / 438mm+

Built at Neilson, Reid & Co in Glasgow, in March 1885, LSWR 488 was renumbered 0488 in March 1914, then sold on to the Ministry of Munitions in 1917. In March 1923, the East Kent Light Railway bought the locomotive, later selling it on to the Southern Railway to join 3125 and 3520 on the Lyme Regis branch, now numbered 3488. Following withdrawal in 1961, the locomotive was sold to the Bluebell Railway for preservation.

R3462	**BR, 42xx Class, 2-8-0T, 4287 - Era 4**				DCC READY	8 PIN CONNECTION

Designer: George Churchward | **Entered Service:** 1921 | **Length:** 163mm | **Motor:** 5 Pole Skew Wound | **Curved Track:** Hornby 2nd Radius + / 438mm+

One of the final batch of 42xx locomotives built to Lot 220 at Swindon in August 1921, 4287 spent its British Rail life allocated to 86H Aberbeeg Shed in South Wales, from where it was withdrawn to Swindon for disposal in 1961, being cut up in April that year.

R3463	**BR, 52xx Class, 2-8-0T, 5231 - Era 4**				DCC READY	8 PIN CONNECTION

Designer: Charles Collett | **Entered Service:** 1924 | **Length:** 163mm | **Motor:** 5 Pole Skew Wound | **Curved Track:** Hornby 2nd Radius + / 438mm+

Class 52xx locomotive 5231 was built at Swindon in June 1924 to Lot 225 and at Nationalisation in 1948 was allocated to 87G Carmarthen Shed. Spells at 86F Aberbeeg and 88A Cardiff East Dock followed, before 5231 was withdrawn from service in April 1964 and cut up at Cashmore's, Newport in July that year.

R3721/X | GWR, Class 61xx 'Large Prairie', 2-6-2T, 6110 - Era 3

DCC FITTED R3721X
DCC READY | 8 PIN CONNECTION

Due Q1

| Designer: Charles Collett | Entered Service: 1931 | Length: 165mm | Motor: 5 Pole Skew Wound | Curved Track: Hornby 2nd Radius + / 438mm+ |

Built at Swindon Works under Lot No. 269 in August 1931, Diagram A10 Class 61xx 'Large Prairie' No. 6110 entered traffic at Slough and was employed on London suburban services, even over London Underground metals.

6110 was the first of the class to be fitted with a cab shutter from new and carried tripcock gear from new for operation on the Underground tracks.

R3723/X | BR, Class 61xx 'Large Prairie', 2-6-2T, 6145 - Era 4

DCC FITTED R3723X
DCC READY | 8 PIN CONNECTION

Due Q1

| Designer: Charles Collett | Entered Service: 1932 | Length: 165mm | Motor: 5 Pole Skew Wound | Curved Track: Hornby 2nd Radius + / 438mm+ |

Built at Swindon Works under Lot No. 278 in December 1932, Diagram A10 Class 61xx 'Large Prairie' No. 6145 entered traffic at Old Oak Common, employed on London suburban services, even over London

Underground metals. Class 61xx locomotives were the mainstays of the Thames Valley suburban services until replaced by DMUs, illustrated by 6145's allocations to Old Oak Common, Slough and Oxford sheds.

R3719/X | GWR, Class 5101 'Large Prairie', 2-6-2T, 4154 - Era 3

DCC FITTED R3719X
DCC READY | 8 PIN CONNECTION

Due Q1

| Designer: Charles Collett | Entered Service: 1947 | Length: 165mm | Motor: 5 Pole Skew Wound | Curved Track: Hornby 2nd Radius + / 438mm+ |

Built at Swindon Works under Lot No. 361 in July 1947, Diagram A9 Class 5101 'Large Prairie' No. 4154 entered traffic at Wellington Shed, remaining there until 11 July, 1953. 4154's remaining shed allocations saw the locomotive

cover much of the Great Western region, with spells at Carmarthen, Worcester, Newton Abbot, Banbury, Stourbridge Junction and Oxley, from where it was withdrawn in October 1965.

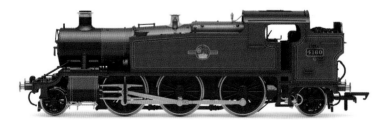

R3725/X | BR, Class 5101 'Large Prairie', 2-6-2T, 4160 - Era 5

DCC FITTED R3725X
DCC READY | 8 PIN CONNECTION

Due Q1

| Designer: Charles Collett | Entered Service: 1948 | Length: 165mm | Motor: 5 Pole Skew Wound | Curved Track: Hornby 2nd Radius + / 438mm+ |

Built at Swindon Works under Lot No. 369 during August 1948, Diagram A9 Class 5101 'Large Prairie' No. 4160 entered traffic on 6 September, 1948 at Barry Shed, where it stayed until 3 October, 1953.

Staying in Wales, 4160 worked from Merthyr Tydfil and Radyr until 5 October, 1964, when it moved to Severn Valley Junction. Condemned in June 1965, it was purchased for preservation and is currently at Llangollen Railway, awaiting restoration.

CENTENARY YEAR 1920 2020 **HORNBY**®

R3404	BR, Fowler 4P Class, 2-6-4T, 42334 - Era 5			DCC READY	8 PIN CONNECTION

Designer: Sir Henry Fowler | **Entered Service:** 1929 | **Length:** 188mm | **Motor:** 5 Pole Skew Wound | **Curved Track:** Hornby 2nd Radius + / 438mm+

Entering service on 12 March, 1929 as LMS No. 2334, the locomotive was renumbered to No. 42334 following Nationalisation, while allocated to Leicester Midland, where it stayed until 4 December, 1954.

Transfers to Bournville, Neasden, Kentish Town and a return to Leicester were followed by allocation to Gorton Shed in 1963, then Trafford Park, from where the locomotive was withdrawn on Christmas Day, 1965.

R3461	LNER, L1 Class, 2-6-4T, 67702 - Era 4			DCC READY	8 PIN CONNECTION

Designer: Edward Thompson | **Entered Service:** 1948 | **Length:** 174mm | **Motor:** 5 Pole Skew Wound | **Curved Track:** Hornby 2nd Radius + / 438mm+

67702 entered service at 30A Stratford Shed on 22 January, 1948, in LNER livery and numbered as 9001. Re-numbering under the British Railways' scheme followed shortly after, on 15 May, 1948 but curiously the locomotive

retained its LNER branding and green livery until its first general repair in mid-November 1948. 67702 was the first of the class to be withdrawn, on 31 October, 1960, at Darlington Works.

R3414	LNER, J15 Class, 0-6-0, 5444 - Era 3			DCC READY	8 PIN CONNECTION

Designer: T.W Worsdell | **Entered Service:** 1899 | **Length:** 218mm | **Motor:** 5 Pole Skew Wound, Loco Drive | **Curved Track:** Hornby 2nd Radius + / 438mm+

Locomotive 5444, built at Stratford Works, entered traffic during July 1899 as NER No. 644. Renumbered to LNER No. 7644 following Grouping, in September 1946 the locomotive was renumbered to 5444.

The locomotive spent its working life allocated between Stratford and Colchester sheds and made it through to Nationalisation in 1948, taking the BR No. 65444, finally being withdrawn in October 1958.

R3529	LNER, J15 Class, 0-6-0, 65477 - Era 3			DCC READY	8 PIN CONNECTION

Designer: T.W Worsdell | **Entered Service:** 1892 | **Length:** 218mm | **Motor:** 5 Pole Skew Wound, Loco Drive | **Curved Track:** Hornby 2nd Radius + / 438mm+

Locomotive 7942 was built at Stratford Works and entered traffic during September 1892 as GER No. 942, allocated to Ipswich. The renumbering to LNER No. 7942 took place quite late after Grouping, on 26 June,

1926 and was following by a move to Colchester Shed on 11 April, 1929. Allocations to Kings Lynn in 1939 and Cambridge in 1949 followed and it was from here that, in October 1956, the locomotive was withdrawn from service.

83

| R3415 | BR, J15 Class, 0-6-0, 65477 - Era 4 | | | DCC READY | 8 PIN CONNECTION |

| Designer: T.W Worsdell | Entered Service: 1913 | Length: 218mm | Motor: 5 Pole Skew Wound, Loco Drive | Curved Track: Hornby 2nd Radius + / 438mm+ |

Locomotive 65477, built at Stratford Works, entered traffic during August 1913 as NER No. 549. Renumbered to LNER No. 7549 following Grouping, in December 1946 the locomotive was renumbered to 5477.

The locomotive spent its working life allocated to Cambridge Shed and at Nationalisation took the BR No. 65477, finally being withdrawn during February 1960.

| R3530 | BR, J15 Class, 0-6-0, 65469 - Era 4 | | | DCC READY | 8 PIN CONNECTION |

| Designer: T.W Worsdell | Entered Service: 1912 | Length: 218mm | Motor: 5 Pole Skew Wound, Loco Drive | Curved Track: Hornby 2nd Radius + / 438mm+ |

Locomotive 65469 entered traffic in May 1912 as GER No. 571, being allocated to Cambridge. Renumbered to 7571 under the LNER, the locomotive moved to Stratford on June 5, 1938. Moving around East Anglia,

allocated in various turns to Norwich, Lowestoft, Yarmouth, Yarmouth Beach, Cambridge and March, it was renumbered as 65469 on 2 December, 1950, being withdrawn from service in August 1962.

| R3416 | BR, J15 Class, 0-6-0, 65464 - Era 5 | | | DCC READY | 8 PIN CONNECTION |

| Designer: T.W Worsdell | Entered Service: 1912 | Length: 218mm | Motor: 5 Pole Skew Wound, Loco Drive | Curved Track: Hornby 2nd Radius + / 438mm+ |

Locomotive 65464, built at Stratford Works, entered traffic during March 1912 as NER No. 566. Renumbered to LNER No. 7566 following Grouping, in January 1947 the locomotive was renumbered to 5464.

The locomotive spent its life at Stratford Shed and at Nationalisation took the BR No. 65464, finally being withdrawn on 16 September, 1962.

| R3559 | SR, Q1 Class, 0-6-0, C24 - Era 3 | | | DCC READY | 8 PIN CONNECTION |

| Designer: O.V.S Bulleid | Entered Service: 1942 | Length: 222mm | Motor: 5 Pole Skew Wound, Loco Drive | Curved Track: Hornby 2nd Radius + / 438mm+ |

Locomotive C24 was built at Ashford and outshopped on June 26, 1942, entering traffic at Feltham.

Renumbered to 33024 under British Railways, C24 was withdrawn from service from Three Bridges on 25 August, 1963.

CENTENARY YEAR 1920 2020 HORNBY®

DCC READY | **8 PIN CONNECTION**

R3735	ROD, J36 Class, 0-6-0, 5662 - Era 2

Due Q3

Designer: Matthew Holmes	**Entered Service:** 1891	**Length:** 200mm	**Motor:** 5 Pole Skew Wound, Loco Drive	**Curved Track:** Hornby 2nd Radius + / 438mm+

Built at Cowlairs in November 1891, NBR No. 662 was rebuilt in May 1915 and was one of twenty five Class C locomotives requisitioned by the Railway Executive on 4 August, 1917 for use by the Railway Operating Division of the Royal Engineers.

Sent to the Western Front on 7 November, 1917, it is thought that ROD 5662 worked around Verquigneul in the Pas-de-Calais, proving reliable in ROD service. Returning on 12 April, 1919 to the UK, NBR 662 was named Birdwood.

DCC READY | **8 PIN CONNECTION**

R3621	LNER, J36 Class, 0-6-0, 722 - Era 3

Designer: Matthew Holmes	**Entered Service:** 1897	**Length:** 200mm	**Motor:** 5 Pole Skew Wound, Loco Drive	**Curved Track:** Hornby 2nd Radius + / 438mm+

Built at Cowlairs in June 1897, 722 was rebuilt with the NBR Standard Boiler by the LNER in May 1923, following Grouping. Renumbered shortly after, in March 1926, as 9722, by June 1926 the locomotive was allocated to St. Margarets Shed.

By April 1930 the locomotive had moved south of the border, being allocated to Carlisle and while there received the 1946 LNER number 5293, changing to 65293 under BR in September 1948.

DCC READY | **8 PIN CONNECTION**

R3734	LNER, J36 Class, 0-6-0, 65235 'Gough' - Era 4

Due Q3

Designer: Matthew Holmes	**Entered Service:** 1891	**Length:** 200mm	**Motor:** 5 Pole Skew Wound, Loco Drive	**Curved Track:** Hornby 2nd Radius + / 438mm+

Built at Cowlairs in August 1891, NBR 659 was rebuilt with the NBR Standard Boiler in September 1915. Sent to the Western Front in October 1917, numbered as ROD 6659, on the locomotive's return it was named

as Gough in April 1914, being renumbered as 9659 in 1926, then 5235 in 1946 under the LNER. In January 1949, under British Railways, Gough was renumbered as 65235 at which point it was allocated to Bathgate.

DCC READY | **8 PIN CONNECTION**

R3521	LNER, D16/3 Class, 4-4-0, 8802 - Era 3

Designer: James Holden	**Entered Service:** 1910	**Length:** 216mm	**Motor:** 3 Pole, Loco Drive	**Curved Track:** Hornby 2nd Radius + / 438mm+

Locomotive No. 8802 was one of the D15s rebuilt by Gresley as a D16/3 in April 1933. Built at Stratford Works in 1910, the locomotive entered traffic as GER No.1802 at Cambridge Shed. Renumbered as 8802 in

August 1924, the locomotive was allocated to Stratford in March 1926 and throughout the rest of its working life, 8802 shuttled between allocations at Norwich, Yarmouth, Yarmouth Beach and Lowestoft Sheds.

85

RAILWAY MUSEUM Produced under licence for SCMG Enterprises Ltd. © SCMGE. *Every purchase supports the museum.*

R3863 | **LSWR, Class T9, 4-4-0, 120 - Era 2** | DCC READY | 8 PIN CONNECTION

NEW Q4

| Designer: Dugald Drummond | Entered Service: 1899 | Length: 229mm | Motor: 5 Pole Skew Wound, Loco Drive | Curved Track: Hornby 2nd Radius + / 438mm+ |

Built in August 1899 at Nine Elms, LSWR 120 entered traffic allocated to the same shed until July 1937. In June 1947, 120 moved to Eastleigh and was renumbered to 30120 and it returned there in November 1961 as the only survivor of the class, preserved as part of the National Collection. 30120 is currently on loan at the Swanage Railway, pending expiry of its boiler certificate in September 2020.

R3458 | **SR, V 'Schools' Class, 4-4-0, 921 'Shrewsbury' - Era 3** | DCC READY | 8 PIN CONNECTION

| Designer: Richard Maunsell | Entered Service: 1933 | Length: 238mm | Motor: 5 Pole Skew Wound, Loco Drive | Curved Track: Hornby 2nd Radius + / 438mm+ |

921 Shrewsbury was built at Eastleigh, entering traffic in November 1933. Allocated to Ramsgate shed until July 1946, Shrewsbury moved to Bricklayers Arms between July 1946 and March 1951, followed by a lengthy period at Dover between May 1951 and June 1957. Final allocations at Stewarts Lane from June 1959 and Nine Elms from August 1961 followed, from where the locomotive was withdrawn in December 1962.

R3541 | **LNER, Q6 Class, 0-8-0, 2265 - Era 3** | DCC READY | 8 PIN CONNECTION

| Designer: Vincent Raven | Entered Service: 1930 | Length: 241mm | Motor: 5 Pole Skew Wound, Loco Drive | Curved Track: Hornby 2nd Radius + / 438mm+ |

An Armstrong Whitworth locomotive, No. 2265 entered traffic in March 1930 at Tyne Dock. Moving between sheds, the locomotive recieved its 50A boiler on 22 December, 1938 and in September 1944 moved to Neville Hall, before returning to Newport in May 1947 as LNER No. 3422. Shortly after, in September, the locomotive moved to West Hartlepool, from where it was withdrawn from service on 18 May, 1964.

R3542 | **BR, Q6 Class, 0-8-0, 63427 - Era 4** | DCC READY | 8 PIN CONNECTION

| Designer: Vincent Raven | Entered Service: 1920 | Length: 241mm | Motor: 5 Pole Skew Wound, Loco Drive | Curved Track: Hornby 2nd Radius + / 438mm+ |

63427 entered traffic in April 1920 at Dairycoates, as NER 2270, having been built at Armstrong Whitworth. On 5 March, 1945, the locomotive moved to West Hartlepool, from where it was fitted with the 50A boiler on 8th March. Renumbered as 3427 in July 1946, then 63427 in November 1949, a move to Consett followed in early 1951. The locomotive briefly moved to North Blyth before being withdrawn on 14 June 1965.

CENTENARY YEAR 1920 2020 **HORNBY**®

2-6-0 Standard 2MT
Locomotives

Developed from the 1946 LMS 2MT 2-6-0 design, the British Railways' Standard Class 2MT 2-6-0 design benefitted from the work carried out in 1949/50 to improve the steaming characteristics of the Ivatt 2-6-0.

Under Robert Riddles, the design principally came from Derby, with input from Swindon, Brighton and Doncaster drawing offices and the sixty-five locomotives ordered were all built at Darlington between December 1952 and November 1956. The principal difference between the two Class 2MT types centred upon the cab, with the BR Standard using an angled cab side, matched to the tender cab, to improve route availability to almost

universal access across the British Railways network. The locomotives were reliable in service, entirely suited to their mixed traffic task and were equally at home hauling short rakes of coaches on rural lines or moving freight across the Pennines. By the end of May 1967 the class had been withdrawn from service, with just four locomotives; 78018, 78019, 78022 and 78059, being saved for preservation.

R3838 — BR, Standard 2MT, 2-6-0, 78010 - Era 4
NEW Q2 | DCC READY | 8 PIN CONNECTION

| Designer: Robert Riddles | Entered Service: 1953 | Length: 215mm | Motor: 5 Pole Skew Wound Loco Drive | Curved Track: Hornby 2nd Radius + / 438mm+ |

78010 entered traffic at West Auckland Shed on 24 December 1953, one of nine 2MT locomotives allocated there for passenger services to Saltburn, Tebay mineral workings over Stainmore summit and the odd excursion working. In March 1955, 78010 was moved to Northallerton shed, displacing the J21, J25 and G5 locomotives on pick up freight workings locally.

In March 1963 the locomotive was sent to Polmadie but was in a poor condition being transferred on to Motherwell, before being returned to Darlington in June that year. 78010 arrived at Farnley Junction in November 1963, before being moved on to Crewe South in April 1964 from where it was withdrawn from service in September 1966.

R3836 — BR, Standard 2MT, 2-6-0, 78047 - Era 5
NEW Q2 | DCC READY | 8 PIN CONNECTION

| Designer: Robert Riddles | Entered Service: 1955 | Length: 215mm | Motor: 5 Pole Skew Wound Loco Drive | Curved Track: Hornby 2nd Radius + / 438mm+ |

78047 entered traffic at Hawick Shed on 25 October 1955, where the locomotive spent most of its lifetime working, even deputising for failed Class 27, 40 and 45 diesels on the Edinburgh-Carlisle route post-1961. In 1966, once local passenger and freight services were discontinued, or

taken over by diesel traction, 78047 moved over to Bathgate, mainly to operate mineral trip freights from local collieries and to haul the occasional enthusiasts' special. Reallocated to St. Margarets prior to withdrawal, 78047 was eventually scrapped in January 1967.

R3839 — BR, Standard 2MT, 2-6-0, 78000 - Era 5
NEW Q2 | DCC READY | 8 PIN CONNECTION

| Designer: Robert Riddles | Entered Service: 1952 | Length: 215mm | Motor: 5 Pole Skew Wound Loco Drive | Curved Track: Hornby 2nd Radius + / 438mm+ |

78000 entered traffic at Oswestry on 27 December 1952 along with the other nine 2MT locomotives from the first batch, displacing the GWR Dean Goods and Cambrian Railways' 0-6-0s from their local passenger and freight duties. As the new locomotives and their crews became accustomed to their new operating areas, they were dispersed to other sheds and so 78000 found itself allocated to Machynlleth for work between

Shrewsbury, Oswestry and the Welsh coast resorts from Aberystwyth to Portmadoc until May 1963.

Moved to Nottingham to cover local freight workings, in January 1964 the locomotive was transferred to Derby for use on the Shirland Colliery Branch until June 1965, when 78000 was withdrawn from service.

R3418 | **BR, K1 Class, 2-6-0, 62006 - Era 4**

DCC READY | 8 PIN CONNECTION

| **Designer:** Arthur Peppercorn | **Entered Service:** 1949 | **Length:** 243mm | **Motor:** 3 Pole, Loco Drive | **Curved Track:** Hornby 2nd Radius + / 438mm+ |

62006 entered traffic, allocated to Darlington Shed, on 15 June, 1949, before moving to Blaydon Shed on 31 January, 1954. 62006 spent its working life in the North East, spending time allocated to Gateshead from 6 May, 1952, Heaton from 23 September of that year and Alnmouth from 4 November. A final spell at Sunderland Shed from June 1966 preceded 62006's withdrawal from service on 4 September, 1966.

R3417 | **BR, K1 Class, 2-6-0, 62065 - Era 5**

DCC READY | 8 PIN CONNECTION

| **Designer:** Arthur Peppercorn | **Entered Service:** 1950 | **Length:** 243mm | **Motor:** 3 Pole, Loco Drive | **Curved Track:** Hornby 2nd Radius + / 438mm+ |

62065 entered traffic, allocated to Darlington Shed, on 23 January, 1950 and in June that year the engine was transferred to Stockton Shed, where it spent nearly nine years. A short spell at Low Moor between June and August 1959 was followed by a final allocation to York, where 62065 spent the rest of its service life. Sold for scrap to A. Draper's of Hull on 4 July, 1967, the locomotive was finally cut up on 28 August, 1967.

R3729 | **LNER, Class O1, 2-8-0, 6359 - Era 3**

DCC READY | 8 PIN CONNECTION

| **Designer:** Edward Thompson | **Entered Service:** 1945 | **Length:** 250mm | **Motor:** 5 Pole Skew Wound, Loco Drive | **Curved Track:** Hornby 2nd Radius + / 438mm+ |

6359 was one of the original Railway Operating Division 2-8-0 locomotives, built by Kitson in August 1918 and numbered as ROD 1625. Transferred to the LNER on 2 February, 1924 as a Class O4/3, the locomotive was renumbered as LNER 6359 and allocated to Gorton, then Sheffield Neepsend, Doncaster and Retford Thrumpton, before being rebuilt as a Class O1 in April/May 1945.

R3730 | **BR, Class O1, 2-8-0, 63806 - Era 4**

DCC READY | 8 PIN CONNECTION

| **Designer:** Edward Thompson | **Entered Service:** 1945 | **Length:** 250mm | **Motor:** 5 Pole Skew Wound, Loco Drive | **Curved Track:** Hornby 2nd Radius + / 438mm+ |

63806 was one of the original Railway Operating Division 2-8-0 locomotives, built by the North British Locomotive Company in May 1918 as ROD 1915. Post-war, the locomotive returned to service with the LNWR, before being transferred to the LNER in March 1928, Rebuilt as a Class O1 in August 1944, the locomotive was allocated to Thornton Junction, from where it entered British Railways ownership in 1948, being renumbered to 63806.

CENTENARY YEAR 1920 2020

HORNBY®

| R3565 | LMS, 8F Class, 2-8-0, 48035 - Era 3 | | | | D C C READY | 8 PIN CONNECTION |

| Designer: Sir William Stanier | Entered Service: 1936 | Length: 258mm | Motor: 5 Pole Skew Wound, Loco Drive | Curved Track: Hornby 2nd Radius + / 438mm+ |

Locomotive 8035 was built at the Vulcan Foundry Works as Works No.4712 and entered traffic in August 1936, avoiding the War Department 'draft'. Post-war, the locomotive operated across the Midland region, operating from ten different sheds, the longest allocation being at Rugby between 16 June, 1957 and 9 January, 1965. Renumbered to 48035 in June 1948, the locomotive was withdrawn from service at Tyseley in March 1967.

| R3411 | SR, S15 Class, 4-6-0, 827 - Era 3 | | | | D C C READY | 8 PIN CONNECTION |

| Designer: Richard Maunsell | Entered Service: 1927 | Length: 266mm | Motor: 5 Pole Skew Wound, Loco Drive | Curved Track: Hornby 2nd Radius + / 438mm+ |

The S15 proved to be an adaptable class of locomotive and were capable of putting up a creditable performance when pressed into passenger service during peak holiday periods. They just outlived the N15 class, the first withdrawals coming in 1962, and the last being in 1966. Locomotive 827 emerged from Eastleigh works during June 1927 and spent its life operating from Exmouth Junction, before being scrapped during February 1964.

| R3412 | BR, S15 Class, 4-6-0, 30842 - Era 4 | | | | D C C READY | 8 PIN CONNECTION |

| Designer: Richard Maunsell | Entered Service: 1936 | Length: 266mm | Motor: 5 Pole Skew Wound, Loco Drive | Curved Track: Hornby 2nd Radius + / 438mm+ |

30842 was one of the last batch of S15s, being built at Eastleigh works during August 1936 and entered traffic at Hither Green shed. The locomotive spent the war years at Feltham shed, moving there in October 1939, before moving to Exmouth Junction in June 1948. 30842 spent alternating periods at 70B Feltham shed and 70D Eastleigh shed from 1963, before being withdrawn from service in September 1965, having covered 898,348 miles.

| R3413 | BR, S15 Class, 4-6-0, 30831 - Era 4 | | | | D C C READY | 8 PIN CONNECTION |

| Designer: Richard Maunsell | Entered Service: 1927 | Length: 266mm | Motor: 5 Pole Skew Wound, Loco Drive | Curved Track: Hornby 2nd Radius + / 438mm+ |

30831 was built at Eastleigh works during October 1927, entering traffic numbered as E831 and received its smoke deflectors during a works visit in November/December 1929. Unusually, the locomotive spent its service life operating from just one shed, Salisbury, before finally being withdrawn from service in November 1963, having covered 1,304,943 miles.

R3635 | **BR, Lord Nelson Class, 4-6-0, 30863 'Lord Rodney' - Era 4** | DCC READY | 8 PIN CONNECTION

Designer: Richard Maunsell | **Entered Service:** 1929 | **Length:** 283mm | **Motor:** 5 Pole Skew Wound, Loco Drive | **Curved Track:** Hornby 2nd Radius + / 438mm+

Built at Eastleigh in October 1929, 863 'Lord Rodney' entered traffic at Stewarts Lane, before moving to Nine Elms in October 1938 following the fitting of an experimental large diameter chimney. Moving south to

Bournemouth in June 1945, 'Lord Rodney' was at Nine Elms when renumbered to 30863 in August 1949. While allocated to Eastleigh in 1956, 'Lord Rodney' had the complete front end renewed following a collision.

R3733 | **BR (Late), Lord Nelson Class, 4-6-0, 30859 'Robert Blake' - Era 4** | DCC READY | 8 PIN CONNECTION

Due Q3 | **Designer:** Richard Maunsell | **Entered Service:** 1929 | **Length:** 283mm | **Motor:** 5 Pole Skew Wound, Loco Drive | **Curved Track:** Hornby 2nd Radius + / 438mm+

Entering traffic as E855 'Robert Blake' in November 1928, smoke deflectors were added a year later in November 1929 and the 'E' prefix was removed in July 1931. Following nationalisation, Robert Blake was renumbered as 30855 in February 1949 while in Malachite Green livery with an

unnumbered tender, not receiving the early BR crest until repainted to BR Green in September 1950. The later BR crest was added in August 1958, with the Lions correctly facing left and right.

R3732 | **BR (Early), Lord Nelson Class, 4-6-0, 30852 'Sir Walter Raleigh' - Era 5** | DCC READY | 8 PIN CONNECTION

Due Q2 | **Designer:** Richard Maunsell | **Entered Service:** 1928 | **Length:** 283mm | **Motor:** 5 Pole Skew Wound, Loco Drive | **Curved Track:** Hornby 2nd Radius + / 438mm+

Entering traffic as E852 'Sir Walter Raleigh' in July 1928, smoke deflectors were added in December 1929 and the 'E' prefix was removed in June 1931. Following nationalisation, 'Sir Walter Raleigh' was renumbered as 30852 in

February 1949, while in Malachite Green with an unlettered tender and was repainted into British Railways Dark Green in December 1951. The late BR totem was added in October 1958.

R3862 | **SR, Lord Nelson Class, 4-6-0, 864 'Sir Martin Frobisher' - Era 3** | DCC READY | 8 PIN CONNECTION

NEW Q3 | **Designer:** Richard Maunsell | **Entered Service:** 1929 | **Length:** 283mm | **Motor:** 5 Pole Skew Wound, Loco Drive | **Curved Track:** Hornby 2nd Radius + / 438mm+

Entering traffic at Stewarts Lane in November 1929 on the Continental services, E864 'Sir Martin Frobisher' was moved to Nine Elms in November 1937 on Link 1 duties for the Southampton Docks and Bournemouth express services, swapping places with 857 Lord Howe.

In January 1939 'Sir Martin Frobisher' was modified with the Lemaitre exhaust and a modified chimney, raising the performance level of the locomotive, a welcomed development as by 1945, somewhat surprisingly, wartime holiday traffic on the Western Section had reached pre-war levels and the introduction of the Merchant Navy class meant that 'Sir Martin Frobisher' could be sent to Bournemouth shed to augment the Lord Nelsons already based there.

| R3408 | BR, 6000 'King' Class, 4-6-0, 6016 'King Edward V' - Era 3 | DCC READY | 8 PIN CONNECTION |

Designer: Charles Collett | **Entered Service:** 1928 | **Length:** 276mm | **Motor:** 5 Pole Skew Wound, Loco Drive | **Curved Track:** Hornby 2nd Radius + / 438mm+

6016, 'King Edward V', was built at Swindon Works in June 1928 and was allocated to Plymouth Laira initially. The Alfloc water treatment was fitted in 1954, with the double chimney being fitted in January 1958.

Post-war, spells at Old Oak Common, Wolverhampton Stafford Road and Plymouth Laira followed, before returning to Wolverhampton Stafford Road, from where it was withdrawn from service in September 1962.

| R3534 | GWR, 6000 'King' Class, 4-6-0, 6023 'King Edward II' - Era 3 | DCC READY | 8 PIN CONNECTION |

Designer: Charles Collett | **Entered Service:** 1930 | **Length:** 276mm | **Motor:** 5 Pole Skew Wound, Loco Drive | **Curved Track:** Hornby 2nd Radius + / 438mm+

6023 'King Edward II' was built at Swindon, entering traffic in June 1930, being first allocated to Newton Abbot Shed in July 1930. A short move across Devon to Plymouth Laira followed, during November 1936 but a

month later, 'King Edward II' was back at Newton Abbot, where the engine stayed until February 1949. Back at Laira until August 1956, allocations at Old Oak Common and Canton followed, until final withdrawal on June 19, 1962.

| R3410 | BR, 6000 'King' Class, 4-6-0, 6025 'King Henry III' - Era 4 | DCC READY | 8 PIN CONNECTION |

Designer: Charles Collett | **Entered Service:** 1930 | **Length:** 276mm | **Motor:** 5 Pole Skew Wound, Loco Drive | **Curved Track:** Hornby 2nd Radius + / 438mm+

6025 'King Henry III', was built at Swindon Works in July 1930 and was allocated at first to Old Oak Common Shed. There were also spells of allocation at Plymouth Laira Shed, but it was from Old Oak Common

that 'King Henry III' was withdrawn from service in December 1962, being scrapped by Swindon Works in May 1964.

| R3409 | BR, 6000 'King' Class, 4-6-0, 6002 'King William IV' - Era 5 | DCC READY | 8 PIN CONNECTION |

Designer: Charles Collett | **Entered Service:** 1927 | **Length:** 276mm | **Motor:** 5 Pole Skew Wound, Loco Drive | **Curved Track:** Hornby 2nd Radius + / 438mm+

6002, 'King William IV', was built in July 1927 at Swindon Works and was allocated initially to Plymouth Laira Shed. The Alfloc water treatment was fitted in 1954, with the double chimney being fitted in March 1956.

'King William IV' spent spells at sheds across the Great Western region, from Plymouth Laira, Newton Abbot and Old Oak Common, to Wolverhampton Stafford Road, from where it was withdrawn in September 1962.

R3447 | **LNER, B17/2 Class, 2-6-0, 2842 'Kilverstone Hall' - Era 3** | DCC READY | 8 PIN CONNECTION

| Designer: Sir Nigel Gresley | Entered Service: 1933 | Length: 249mm | Motor: 5 Pole Skew Wound, Loco Drive | Curved Track: Hornby 2nd Radius + / 438mm+ |

2842 'Kilverstone Hall' was the last B17/2 built at Darlington during May 1933 and was converted to a B17/6 in January 1949, at which point it was renumbered under British Railways as 61642.

'Kilverstone Hall' was withdrawn from service from Cambridge Shed on 15 September, 1958.

R3448 | **BR, B17/4 Class, 4-6-0, 61619 'Welbeck Abbey' - Era 4** | DCC READY | 8 PIN CONNECTION

| Designer: Sir Nigel Gresley | Entered Service: 1930 | Length: 249mm | Motor: 5 Pole Skew Wound, Loco Drive | Curved Track: Hornby 2nd Radius + / 438mm+ |

61619 'Welbeck Abbey' entered service on 8 November, 1930, having been built at Darlington in the first batch of B17/2 locomotives and was converted to a B17/6 in January 1953, while allocated to March Shed.

Renumbered under British Railways in August 1948 to 61619, 'Welbeck Abbey' was withdrawn from service on September 19, 1958.

R3523 | **BR, B17/6 Class, 4-6-0, 61665 'Leicester City' - Era 4** | DCC READY | 8 PIN CONNECTION

| Designer: Sir Nigel Gresley | Entered Service: 1937 | Length: 249mm | Motor: 5 Pole Skew Wound, Loco Drive | Curved Track: Hornby 2nd Radius + / 438mm+ |

61665 'Leicester City' entered service as LNER No.2865 in January 1937, having been built at the Robert Stephenson works as a B17/4. The locomotive's first allocation was to Sheffield, followed by a short period

at Gorton until late July 1938, when it was allocated to its 'home' town of Leicester. Further spells at Cambridge and Doncaster were followed by a return to East Anglian sheds at Ipswich, Yarmouth and Norwich.

  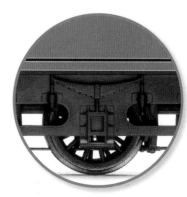

CENTENARY YEAR 1920 2020

HORNBY®

R3451 | **BR, B1 Class, 4-6-0, 61032 'Stembok' - Era 4** | DCC READY | 8 PIN CONNECTION

Designer: Edward Thompson | **Entered Service:** 1947 | **Length:** 246mm | **Motor:** 5 Pole Skew Wound, Loco Drive | **Curved Track:** Hornby 2nd Radius + / 438mm+

1032 'Stembok' entered service on 7 August, 1947 and was initially allocated to Stockton Shed. Renumbered under British Railways as No. 61032, 'Stembok' stayed at Stockton until 1959, when the locomotive was transferred to 51L Thornaby Shed. Allocations to 51A Darlington and 50B Hull Dairycoates followed, from where 61052 'Stembok' was withdrawn on 27 November, 1966.

R3544 | **LNER, B12 Class, 4-6-0, 8527 - Era 3** | DCC READY | 8 PIN CONNECTION

Designer: Stephen Holden | **Entered Service:** 1914 | **Length:** 236mm | **Motor:** 5 Pole Skew Wound, Loco Drive | **Curved Track:** Hornby 2nd Radius + / 438mm+

8527 was built at Stratford and entered traffic at Cambridge in August 1914 where it remained until 31 October, 1927 when it was transferred to Ipswich. In April 1928, 8527 moved to Parkeston, followed by a brief move to Norwich in March 1929 before heading back to Cambridge in April that year. The ACFI feed was fitted in January 1932 at Stratford, being removed when the locomotive was rebuilt to a B12/3 in January 1935.

R3545 | **BR, B12 Class, 4-6-0, 61556 - Era 4** | DCC READY | 8 PIN CONNECTION

Designer: Stephen Holden | **Entered Service:** 1921 | **Length:** 236mm | **Motor:** 5 Pole Skew Wound, Loco Drive | **Curved Track:** Hornby 2nd Radius + / 438mm+

61556 was built at Beardmore's Glasgow Works and entered traffic at Stratford during February 1921, remaining there until 15 December, 1927 when it was moved to Ipswich. The locomotive moved between Colchester, Norwich and Stratford, receiving the ACFI feed in late 1931 whilst at Stratford, before being rebuilt as a B12/3 in May 1935. 61556 was withdrawn from service whilst allocated to Norwich, in December 1957.

R3546 | **BR, B12 Class, 4-6-0, 61576 - Era 4** | DCC READY | 8 PIN CONNECTION

Designer: Stephen Holden | **Entered Service:** 1928 | **Length:** 236mm | **Motor:** 5 Pole Skew Wound, Loco Drive | **Curved Track:** Hornby 2nd Radius + / 438mm+

61576 was built at Beyer Peacock as a B12/2 and entered traffic at Gorton on August 31, 1928, remaining there until September 20, 1928 when it was transferred to Stratford. Spells at Colchester and Ipswich followed, the B12/3 rebuild taking place in August 1932. In April 1944, whilst allocated to Colchester, 61576 was adapted to work with the ambulance trains and it continued in service until January 1959, when it was withdrawn from Cambridge Shed.

| R3452 | **BR, 6800 'Grange' Class, 4-6-0, 6825 'Llanvair Grange' - Era 5** | | | | DCC READY | 8 PIN CONNECTION |

| **Designer:** Charles Collett | **Entered Service:** 1937 | **Length:** 253mm | **Motor:** 5 Pole Skew Wound, Loco Drive | **Curved Track:** Hornby 2nd Radius + / 438mm+ |

6825 'Llanvair Grange' was built at Swindon and entered service in February 1937, allocated to Exeter Shed. Between 1946 and October 1960 the locomotive operated from Penzance before being moved around the region, finally being withdrawn from St. Philip's Marsh, Bristol in June 1964.

| R3552 | **GWR, 6800 'Grange' Class, 4-6-0, 6860 'Aberporth Grange' - Era 3** | | | | DCC READY | 8 PIN CONNECTION |

| **Designer:** Charles Collett | **Entered Service:** 1939 | **Length:** 253mm | **Motor:** 5 Pole Skew Wound, Loco Drive | **Curved Track:** Hornby 2nd Radius + / 438mm+ |

6860 'Aberporth Grange' was built at Swindon and entered service on 11 February, 1939, allocated to Tyseley. The first of the final batch of 'Granges' to be completed, 'Aberporth Grange' stayed at Tyseley until March 1959, when it moved to Penzance and was finally withdrawn from service in February 1965 from Cardiff East Dock.

| R3454 | **GWR, Castle Class, 4-6-0, 5076 'Drysllwyn Castle' - Era 3** | | | | DCC READY | 8 PIN CONNECTION |

| **Designer:** Charles Collett | **Entered Service:** 1938 | **Length:** 265mm | **Motor:** 5 Pole Skew Wound, Loco Drive | **Curved Track:** Hornby 2nd Radius + / 438mm+ |

5076 'Drysllwyn Castle' was built at Swindon in August 1938 and was allocated initially to Exeter Shed. However, in January 1941 while at Bath Road, the locomotive was renamed to 'Gladiator', one of twelve locomotives renamed to carry aircraft names.

| R3619 | **BR, Castle Class, 4-6-0, 5013 'Abergavenny Castle' - Era 5** | | | | DCC READY | 8 PIN CONNECTION |

| **Designer:** Charles Collett | **Entered Service:** 1932 | **Length:** 265mm | **Motor:** 5 Pole Skew Wound, Loco Drive | **Curved Track:** Hornby 2nd Radius + / 438mm+ |

5013 'Abergavenny Castle' was built at Swindon in June 1932, entering traffic at Newton Abbot on June 27th. During the course of its lifespan, 'Abergavenny Castle' served throughout the GWR territory, from Penzance to Carmarthen, before finally being withdrawn from Llanelly in July 1962.

CENTENARY YEAR 1920 2020 HORNBY®

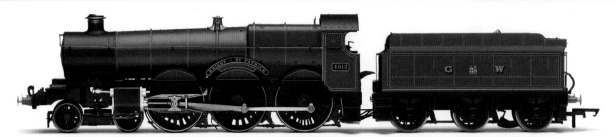

R3455 | **GWR, Star Class, 4-6-0, 4013 'Knight of St. Patrick' - Era 3** | DCC READY | 8 PIN CONNECTION

| Designer: George Jackson Churchward | Entered Service: 1908 | Length: 251mm | Motor: 5 Pole Skew Wound, Loco Drive | Curved Track: Hornby 2nd Radius + / 438mm+ |

4013 'Knight of St. Patrick' was from the second batch of 'Stars'; built at GWR's Swindon Works as No.2302, to Lot 173, in March 1908 and allocated to Old Oak Common initially. Built with improved, french style bogies, modifications followed in December 1910 when a half-cone boiler and No.3 superheater was fitted, although the locomotive reverted to a full-cone boiler in September 1915.

RAILWAY MUSEUM Produced under licence for SCMG Enterprises Ltd. © SCMGE. Every purchase supports the museum.

R3864 | **GWR, Star Class, 4-6-0, 4003 'Lode Star' - Era 3** | DCC READY | 8 PIN CONNECTION

NEW Q4

| Designer: George Jackson Churchward | Entered Service: 1907 | Length: 251mm | Motor: 5 Pole Skew Wound, Loco Drive | Curved Track: Hornby 2nd Radius + / 438mm+ |

4003 'Lode Star' entered service with the Great Western Railway in February 1907 and received the first of its modifications, the superheated boiler, in May 1911. The second major alteration took place in in March 1949 when 'elbow' pattern outside steam pipes were fitted however just two years later, in July 1951, 4003 'Lode Star' was withdrawn from service while allocated to Landore.

Added to the National Collection, 'Lode Star' remained in storage at Swindon until 1962, when it was moved to Swindon Railway Museum as a static exhibit until 1 March 1992, when it was sent to the National Railway Museum in York. The locomotive has since been exhibited again in Swindon at STEAM, the Museum of the Great Western Railway and more recently back at the Railway Musuem in York.

R3527 | **SR, N15 'King Arthur' Class, 4-6-0, 742 'Camelot' - Era 3** | DCC READY | 8 PIN CONNECTION

| Designer: Robert Urie | Entered Service: 1919 | Length: 270mm | Motor: 5 Pole Skew Wound, Loco Drive | Curved Track: Hornby 2nd Radius + / 438mm+ |

742 'Camelot' was built at Eastleigh Works, being one of the 'Urie Arthurs' and entered traffic in June 1919, although the naming ceremony did not take place until December 1925.

Smoke deflectors were fitted in June 1928 and the Maunsell boiler first fitted in September 1932. 'Camelot' was finally withdrawn from service while at Bournemouth Shed, on 9 February, 1957.

R3456 | **BR, N15 'King Arthur' Class, 4-6-0, 30792 'Sir Hervis de Revel' - Era 4** | DCC READY | 8 PIN CONNECTION

| Designer: Robert Urie | Entered Service: 1925 | Length: 270mm | Motor: 5 Pole Skew Wound, Loco Drive | Curved Track: Hornby 2nd Radius + / 438mm+ |

30792 'Sir Hervis de Revel', was one of the 'Scotch Arthurs', being built at North British Locomotive Company's works in Glasgow, and entered traffic in September 1925 at Bournemouth Shed.

Smoke deflectors were fitted to the locomotive in April 1928 and a Lemaitre exhaust was fitted between September 1940 and March 1952, 30792 being the only 'King Arthur' to receive this.

R3548 | **BR, Standard 4MT Class, 4-6-0, 75053 - Era 4** | DCC READY | 8 PIN CONNECTION

| Designer: R. A Riddles | Entered Service: 1956 | Length: 230mm | Motor: 5 Pole Skew Wound, Loco Drive | Curved Track: Hornby 2nd Radius + / 438mm+ |

75053 was built at Swindon, to Lot 408, in late 1956 and entered traffic with the London Midland Region at Chester Midland. A well-travelled locomotive, 75053 spent alternate spells at Ryhll and Chester Midland before moving on to Mold Junction in September 1960. In April 1962, a move to Bletchley was followed in January 1965 by allocation to Stoke-on-Trent, from where 75053 was withdrawn in September 1966.

R3547 | **BR, Standard 4MT Class, 4-6-0, 75008 - Era 5** | DCC READY | 8 PIN CONNECTION

| Designer: R. A Riddles | Entered Service: 1951 | Length: 230mm | Motor: 5 Pole Skew Wound, Loco Drive | Curved Track: Hornby 2nd Radius + / 438mm+ |

75008 was built at Swindon, to Lot 390, in 1951 and entered traffic with the Western Region at Shrewsbury. In October 1953 the locomotive was transferred to Cardiff Canton, before moving across the region to Oxford in October 1958. A move to Templecombe in July 1964 was followed by allocation to Exmouth Junction and then a move to Worcester, from where 75008 was withdrawn in December 1965.

R3557 | **LMS, Royal Scot Class, 4-6-0, 6126 'Royal Army Service Corps' - Era 3** | DCC READY | 8 PIN CONNECTION

| Designer: Sir Henry Fowler | Entered Service: 1927 | Length: 259mm | Motor: 5 Pole Skew Wound, Loco Drive | Curved Track: Hornby 2nd Radius + / 438mm+ |

6126 'Royal Army Service Corps' was built at the North British Hyde Park Works and entered traffic at Crewe North on 20 August, 1927. On 30 June, 1945, 'Royal Army Service Corps' received Stanier's tapered boiler and continued in service until October 1963, when it was withdrawn from Annesley Shed.

R3558 | **BR, Royal Scot Class, 4-6-0, 46165 'The Ranger' - Era 5** | DCC READY | 8 PIN CONNECTION

| Designer: Sir Henry Fowler | Entered Service: 1930 | Length: 259mm | Motor: 5 Pole Skew Wound, Loco Drive | Curved Track: Hornby 2nd Radius + / 438mm+ |

46165 'The Ranger' (12th London Regiment) was built at the LMSR's Derby works and entered traffic at Longsight on 22 October, 1930. On June 24, 1952 'The Ranger' (12th London Regiment), received Stanier's tapered boiler, continuing in service until being withdrawn from Crewe North in November 1964.

R3614 | LMS, Patriot Class, 4-6-0, 5521 'Rhyl' - Era 3 | DCC READY | 8 PIN CONNECTION

| **Designer:** Sir Henry Fowler | **Entered Service:** 1933 | **Length:** 259mm | **Motor:** 5 Pole Skew Wound, Loco Drive | **Curved Track:** Hornby 2nd Radius + / 438mm+ |

5521 'Rhyl' was rebuilt at Derby in March 1933 and re-entered traffic at Kentish Town later that month. Allocations to Edge Hill, Bushbury, Crewe North and Rugby followed, before the 6P conversion with the 2A tapered boiler came in October 1946, the second Patriot to be converted. Now numbered 45521, 'Rhyl' was withdrawn from Springs Branch in September 1963 and scrapped at Crewe that November.

R3633 | BR, Patriot Class, 4-6-0, 45534 'E. Tootal Broadhurst' - Era 4 | DCC READY | 8 PIN CONNECTION

| **Designer:** Sir Henry Fowler | **Entered Service:** 1933 | **Length:** 259mm | **Motor:** 5 Pole Skew Wound, Loco Drive | **Curved Track:** Hornby 2nd Radius + / 438mm+ |

5534 'E. Tootal Broadhurst' was rebuilt at Derby in April 1933 and re-entered traffic at Leeds later that month. Allocations to Longsight and Edge Hill followed, before the 6P conversion with the 2A tapered boiler came in December 1948, the penultimate Patriot to be converted. Now numbered 45534, 'E. Tootal Broadhurst' was withdrawn from Crewe North in May 1964 after a period of storage.

R3616 | LMS, Class 5MT, 4-6-0, 5089 - Era 3 | DCC READY | 8 PIN CONNECTION

| **Designer:** Sir William Stanier | **Entered Service:** 1935 | **Length:** 256mm | **Motor:** 5 Pole Skew Wound, Loco Drive | **Curved Track:** Hornby 2nd Radius + / 438mm+ |

Built as 5089 at the Vulcan Foundry in April 1935, the locomotive entered traffic on April 14th, allocated to Crewe Shed. followed six months later by a move to Sheffield.

Like the majority of the 'Black Five' class, 5089 served across the LMS region, but prior to nationalisation it spent much of its time in Yorkshire and Cheshire, being renumbered under British Railways to 45089 in October 1948 whilst at Crewe North.

97

HOME TO ROOST
1:1 Collection Museum at Margate

Imagine a collection of railway locomotives and other vehicles in which the subjects are not scale models but the real thing. The 1:1 Collection is a unique gathering of some of the most iconic and historically important railway locomotives, rolling stock and memorabilia in the United Kingdom.

At present there are twenty-four steam and diesel locomotives in The 1:1 Collection, as well as fully restored coaches and rolling stock. Each vehicle in the collection has either undergone, or is undergoing, painstaking restoration to return it to museum quality presentation, with many of the vehicles being certified for use on the United Kingdom's rail network.

From the Summer of 2018, The 1:1 Collection Museum began to take shape in the converted Margate warehouse adjacent to the Hornby Visitor Centre, with the Class A4 locomotive 4464 'Bittern' being the very first to arrive. Visitors to The 1:1 Collection Museum will be able to view 'up close' and see 'Bittern' alongside other magnificent engines and rolling stock in a building specially adapted to display these historic vehicles to museum conditions. From time to time The 1:1 Collection Museum will host guest locomotives for periods of medium or long term storage and display.

During the time that these locomotives are at the Margate warehouse, they will become 'honorary' members of The 1:1 Collection for promotion and merchandising purposes and so, as part of The 1:1 Collection, Hornby are pleased to be able to present two of the locomotives to be housed at Margate, the Mid-Hants Railway's 'Black Five', 45379 and Locomotive Services' own Class 9F, 92212.

Limited Edition
1000
Models

| R3805 | BR, Class 5MT, 4-6-0, 45379 - 1:1 Collection - Era 11 | DCC READY | 8 PIN CONNECTION |

| **Designer:** Sir William Stanier | **Entered Service:** 1937 | **Length:** 256mm | **Motor:** 5 Pole Skew Wound, Loco Drive | **Curved Track:** Hornby 2nd Radius + / 438mm+ |

The 'Black Fives' were mixed traffic class locomotives, a 'do-anything-go-anywhere' type, designed by Sir William Stanier. In their early days the locomotives were known as the 'Black Staniers' from their black livery but later on they became known as 'Black Fives'; the number referring to the power classification. 'Black Fives' occasionally worked as far south as Bournemouth and even ran over the Mid Hants Railway, 'the 'Watercress Line'. This locomotive class was large enough for the steep gradients but small enough to be economical.

Eighteen of the Class have been preserved. In 1974, '45379' was bought for restoration and taken to the Avon Valley Railway, then later to The Great Central Railway. It was bought from there by MHRPS, coming to Alresford on 1 March, 2002. The restoration of '45379' was completed in time for the Somerset & Dorset Steam Spectacular that ran between 10-12 September appearing alongside the visiting S&DJR Class 7F No. 88, the five year restoration effort visible for all to see. '45379' is currently a welcome guest of The 1:1 Collection, awaiting overhaul for its return to steam.

Limited Edition
500
Models

| R3941 | BR, Class 9F, 2-10-0, 92212 - 1:1 Collection - Era 11 | DCC READY | 8 PIN CONNECTION |

| NEW Q4 | **Designer:** Robert Riddles | **Entered Service:** 1959 | **Length:** 266mm | **Motor:** 5 Pole Skew Wound, Loco Drive | **Curved Track:** Hornby 2nd Radius + / 438mm+ |

One of fifty-three Class 9Fs completed at Swindon Works, 92212 entered service on 22 September 1959 and was first allocated to Banbury shed in the Western Region. By withdrawal from Carnforth shed in January 1968, 92212 had gone on to work for the remaining three British Railways' regions, having covered over 78,000 miles in just over eight years' service. Sold to Woodham Brothers at Barry for scrap in September 1968, 92212 spent eleven years in storage before being purchased by 92212 Holdings Ltd for storage and eventual restoration, returning to traffic in September 1996.

Spending two loan periods at the Severn Valley Railway, during Winter 2000/1 and Summer 2011, it was while being overhauled at the Mid-Hants Railway between 2007 and 2009 that the locomotive was purchased by Jeremy Hosking. Since returning to service on 11 September 2009, 92212 has been based at the Mid Hants Railway, and following the expiration of 92212's boiler certificate in December 2019, the locomotive is expected to be moved to The 1:1 Collection Museum at Margate during the course of 2020, although this is yet to be confirmed.

CENTENARY YEAR 1920 2020

HORNBY®

To place an order contact Hornby Customer Services on: **01843 233512** or visit your local stockist.

R3617 | **BR, Rebuilt Merchant Navy Class, 4-6-2, 35030 'Elder Dempster Lines' - Era 5** | **DCC READY** | **8 PIN CONNECTION**

| **Designer:** O.V.S Bulleid | **Entered Service:** 1949 | **Length:** 285mm | **Motor:** 5 Pole Skew Wound, Loco Drive | **Curved Track:** Hornby 2nd Radius + / 438mm+ |

35030 'Elder Dempster Lines' was the last of the Merchant Navy class to be built, entering traffic on 1 April, 1949. The rebuilding from its original air-smoothed form came between March and the end of April 1958, having covered just over 350,000 miles.

Re-entering traffic at Nine Elms, in September 1964, 35030 moved to Weymouth where it stayed up to April 1967. There was then a brief return to Nine Elms for three months, prior to withdrawal in July.

R3717 | **SR, Merchant Navy Class, 4-6-2, 21C7 'Aberdeen Commonwealth' - Era 3** | **DCC READY** | **8 PIN CONNECTION**

Due Q2 | **Designer:** O.V.S Bulleid | **Entered Service:** 1942 | **Length:** 285mm | **Motor:** 5 Pole Skew Wound, Loco Drive | **Curved Track:** Hornby 2nd Radius + / 438mm+ |

21C7 'Aberdeen Commonwealth' entered traffic in June 1942 liveried in Wartime Black, despite having been built in Malachite Green. Named at a ceremony on 30 July, 1942, 21C7 took part in smoke clearance trials during 1944 prior to receiving the standard deflectors during May 1947.

Malachite Green was restored to 21C7 in July 1947, but less than three years later 'Aberdeen Commonwealth' had received the experimental BR Steam Blue.

R3632 | **BR, Merchant Navy Class, 4-6-2, 35024 'East Asiatic Company' - Era 4** | **DCC READY** | **8 PIN CONNECTION**

| **Designer:** O.V.S Bulleid | **Entered Service:** 1948 | **Length:** 285mm | **Motor:** 5 Pole Skew Wound, Loco Drive | **Curved Track:** Hornby 2nd Radius + / 438mm+ |

35024 'East Asiatic Company' entered traffic on 13 November, 1948 at Exmouth Junction and was named during a ceremony at Waterloo Station on 5 May, 1949, where HRH Prince Axel of Denmark officially named the

locomotive. 35024 'East Asiatic Company' remained at Exmouth until 26 February, 1959, when it entered the works for its rebuild.

R3649 | **BR, Merchant Navy Class, 4-6-2, 35029 'Ellerman Lines' - Era 4** | **DCC READY** | **8 PIN CONNECTION**

| **Designer:** O.V.S Bulleid | **Entered Service:** 1949 | **Length:** 285mm | **Motor:** 5 Pole Skew Wound, Loco Drive | **Curved Track:** Hornby 2nd Radius + / 438mm+ |

35029 'Ellerman Lines' entered traffic on 19 February, 1949 at Bournemouth and was named during a ceremony at Southampton Docks on 1 March, 1951, the Chairman of the company, Mr A.F Hull, officially naming the locomotive.

Allocated to Dover in October 1949, 'Ellerman Lines' was selected to haul the Danish Royal train from Dover Marine to London Victoria for the State visit of King Frederik IX and Queen Ingrid in May 1951.

R3716 | **BR, Merchant Navy Class, 4-6-2, 35022 'Holland America Line' - Era 4** | DCC READY | 8 PIN CONNECTION

Due Q2

| **Designer:** O.V.S Bulleid | **Entered Service:** 1948 | **Length:** 285mm | **Motor:** 5 Pole Skew Wound, Loco Drive | **Curved Track:** Hornby 2nd Radius + / 438mm+ |

35023 'Holland America Line' entered traffic on 9 October, 1948 and was named at a ceremony at Southampton Docks on 24 January, 1949. Repainted into British Railways experimental Steam Blue in July 1950, by the beginning of February 1952 the locomotive had reverted to British Railways Green and it was in this livery that 35023 'Holland America Line' was sent to BR's Test Facility at Rugby in order to work on improvements to the operation of the class.

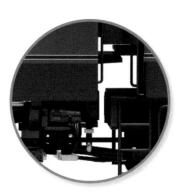

R3638 | **BR (Original) West Country Class, 4-6-2, 34019 'Bideford' - Era 5** | DCC READY | 8 PIN CONNECTION

| **Designer:** O.V.S Bulleid | **Entered Service:** 1945 | **Length:** 272mm | **Motor:** 5 Pole Skew Wound, Loco Drive | **Curved Track:** Hornby 2nd Radius + / 438mm+ |

Entering traffic on 24 December, 1945, 21C119 'Bideford' was first allocated to Exmouth Junction, where it stayed apart from a brief move to Eastleigh, until April 1951. The allocation at Nine Elms lasted until October 1958, with a move to Brighton, which was followed by a move to Salisbury in September 1963. Moves to Feltham and Eastleigh in 1964 were followed in 1966 by a return to Nine Elms, from where 34019 was withdrawn on 19 March, 1967.

R3525 | **BR, Battle of Britain Class, 4-6-2, 21C159 'Sir Archibald Sinclair' - Era 4** | DCC READY | 8 PIN CONNECTION

| **Designer:** O.V.S Bulleid | **Entered Service:** 1947 | **Length:** 272mm | **Motor:** 5 Pole Skew Wound, Loco Drive | **Curved Track:** Hornby 2nd Radius + / 438mm+ |

21C159 'Sir Archibald Sinclair', built at Brighton Works, entered traffic on 3 April, 1947, allocated to Nine Elms. Transferred to Stratford in April 1949, a second spell at Nine Elms from May 1949 was followed by a transfer west, to Exmouth Junction, on 11 April, 1951. Transferred again on 10 October, 1955, this time to Salisbury, the locomotive was rebuilt between February and March 1960, before being withdrawn from service on 29 May, 1966.

CENTENARY YEAR 1920 2020 HORNBY®

| R3856 | BR, Princess Coronation Class, 4-6-2, 46257 'City of Salford' - Era 5 | D C C READY | 8 PIN CONNECTION |

NEW Q3

| **Designer:** Sir William Stanier | **Entered Service:** 1948 | **Length:** 301mm | **Motor:** 5 Pole Skew Wound, Loco Drive | **Curved Track:** Hornby 2nd Radius + / 438mm+ |

The last of the class, 46257 'City of Salford' entered traffic on 19 May 1948 at Camden shed straight into British Railways' service, albeit that the livery was the lined LMS black with an M prefix to the BR number. Black gave way to BR Green on 10 December 1952 and by this time the Pony truck had been changed for a welded type, but the addition of AWS on 6 August 1959 cluttered the appearance beneath the cab on the left hand side. Withdrawn from service on 12 September 1964 from Carlisle shed, 46257 'City of Salford' was moved to Preston for storage until disposal.

Limited Availability

| R3642 | BR, Princess Coronation Class, 4-6-2, 46232 'Duchess of Montrose' - Era 4 | D C C READY | 8 PIN CONNECTION |

| **Designer:** Sir William Stanier | **Entered Service:** 1938 | **Length:** 301mm | **Motor:** 5 Pole Skew Wound, Loco Drive | **Curved Track:** Hornby 2nd Radius + / 438mm+ |

Built as one of the ten conventional 1938 Locomotive Programme 'Duchesses' that Stanier had yearned for, 46232 'Duchess of Montrose' entered traffic at Camden on 2 July, 1938. 'Duchess of Montrose' was sent to Polmadie at the beginning of January 1940 and was damaged by enemy action while allocated there, on 18 November, 1940. Returning to traffic on Boxing Day 1940, the locomotive remained at Polmadie until its withdrawal on 29 December, 1962.

| R3682 | BR, Princess Coronation Class, 4-6-2, 46225 'Duchess of Gloucester' - Era 4 | D C C READY | 8 PIN CONNECTION |

| **Designer:** Sir William Stanier | **Entered Service:** 1938 | **Length:** 301mm | **Motor:** 5 Pole Skew Wound, Loco Drive | **Curved Track:** Hornby 2nd Radius + / 438mm+ |

46225 'Duchess of Gloucester' was built streamlined at Crewe and entered traffic at Camden on 21 May, 1938. The streamlined casing was removed on 24 March, 1947 whilst the locomotive was allocated to Crewe North. Between January and June 1955, 'Duchess of Gloucester' was the subject of drawbar power tests by British Railways that confirmed the Princess Coronation class were the most powerful of British steam locomotives.

101

| R3681 | LMS, Princess Coronation Class, 4-6-2, 6241 'City of Edinburgh' - Era 3 | DCC READY | 8 PIN CONNECTION |

| **Designer:** Sir William Stanier | **Entered Service:** 1940 | **Length:** 301mm | **Motor:** 5 Pole Skew Wound, Loco Drive | **Curved Track:** Hornby 2nd Radius + / 438mm+ |

6241 'City of Edinburgh' was built streamlined at Crewe and entered traffic at Camden on 13 April, 1940, being paired with tender 9804. The streamlined casing was removed on 2 February, 1947 while the locomotive was still at Camden, a shed where 6241 spent the majority of its working life.

In storage between November 1962 and February 1963, then again between October 1963 and March 1964, 6241 'City of Edinburgh' was withdrawn in September 1964.

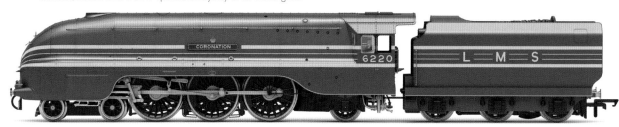

| R3857 | LMS, Princess Coronation Class, 4-6-2, 6220 'Coronation' - Era 3 | DCC READY | 8 PIN CONNECTION |
| NEW Q3 | | | |

| **Designer:** Sir William Stanier | **Entered Service:** 1937 | **Length:** 301mm | **Motor:** 5 Pole Skew Wound, Loco Drive | **Curved Track:** Hornby 2nd Radius + / 438mm+ |

The lead locomotive of the class, 6220 'Coronation' entered the LMS stock book on 1 June 1937, having been displayed to the Press at Crewe Works on 26 May. Regular Coronation Scot services commenced on 5 July, but prior to that 6220 'Coronation' was filmed for a publicity feature with the train between Colwyn Bay and Llandudno Junction.

From 20 December 1938, 6220 ran as 6229 'Duchess of Hamilton', as 6229 was masquerading as 6220 'Coronation' during a visit to the USA and even after returning in 1942, it was not until 14 May 1943 that 6220 'Coronation' was restored to its correct identity.

R3715 | **LMS, Princess Coronation Class, 4-6-2, 6224 'Princess Alexandra' - Era 3** | DCC READY | 8 PIN CONNECTION

| Designer: Sir William Stanier | Entered Service: 1937 | Length: 301mm | Motor: 5 Pole Skew Wound, Loco Drive | Curved Track: Hornby 2nd Radius + / 438mm+ |

6224 'Princess Alexandra' left Crewe Works for Camden Shed on 17 July, 1937, where it remained until 16 September, 1939 at the outbreak of war. Briefly put into storage at Bletchley, 'Princess Alexandra' re-entered traffic on October 21, 1939. Sent on loan to Polmadie on 25th November, the locomotive remained allocated there until its withdrawal in October 1963 and while there, the streamlined casing was removed on 27 June, 1946.

R3639 | **LMS, Princess Coronation Class, 4-6-2, 6244 'King George VI' - Era 3** | DCC READY | 8 PIN CONNECTION

| Designer: Sir William Stanier | Entered Service: 1940 | Length: 301mm | Motor: 5 Pole Skew Wound, Loco Drive | Curved Track: Hornby 2nd Radius + / 438mm+ |

6244 'King George VI' left Crewe works in July 1940 for Camden shed, having been originally named as 'City of Leeds' and covered just over 33,000 miles during the rest of 1940. Loaned to Polmadie briefly for a month in 1940, the locomotive spent the war years allocated to Camden and it was while there that it was renamed as 'King George VI' in April 1941. The streamlined casing was finally removed on 4 September, 1947.

RAILWAY MUSEUM Produced under licence for SCMG Enterprises Ltd. © SCMGE. Every purchase supports the museum.

R3677 | **LMS, Princess Coronation Class, 4-6-2, 6229 'Duchess of Hamilton' - Era 3** | DCC READY | 8 PIN CONNECTION

| Designer: Sir William Stanier | Entered Service: 1938 | Length: 301mm | Motor: 5 Pole Skew Wound, Loco Drive | Curved Track: Hornby 2nd Radius + / 438mm+ |

Built at Crewe in 1938 as the last of the streamlined 'Coronations', 'Duchess of Hamilton' entered service on 10th September. At the same time, the LMSR had accepted an invitation from the organisers of the 1939 World's Fair in New York to send a streamlined train to the exposition and as the newest of the 'Coronations', 6229 was selected, the name and numbers being swapped between 6229 'Duchess of Hamilton' and 6220 'Coronation'.

Princess Coronation Class
Locomotives

103

'Hush Hush'

Class W1 Locomotives

Introducing Sir Nigel Gresley's experimental 4-6-4HP Baltic, Engine No. 10000; the 'Hush-Hush'.

How Nigel Gresley came to consider a high pressure water-tube boiler to power a locomotive is a matter of some conjecture, but having considered it, in September 1924 he approached Harold Yarrow, a shipbuilder from Glasgow, with a proposal to build a high pressure water tube boiler to power a new 3 cylinder compound 4-6-2 design, comparable to the existing A1 Pacifics. By 1927 an outline diagram had been produced showing a 4-6-2-2 arrangement, although officially the design was designated as a 4-6-4 Baltic and on the 1st February 1928 the order for the locomotive was confirmed, initially referred to as 4-6-4HP on the drawings, then subsequently as 'Engine No. 10000'.

The widely adopted name of 'Hush-Hush' possibly arose in the late Summer of 1928, as news of Gresley's new locomotive began to leak out but it also possibly refers to an internal Darlington name that came from the distinctively quiet motion sound the loco made, or possibly even because of a mistaken caption that featured in a Pathé News item.

On 20 November 1929, nameplates were drawn up featuring the name British Enterprise and were cast soon after but these plates were never fitted and the loco remained unnamed, being referred to as 'Hush-Hush' ever since.

R3840	LNER, Class W1 'Hush Hush', 4-6-4, 10000 - Era 3					DCC READY	8 PIN CONNECTION
NEW Q4	Designer: Sir Nigel Gresley	Entered Service: 1928	Length: 307mm	Motor: 5 Pole Skew Wound, Loco Drive	Curved Track: Hornby 2nd Radius + / 438mm+		

R3841	LNER, Class W1 'Hush Hush', 4-6-4, 10000 'British Enterprise' - Era 3					DCC READY	8 PIN CONNECTION
NEW Q4	Designer: Sir Nigel Gresley	Entered Service: 1928	Length: 307mm	Motor: 5 Pole Skew Wound, Loco Drive	Curved Track: Hornby 2nd Radius + / 438mm+		

R3842	LNER (Promotional), Class W1 'Hush Hush', 4-6-4, 10000 - Era 3					DCC READY	8 PIN CONNECTION
NEW Q4	Designer: Sir Nigel Gresley	Entered Service: 1928	Length: 307mm	Motor: 5 Pole Skew Wound, Loco Drive	Curved Track: Hornby 2nd Radius + / 438mm+		

To place an order contact Hornby Customer Services on: **01843 233512** or visit your local stockist.

Class W1
Locomotives

Having completed nearly 90,000 miles of test running since new, the W1 entered Darlington Works on 21 August 1935 for what was anticipated to be a major overhaul and modification.

Sir Nigel Gresley decided that the time had come to rebuild 10000 as a three cylinder locomotive with a conventional firetube boiler and on 13 October 1936, 10000 was moved to Doncaster Works. What emerged in November 1937 was a significantly different locomotive fitted with a diagram 111 boiler similar to that fitted to 2006 'Wolf of Badenoch' and with a streamlined casing to the same pattern as the A4 class.

Up to the outbreak of War in 1939, and during the War years, 10000 worked mainly on Kings Cross main line duties and with its power and smooth riding it was a popular engine with the LNER drivers. Post War, and now numbered 60700, the corridor tender was swapped for a streamlined non-corridor tender and the locomotive was engaged in more varied duties, working occasional passenger services to Leeds and Cambridge from Kings Cross alongside the occasional 'lodging' turns to Newcastle.

As 10000 never received its proposed name of 'British Enterprise' in November 1929, 60700 never received its intended name of 'Pegasus', for which the nameplates were cast on 13 April 1951.

R3843	LNER, Rebuilt Class W1, 4-6-4, 10000 - Era 3				DCC READY	8 PIN CONNECTION
NEW Q4	Designer: Sir Nigel Gresley	Entered Service: 1937	Length: 307mm	Motor: 5 Pole Skew Wound, Loco Drive	Curved Track: Hornby 2nd Radius + / 438mm+	

R3844	BR, Rebuilt Class W1, 4-6-4, 60700 - Era 4				DCC READY	8 PIN CONNECTION
NEW Q4	Designer: Sir Nigel Gresley	Entered Service: 1937	Length: 307mm	Motor: 5 Pole Skew Wound, Loco Drive	Curved Track: Hornby 2nd Radius + / 438mm+	

To place an order contact Hornby Customer Services on: **01843 233512** or visit your local stockist.

R3522 | **BR, A4 Class, 4-6-2, 60026 'Miles Beevor' - Era 3** | DCC READY | 8 PIN CONNECTION

Designer: Sir Nigel Gresley | **Entered Service:** 1937 | **Length:** 291mm | **Motor:** 5 Pole Skew Wound, Loco Drive | **Curved Track:** Hornby 2nd Radius + / 438mm+

Built at Doncaster, 4485 'Miles Beevor' left the works for Haymarket shed on 20 February, 1937 with the name 'Kestrel'. While at Kings Cross in April/May 1946, 4485 was renumbered twice, as 587 and 26, within the space of a month.

In November 1947, at Doncaster, the locomotive was renamed as 'Miles Beevor', before being moved back to Kings Cross Shed, eventually receiving the BR number 60026 in September 1949.

R3701 | **BR, A4 Class, 4-6-2, 60028 'Walter K Whigham' - Era 4** | DCC READY | 8 PIN CONNECTION

Designer: Sir Nigel Gresley | **Entered Service:** 1937 | **Length:** 291mm | **Motor:** 5 Pole Skew Wound, Loco Drive | **Curved Track:** Hornby 2nd Radius + / 438mm+

Entering traffic on 20 March, 1937 as 4487 'Sea Eagle', the locomotive was allocated to Gateshead and Haymarket sheds until 9 May, 1939, moving to Kings Cross for the duration of the Second World War. Returning to Kings Cross in May 1948 as LNER No. 28 and renamed as 'Walter K. Whigham',

the move coincided with a repaint into British Railways' experimental express blue/purple livery, with lining in red, cream and grey, as well as a renumbering to 60028.

RAILWAY MUSEUM | Produced under licence for SCMG Enterprises Ltd. © SCMGE. Every purchase supports the museum.

R3737 | **BR, A4 Class, 4-6-2, 60022 'Mallard' - Era 4** | DCC READY | 8 PIN CONNECTION

Designer: Sir Nigel Gresley | **Entered Service:** 1938 | **Length:** 291mm | **Motor:** 5 Pole Skew Wound, Loco Drive | **Curved Track:** Hornby 2nd Radius + / 438mm+

Having been neglected during the wartime years while based at Grantham Shed, numbered as 22 and having been paired with a Corridor Tender, 'Mallard's' prestige was restored with a move back to Kings Cross on 11 April, 1948, the last A4 to regain the Garter Blue Livery.

British Railways experimented with their own versions of Blue and on 16 September, 1949, 'Mallard', now numbered 60022, emerged from Doncaster Works in the new BR Blue for Steam Locomotives.

| R3711 | BR, Princess Royal Class, 4-6-2, 46206 'Princess Marie Louise' (with flickering firebox) - Era 4 | DCC READY | 8 PIN CONNECTION |

| Designer: Sir William Stanier | Entered Service: 1935 | Length: 300mm | Motor: 5 Pole Skew Wound, Loco Drive | Curved Track: Hornby 2nd Radius + / 438mm+ |

Originally proposed to be named as 'Princess Maud', 6206 Princess 'Marie Louise' entered service on loan at Crewe North, before heading on to Camden as the majority of the class did from new. Renumbered as 46206 on 27 November, 1948 while at Crewe North Shed, 'Princess Marie Louise'

was one of four 'Princess Royals' to receive the experimental British Railways Blue livery in November 1950, before switching to BR Green with emblems in August 1953.

DCC FITTED R3854X

| R3854/X | LMS, Princess Royal Class, 4-6-2, 6212 'Duchess of Kent' (with flickering firebox) - Era 3 | DCC READY | 8 PIN CONNECTION |

NEW Q2

| Designer: Sir William Stanier | Entered Service: 1935 | Length: 300mm | Motor: 5 Pole Skew Wound, Loco Drive | Curved Track: Hornby 2nd Radius + / 438mm+ |

6212 'Duchess of Kent' entered traffic on 21 October 1935, being allocated to Camden shed and fitted with a riveted 9-ton LMS tender. Oddly, out of all the 'Princess Royals' built at Crewe, 6212 was the only one to be fitted with a Derby style smokebox door, but by 1939 this had been removed.

Spread across three different allocation periods, 6212 'Duchess of Kent' spent the majority of its service life running out of Crewe North and was finally withdrawn from service while at this shed at the beginning of October 1961.

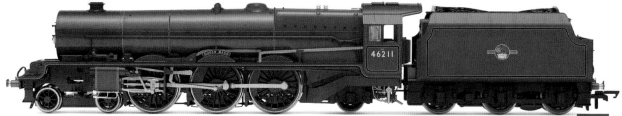

DCC FITTED R3855X

| R3855/X | BR, Princess Royal Class, 4-6-2, 46211 'Queen Maud' (with flickering firebox) - Era 5 | DCC READY | 8 PIN CONNECTION |

NEW Q3

| Designer: Sir William Stanier | Entered Service: 1935 | Length: 300mm | Motor: 5 Pole Skew Wound, Loco Drive | Curved Track: Hornby 2nd Radius + / 438mm+ |

6211 'Queen Maud' entered traffic on 21 October 1935 allocated to Camden shed and fitted with the riveted 9-ton LMS tender, which it retained until the first heavy service at Crewe during July 1936, when a riveted 10-ton tender was attached. Fleetingly allocated to Crewe North at the outbreak

of War in 1939, 'Queen Maud' moved to the shed permanently on 22 May 1943 where it remained, apart from a two month stint at Edge Hill in 1956, until withdrawn on 7 October 1961.

| R3713 | BR, Princess Royal Class, 4-6-2, 46207 'Princess Arthur of Connaught' (with flickering firebox) - Era 5 | DCC READY | 8 PIN CONNECTION |

| Designer: Sir William Stanier | Entered Service: 1935 | Length: 300mm | Motor: 5 Pole Skew Wound, Loco Drive | Curved Track: Hornby 2nd Radius + / 438mm+ |

Originally proposed to be named as 'Princess Alice', 6207 'Princess Arthur of Connaught' entered service on loan at Crewe North on 10 August, 1935, before heading on to be allocated to Camden from 1st September.

During 1958/59, four 'Princess Royals' were repainted into British Railways' version of the LMS pre-war Crimson Lake livery, 46207 'Princess Arthur of Connaught' being the first on 9 May, 1958, while allocated to Edge Hill Shed.

CENTENARY YEAR 1920 2020

HORNBY®

Produced under licence for SCMG Enterprises Ltd. © SCMGE. Every purchase supports the museum.

R3865 | BR, Standard 7 'Britannia' Class, 4-6-2, 70013 'Oliver Cromwell' - Era 5 | DCC READY | 8 PIN CONNECTION

NEW Q4

| Designer: Robert Riddles | Entered Service: 1951 | Length: 287mm | Motor: 5 Pole Skew Wound, Loco Drive | Curved Track: Hornby 2nd Radius + / 438mm+ |

70013 'Oliver Cromwell' famously took part in the very last British Rail Steam railtour, the 'Fifteen Guinea Special', on 11 August 1968 and was withdrawn from service the following day, the locomotive's final trip in BR service being to Norwich, via Doncaster, then on to Diss from where it was transferred by road to Alan Bloom's Bressingham Steam Museum on 19th August. Part of the National Collection, at Bressingham 70013 'Oliver Cromwell' continued in use on a 200 yard track, giving guards van and footplate rides and ran until 1973, when it was moved to the museum. 70013 'Oliver Cromwell' remained at Bressingham until the long-term loan agreement was terminated and left East Anglia on 21 May 2004, travelling by road to York, before heading to Loughborough and the Great Central Railway for a thorough overhaul. 70013 'Oliver Cromwell' returned to passenger service on 3rd May 2008 and worked until the final day of 2018, the locomotive's boiler certificate expiring on 1 January 2019.

R3643 | BR, Standard 7 'Britannia' Class, 4-6-2, 70046 'ANZAC' - Era 5 | DCC READY | 8 PIN CONNECTION

| Designer: Robert Riddles | Entered Service: 1954 | Length: 287mm | Motor: 5 Pole Skew Wound, Loco Drive | Curved Track: Hornby 2nd Radius + / 438mm+ |

70046 'ANZAC' entered traffic on 22 June, 1954, being allocated to 6J Holyhead for the first five years of service. With further allocations to Holyhead coming in December 1962 and June 1965, 70046 spent over half of its service life operating from this shed. The final allocation was to 12A Carlisle Kingsmoor on 8 January, 1966 and it was from here that 70046 was withdrawn on 8 July, 1967, having completed just thirteen years and sixteen days in service.

Produced under licence for SCMG Enterprises Ltd. © SCMGE. Every purchase supports the museum.

R3627 | BR, Class A3, 4-6-2, 60103 'Flying Scotsman' - Era 4 | DCC READY | 8 PIN CONNECTION

| Designer: Sir Nigel Gresley | Entered Service: 1923 | Length: 293mm | Motor: 5 Pole Skew Wound, Loco Drive | Curved Track: Hornby 2nd Radius + / 438mm+ |

A1 Class 4472 'Flying Scotsman' entered traffic in February 1923 as LNER No. 1472, being allocated initially to Doncaster. Renumbered as 4472 in March 1924, the locomotive was also renumbered as No. 502 and No. 103 before entering Doncaster workshops in November 1946 for rebuilding as an A3. In 1949 the locomotive was repainted into British Railways' experimental Express Blue livery and carried the new number of 60103.

Produced under licence for SCMG Enterprises Ltd. © SCMGE. Every purchase supports the museum.

R3736 | LNER, Class A1, 4-6-2, 4472 'Flying Scotsman' - Era 3 | DCC READY | 8 PIN CONNECTION

| Designer: Sir Nigel Gresley | Entered Service: 1923 | Length: 293mm | Motor: 5 Pole Skew Wound, Loco Drive | Curved Track: Hornby 2nd Radius + / 438mm+ |

A1 Class 4472 'Flying Scotsman' entered traffic on 24 February, 1923, unnamed, as LNER No. 1472. Selected as the LNER's presitige exhibit for the forthcoming British Empire Exhibition at Wembley, 1472 emerged from Doncaster Works on 2 March, 1924 with the Company's Coat-of-Arms adorning the cabside, a new number; 4472 and named as 'Flying Scotsman'. On 1 May, 1928, and fitted with a Corridor Tender, 'Flying Scotsman' undertook the first non-stop run from London to Edinburgh.

'Thompson Class'
A2/2 & A2/3 Locomotives

Thompson Class A2/2 Locomotives.

Edward Thompson's heavy mixed traffic 4-6-2 conversion of Sir Nigel Gresley's six 2-8-2 P2 class locomotives.

Initially, Thompson's modifications involved cutting away the front ring of the existing 106A (and sole 108A) boilers and fitting shorter super-heater elements but with only six 106A boilers in stock the lack of spare boilers led to lengthy works visits. To counter this, authority was granted on 9 July 1948 to replace these boilers with Arthur Peppercorn's new issue

Diagram 118 boilers as renewals became necessary. Eventually four of the A2/2s were converted during 1951/52; 60501 'Cock o' the North', 60502 'Earl Marischal', 60505 'Thane of Fife' and 60506 'Wolf of Badenoch', with 60505 'Thane of Fife' receiving a Diagram 107 Boiler as a replacement five years later in 1957.

R3830	BR, Thompson Class A2/2, 4-6-2, 60501 'Cock o' the North' - Era 4				DCC READY	8 PIN CONNECTION
NEW Q4	Designer: Edward Thompson	Entered Service: 1944	Length: 295mm	Motor: 5 Pole Skew Wound, Loco Drive	Curved Track: Hornby 2nd Radius + / 438mm+	

R3831	BR, Thompson Class A2/2, 4-6-2, 60505 'Thane of Fife' - Era 5				DCC READY	8 PIN CONNECTION
NEW Q4	Designer: Edward Thompson	Entered Service: 1943	Length: 295mm	Motor: 5 Pole Skew Wound, Loco Drive	Curved Track: Hornby 2nd Radius + / 438mm+	

To place an order contact Hornby Customer Services on: **01843 233512** or visit your local stockist.

Thompson Class A2/3 Locomotives.

The design of Edward Thompson's new A2/3 4-6-2 class locomotives was based on his previous rebuild of the 2-8-2 P2 class.

Orders were placed for ten locomotives initially, to be followed by a further five. The A2/3s were fitted with a Diagram 117 boiler from Darlington, with a round dome rather than the more familiar Gresley 'banjo' dome.

Thompson reverted to his favoured GNR style flat fronted cab for the A2/3 and at the front end traditional large deflectors were mounted either side of the smokebox, as opposed to the small winglet style deflectors that were in vogue with the LNER at the time. The first A2/3 was completed in May 1946, just a month before Thompson's retirement and was the 2000th locomotive to be built at Doncaster.

Thompson never really had the opportunity to develop his A2/3 locomotives and while steps were taken to iron out the locomotive's initial flaws under the new CME, Arthur Peppercorn, he amended the design of the remaining fifteen locomotives from Thompson's 1945 order, creating his own A2 class in the process.

R3832	LNER, Thompson Class A2/3, 4-6-2 500 'Edward Thompson' - Era 3				DCC READY	8 PIN CONNECTION
NEW Q4	Designer: Edward Thompson	Entered Service: 1946	Length: 295mm	Motor: 5 Pole Skew Wound, Loco Drive	Curved Track: Hornby 2nd Radius + / 438mm+	
R3833	LNER, Thompson Class A2/3, 4-6-2, 514 'Chamossaire' - Era 3				DCC READY	8 PIN CONNECTION
NEW Q4	Designer: Edward Thompson	Entered Service: 1946	Length: 295mm	Motor: 5 Pole Skew Wound, Loco Drive	Curved Track: Hornby 2nd Radius + / 438mm+	
R3834	BR, Thompson Class A2/3, 4-6-2, 60512 'Steady Aim' - Era 4				DCC READY	8 PIN CONNECTION
NEW Q4	Designer: Edward Thompson	Entered Service: 1946	Length: 295mm	Motor: 5 Pole Skew Wound, Loco Drive	Curved Track: Hornby 2nd Radius + / 438mm+	
R3835	BR, Thompson Class A2/3, 4-6-2, 60523 'Sun Castle' - Era 5				DCC READY	8 PIN CONNECTION
NEW Q4	Designer: Edward Thompson	Entered Service: 1947	Length: 295mm	Motor: 5 Pole Skew Wound, Loco Drive	Curved Track: Hornby 2nd Radius + / 438mm+	

DIESEL
& ELECTRIC Locomotives

In 2020, diesel and electric powered locomotives and trains exist side by side on the United Kingdom's railway network and even, in some cases, provide dual power sources, but as diesel traction is gradually phased out as a primary power source, familiar trains are being replaced by new rolling stock.

The biggest change has arguably taken place on the West Country routes, with the replacement of the venerable HST fleet on long haul passenger services by Hitachi's Class 800 bi-mode InterCity Express Trains and the gradual extension of overhead power masts westwards from London Paddington but an equally big change is currently taking place on the East Coast Main Line, as HSTs and Class 91 sets are slowly withdrawn from service and replaced by both electric and bi-mode Class 800 Azuma, Novo and Paragon sets serving LNER, TransPennine Express and Hull Trains. On the West Coast Main Line, Pendolino and Super Voyager are now seen with their new liveries while the Midland Main Line, under East Midlands Railway, is preparing to replace its HSTs and Meridian sets with new Hitachi AT300 bi-mode trains. Even East Anglia is benefitting from new rolling stock, as Stadler's bi-mode Class 755 'Flirt' sets are introduced.

As the Class 91 locomotives are withdrawn from the ECML under LNER, their future use remains unclear but Hornby are honouring the thirty plus year service of this record breaking locomotive with a completely new model featuring 21st Century tooling that covers the entire service history of the locomotive, from the early InterCity 225 examples, through to the Project Delta refurbishments under GNER and on to the final variants running under LNER.

There are probably more locomotive liveries on the network at the present time than there have been since the pre-grouping era and the UK Class 66 fleets are a perfect example of this. Building on the Class 66 models offered in 2019, Hornby are producing a further range of locomotives from the class, in a myriad of liveries that illustrate the flexibility of this remarkable diesel locomotive workhorse.

71012

50 040

NEW Q3

R3852	DVLR, Ruston & Hornsby 48DS, 0-4-0, 417892 'Jim' - Era 8	DCC READY	6 PIN CONNECTION

Designer: Ruston & Hornsby	Entered Service: 1958

Length: 55mm	Motor: 3 Pole Skew Wound.	Curved Track: Hornby 1st Radius + / 371mm+

R&H No. 417892 left Boultham Works on 25 August 1958 fitted with the newer R&H VRH engine No. 441501, ordered by Sir William Arrol & Co. Ltd at Glasgow's Parkhead Crane Works. In 1975 the locomotive was sold on to Crossley Scrap Merchants in Shipley, where it worked until 1982. Sold into preservation, 417892 was restored and moved to the Derwent Valley Light Railway at Murton Park on 18 August 1990, where it still resides.

NEW Q3

R3853	GrantRail Ltd, Ruston & Hornsby 48DS, 0-4-0, GR5090 - Era 9	DCC READY	6 PIN CONNECTION

Designer: Ruston & Hornsby	Entered Service: 1940

Length: 55mm	Motor: 3 Pole Skew Wound.	Curved Track: Hornby 1st Radius + / 371mm+

R&H 200793 left Boultham Works on 26 October 1940, heading for William Evans & Co. Old Mills Colliery in Somerset. The colliery closed in 1966 and 200793 made its way into the fleet of rail construction contractor Grant, Lyon & Eagre Ltd, at one point being used at the Cheriton site during construction of the Channel Tunnel. GLE Ltd became a subsidiary of British Steel in 1989 and was subsequently rebranded as GrantRail Ltd in August 1996. Sold into preservation at the Pontypool & Blaenavon Railway as 'Gower Princess', 200793 has now been fully restored and is the yard shunter at Williton at the West Somerset Railway.

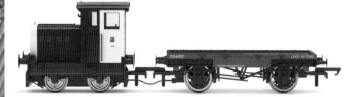

R3705	John Dewar & Sons, R&H 48DS, 0-4-0, No. 458957 - Era 8	DCC READY	6 PIN CONNECTION

Designer: Ruston & Hornsby	Entered Service: 1961

Length: 55mm	Motor: 3 Pole Skew Wound.	Curved Track: Hornby 1st Radius + / 371mm+

R&H No. 458957 left Boultham Works on 6 July, 1961, being one of the final ten 48DS locomotives built and was purchased by John Dewar & Sons for use at their Inveralmond distillery, until its closure in 1994. The locomotive was saved for preservation and is currently operating at the Bridge of Dun station on the Caledonian Railway as 'Dewar Highlander'.

NEW Q4

R3943	Express Dairy Co. Ltd, Ruston & Hornsby 48DS, 0-4-0, 235511 - Era 4/5/6	DCC READY	6 PIN CONNECTION

Designer: Ruston & Hornsby	Entered Service: 1945

Length: 55mm	Motor: 3 Pole Skew Wound.	Curved Track: Hornby 1st Radius + / 371mm+

R&H 235511 left Boultham Works on 24 August 1945, having been ordered by Express Dairy Co. Ltd for shunting use at their bottling plant in Cricklewood, the locomotive remaining there until 1954.

235511 was then transferred over to the Express Dairy's bottling plant at South Morden where it worked until the spring of 1972, being replaced by a Hunslet Yardmaster 0-4-0. In July 1972 235511 was sold to Esmond Lewis-Evans and moved to Ashford, at the South Eastern Steam Centre.

PLEASE NOTE: R3852, R3853 and R3705 fit is incompatible with R7150 and requires 6-pin Nano Decoder.

R3576	Barrington Light Railway, Sentinel 4wDH, No. 19 - Era 8	DCC READY	4 PIN CONNECTION

Designer: Sentinel	Entered Service: 1966

Length: 98mm	Motor: 3 Pole Skew Wound.	Curved Track: Hornby 1st Radius + / 371mm+

Locomotive '19' (Works No.10260, built in 1966) is a chain drive 4wDH type, of which 104 were built. '19' was the locomotive used on the Barrington Light Railway at Rugby Cement, Barrington, in Cambridgeshire, which connected the Cement Works with the British Rail exchange sidings at Foxton.

R3577	Oxfordshire Ironstone Company, Sentinel 0-4-0, 'Graham' - Era 11	DCC READY	4 PIN CONNECTION

Designer: Sentinel	Entered Service: 1965

Length: 98mm	Motor: 3 Pole Skew Wound.	Curved Track: Hornby 1st Radius + / 371mm+

Delivered ex-works as Locomotive No. 10207 in May 1965 as one of a series of locomotives ordered by the Oxfordshire Ironstone Company, Graham was fitted with vacuum braking and a higher ratio gearbox for mainline working. The locomotive is now preserved at the Living Ironstone Museum at Cottesmore in Rutland.

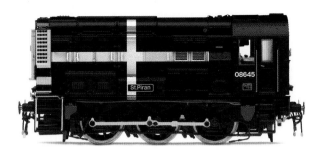

NEW Q3

R3900	BR, Class 08, 0-6-0, 08645 'St. Piran' - Era 11	DCC READY	8 PIN CONNECTION

Designer: BREL	**Entered Service:** 1959

Length: 124mm	**Motor:** 5 Pole Skew Wound.	**Curved Track:** Hornby 1st Radius + / 371mm+

Built at Horwich Works, D3812 entered traffic on 13 February 1959 allocated to Newport Pill and the locomotive was to remain in Wales, albeit allocated to different depots, until the closure of Landore in December 2018. During this period, air brakes were fitted to D3812 in October 1971 and in March 1974 the locomotive was renumbered as 08645 under TOPS. On leaving Landore, 08645 was moved across to GWR's Long Rock Maintenance Depot and on 13 April 2019 at the public open day held to raise money for the Penlee Lifeboat Station and RNLI, the locomotive was unveiled in a special 'Kernow' livery and bearing the name 'St. Piran', after the patron saint of Cornwall.

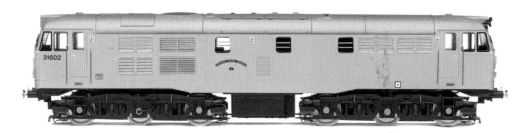

R3745 — Network Rail, Class 31, A1A-A1A, 31602 'Driver Dave Green' - Era 9

DCC READY **8 PIN CONNECTION**

Designer: Brush Traction Ltd | **Entered Service:** 1960 | **Length:** 225mm | **Motor:** 5 Pole Skew Wound | **Curved Track:** Hornby 2nd Radius + / 438mm+

Entering traffic on 12 May, 1960 as D5614, in April 1998 it was withdrawn for modification to Class 31/6, and renumbered 31602. The locomotive re-entered traffic with Fragonset, as Chimera, then Network Rail, and was named as Driver Dave Green at Derby RTC in November 2007, marking 52 years of railway service by the driver.

R3746 — BR, Class 31, A1A-A1A, 31102 - Era 7

DCC READY **8 PIN CONNECTION**

Designer: Brush Traction Ltd | **Entered Service:** 1960 | **Length:** 225mm | **Motor:** 5 Pole Skew Wound | **Curved Track:** Hornby 2nd Radius + / 438mm+

Entering traffic at Stratford as D5520 on 26 February, 1959, the locomotive was soon moved to Ipswich, where it remained until 11 May, 1968.

D5520 was renumbered to 31102 at the beginning of 1973 while allocated to York, moving to Stratford in 1976. Sold to Network Rail for spares, 31102 was scrapped in 2007.

R3661 — BR, Class 31, A1A-A1A, D5509 - Era 6

DCC READY **8 PIN CONNECTION**

Designer: Brush Traction Ltd | **Entered Service:** 1958 | **Length:** 225mm | **Motor:** 5 Pole Skew Wound | **Curved Track:** Hornby 2nd Radius + / 438mm+

D5509 entered traffic on 1 May, 1958 and led the most unremarkable service life, allocated to Stratford right up until being transferred to storage on 9 May, 1976.

Along with fourteen other examples of the original twenty Pilot Scheme 'Toffee Apples', D5509 (as 31009) met the cutter's torch at Doncaster in November 1977.

R3917 — BR, Class 31, A1A-A1A, D5627 - Era 6

NEW Q4 **DCC READY** **8 PIN CONNECTION**

Designer: Brush Traction | **Entered Service:** 1960 | **Length:** 225mm | **Motor:** 5 Pole Skew Wound | **Curved Track:** Hornby 2nd Radius + / 438mm+

D5627 entered traffic on 23 June 1960 allocated to Ipswich Shed and the locomotive spent much of its early career operating in the East of England, with additional allocations to Stratford, March and Finsbury Park. Numbered 31203 under the TOPS scheme, from the late 1970s 31203 operated from Bescot and Immingham on freight duties, before moving to Civil Engineer duties in the 1990s. Placed into storage in July 2000, 31203 was purchased for preservation by Les Emery and was restored at the Chasewater Railway, before being moved to the Pontypool & Blaenavon Railway where the locomotive was named Steve Organ G.M on 26 July 2009.

| R3880 | BR, Class 31, A1A-A1A, 31147 'Floreat Salopia' - Era 8 | | | | DCC READY | 8 PIN CONNECTION |

NEW Q3

| **Designer:** Brush Traction | **Entered Service:** 1959 | **Length:** 225mm | **Motor:** 5 Pole Skew Wound | **Curved Track:** Hornby 2nd Radius + / 438mm+ |

31147 'Floreat Salopia' entered traffic on 19 November 1959 as D5565, allocated to March Shed and the locomotive remained in East Anglia until 9 October 1965, when it moved north to Tinsley. Renumbered to 31147 under the TOPS scheme, the locomotive was one of three Class 31s fitted with Radio Electronic Token Blocks for use over the Cambrian route, 31147 also carrying BR Regional Railways branding over its 'Dutch' livery, until it was named 'Floreat Salopia' by John Thompson, a Shropshire Star competition winner, at Shrewsbury Cotton Hill Depot's Open Day on 30 May 1993.

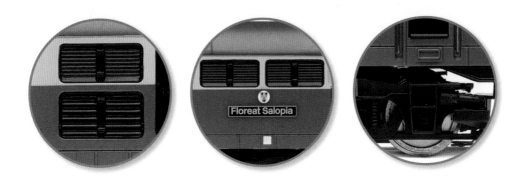

| R3882 | GBRf, Class 50, Co-Co, 50007 'Hercules' - Era 11 | | | | DCC READY | 8 PIN CONNECTION |

NEW Q3

| **Designer:** BREL | **Entered Service:** 1968 | **Length:** 275mm | **Motor:** 5 Pole Skew Wound | **Curved Track:** Hornby 2nd Radius + / 438mm+ |

50007 'Hercules' entered service in August 1968 as D407 and was named 'Hercules' on 6 April 1978, then renamed 'Sir Edward Elgar' on 25 February 1984 to celebrate the 150th anniversary of the Great Western Railway.

Retired from service on 26 March 1994, 50007 was preserved by the Class 40 Appeal at Midland Railway Butterley, then sold into private hands, before being acquired by the Class 50 Alliance in November 2016.

| R3883 | GBRf, Class 50, Co-Co, 50049 'Defiance' - Era 11 | | | | DCC READY | 8 PIN CONNECTION |

NEW Q3

| **Designer:** BREL | **Entered Service:** 1968 | **Length:** 275mm | **Motor:** 5 Pole Skew Wound | **Curved Track:** Hornby 2nd Radius + / 438mm+ |

50049 'Defiance' entered service in December 1968 as D449 and was named 'Defiance' on 2 May 1978. Part of the 1987 freight experiment, the locomotive was renumbered to 50149 and spent two years working china clay and heavy aggregate trains before reverting back to being numbered as 50049.

Retired from service in August 1991, 50049 'Defiance' was preserved by The Class 50 Society (later Project Defiance), first at the West Somerset Railway and then the Severn Valley Railway, before Project Defiance merged with The Fifty Fund to form the Class 50 Alliance, to whom ownership of the locomotive passed to in November 2006.

| R3473 | BR Railfreight, Class 56, Co-Co, 56108 - Era 8 | | | | DCC READY | 8 PIN CONNECTION |

Designer: British Rail | **Entered Service:** 1982 | **Length:** 254mm | **Motor:** 5 Pole Skew Wound | **Curved Track:** Hornby 2nd Radius + / 438mm+

56108 was built at BREL at Doncaster in June 1982 and allocated to Healey Mills Depot as part of the Railfreight fleet. Withdrawn in June 1999, in 2010, 56108 was put up for sale by DB Schenker while at Tees Yard. Sold to EMR Hartlepool for scrap, it was cut up in November 2011.

| R3888 | Floyd Zrt. Class 56, Co-Co, 659 002 (ex-56115) - Era 10 | | | | DCC READY | 8 PIN CONNECTION |

NEW Q3

Designer: BREL | **Entered Service:** 1983 | **Length:** 254mm | **Motor:** 5 Pole Skew Wound | **Curved Track:** Hornby 2nd Radius + / 438mm+

Floyd Zrt. was one of the first open-access freight operators in Hungary and currently operates a varied traction fleet which includes a number of ex-BR locomotives. 56115 was exported to Floyd in September 2012 from Immingham Docks, after first being prepared at Nemesis, in Burton. Arriving with Floyd, the locomotive was given the distinctive 'Pink Floyd' livery and running number 659 002.

| R3660 | DCR, Class 56, Co-Co, 56303 - Era 10 | | | | DCC READY | 8 PIN CONNECTION |

Designer: British Rail | **Entered Service:** 1983 | **Length:** 254mm | **Motor:** 5 Pole Skew Wound | **Curved Track:** Hornby 2nd Radius + / 438mm+

56108 was built at BREL at Crewe, entering traffic on 20 October, 1983. Allocated to Tinsley. 56103 was withdrawn from service in February 2000, before being overhauled by Brush Traction in May 2006 and then reclassified as Class 56/3. Renumbered 56303 on May 18, 2005, it is now in Devon & Cornwall Railways ownership.

| R3901 | Colas Rail, Class 60, Co-Co, 60021 - Era 10 | | | | DCC READY | 8 PIN CONNECTION |

NEW Q3

Designer: BREL | **Entered Service:** 1991 | **Length:** 280mm | **Motor:** 5 Pole Skew Wound | **Curved Track:** Hornby 2nd Radius + / 438mm+

60021 Pen-y-Ghent was allocated to the Railfreight Metals subsector at Thornaby once it had entered British Rail service on 14 December 1991 and it subsequently carried the name Star of the East during EWS service.

In 2014 Colas purchased ten Class 60s from DB Schenker, including 60021, but in June 2018 Colas sold these locomotives on to GBRf. Still running in Colas' orange and yellow livery, GBRf removed 'Colas' from the locomotive sides and gave 60021 the name of Bustler, which it held until 21 May 2019, emerging from Eastleigh Works with a full GBRf livery and reverting to its original name, Pen-y-Ghent.

| R3743 | BR Railfreight, Class 60, Co-Co, 60015 'Bow Fell' - Era 8 | | | | DCC READY | 8 PIN CONNECTION |

| **Designer:** British Rail | **Entered Service:** 1993 | **Length:** 280mm | **Motor:** 5 Pole Skew Wound | **Curved Track:** Hornby 2nd Radius + / 438mm+ |

60015 'Bow Fell' was the last of the class to be accepted into service by British Rail, entering traffic on 24 March, 1993 being allocated to the Railfreight Construction sub-sector at Immingham.

When Transrail was launched on 29 August, 1994 at Arpley Yard, it was 60015 that was selected to unveil the new Transrail livery.

| R3884 | DB Cargo UK, Class 60, Co-Co, 60100 'Midland Railway - Butterley' - Era 11 | | | | DCC READY | 8 PIN CONNECTION |
| NEW Q3 | | | | | | |

| **Designer:** BREL | **Entered Service:** 1992 | **Length:** 280mm | **Motor:** 5 Pole Skew Wound | **Curved Track:** Hornby 2nd Radius + / 438mm+ |

The last Class 60 to be built, 60100 entered service on 9 December 1992 with Railfreight (Construction) named as 'Boar of Badenoch', a name the locomotive retained until May 2003. On 28 June 2003 the locomotive was renamed 'Pride of Acton', retaining that name until March 2010, after which

the locomotive was moved to storage, pending overhaul as a 'Super Sixty'. Returning to traffic, on 16 June 2018 60100 was named 'Midland Railway – Butterley' during Butterley's Diesel Gala.

| R3885 | DB Cargo UK, Class 60, Co-Co, 60062 'Stainless Pioneer' - Era 11 | | | | DCC READY | 8 PIN CONNECTION |
| NEW Q3 | | | | | | |

| **Designer:** BREL | **Entered Service:** 1991 | **Length:** 280mm | **Motor:** 5 Pole Skew Wound | **Curved Track:** Hornby 2nd Radius + / 438mm+ |

60062 entered service on 17 June 1991 with Railfreight (Petroleum) named as 'Samuel Johnson', a name the locomotive retained until November 1996. Having been absorbed into the EWS fleet, like the rest of the class 60062 was subjected to the EWS seasonal storage roundabout; returning to service for the Winter traffic peak and then being returned to storage during the

quieter Summer period. On being sold to Deutsche Bahn, 60062 was selected for the 'Super Sixty' overhaul programme and on returning to traffic was named 'Stainless Pioneer' at a ceremony that took place on 14 June 2013 at Tinsley, Sheffield to celebrate the centenary of the invention of stainless steel.

| R3657 | Loadhaul, Class 60, Co-Co, 60070 'John Loundon McAdam' - Era 9 | | | | DCC READY | 8 PIN CONNECTION |

| **Designer:** British Rail | **Entered Service:** 1991 | **Length:** 280mm | **Motor:** 5 Pole Skew Wound | **Curved Track:** Hornby 2nd Radius + / 438mm+ |

60070 'John Loudon McAdam' was built at Brush Traction's works in October 1991 and named on 28 October, 1991.

Along with 60050 and 60064, 60070 was one of only three locomotives to carry the Loadhaul branding over the existing Railfreight triple grey livery.

CLASS 66 Locomotives

| R3573 | GBRf, Class 66, Co-Co, 66751 'Inspiration Delivered - Hitach Rail Europe' - Era 10 | | | | DCC READY | 8 PIN CONNECTION |

| **Designer:** Electro-Motive Diesel | **Entered Service:** 2003 | **Length:** 280mm | **Motor:** 5 Pole Skew Wound | **Curved Track:** Hornby 2nd Radius + / 438mm+ |

On 27 April, 2015 Beacon Rail/GBRf's 66751 received the name 'Inspiration Delivered - Hitachi Rail Europe' at the Rail Innovation and Development Centre. The locomotive was repainted into the latest GBRf livery and fitted with a special retractable coupler for transporting the new Hitachi Class 800 IEP trains during testing.

| R3881 | GBRf, Class 66, Co-Co, 66727 'Andrew Scott CBE' - Era 10 | | | | DCC READY | 8 PIN CONNECTION |

NEW Q1

| **Designer:** Electro-Motive Diesel | **Entered Service:** 2006 | **Length:** 280mm | **Motor:** 5 Pole Skew Wound | **Curved Track:** Hornby 2nd Radius + / 438mm+ |

Delivered into Newport Docks on board the MV Fairload on 20 December, 2006, 66727 went into service with First GBRf, appearing at GBRf's new livery press launch on 8 January 2007 along with 66723, 66724, 66725 and 66726.

On 22 October 2009, 66727 was named 'Andrew Scott CBE' at the National Railway Museum in a ceremony honouring the outgoing Director of the museum. 66727 retained the name until 20 September 2016, when the locomotive was renamed as 'Maritime One'.

CENTENARY YEAR 1920 2020

HORNBY®

| R3916 | GBRf, Class 66, Co-Co, 66733 'Cambridge PSB' - Era 11 | DCC READY | 8 PIN CONNECTION |
| NEW Q1 | | | |

Designer: Electro-Motive Diesel | **Entered Service:** 2003 | **Length:** 280mm | **Motor:** 5 Pole Skew Wound | **Curved Track:** Hornby 2nd Radius + / 438mm+

66733 'Cambridge PSB' has had an interesting numbering system, having initially been numbered as 66401 at import, when the locomotive joined the DRS fleet. One of five Class 66 locomotives sold to GBRf, the locomotive was renumbered as 66733 on March 2, 2011 but due to GBRf being short of traction it was put back into traffic before the number could be physically applied and retained 66401 as its number, this being rectified on 10 April 2011. On 10 September 2014 the locomotive was named 'Cambridge PSB' by GBRf Managing Director John Smith to celebrate over 30 years of Cambridge Power Signal Box serving the Fen Line and Cross Country routes.

| R3902 | GBRf, Class 66, Co-Co, 66725 'Sunderland' - Era 11 | DCC READY | 8 PIN CONNECTION |
| NEW Q2 | | | |

Designer: Electro-Motive Diesel | **Entered Service:** 2006 | **Length:** 280mm | **Motor:** 5 Pole Skew Wound | **Curved Track:** Hornby 2nd Radius + / 438mm+

Entering service with GBRf in December 2006, on Friday 10 August 2007 66725 was named 'Sunderland' by Niall Quinn, Sunderland Football Club's chairman. The naming ceremony celebrated the new contract between GBRf and Drax Power Ltd to haul coal trains from Tyne Dock to Drax Power Station and marked the 70th anniversary of Sunderland's victory over Preston North End in the 1937 FA Cup Final. When the base livery changed in September 2017, 66725's revised livery was adapted to include the Sunderland FC crests and nameplate.

R3951	GBRf, Class 66, Co-Co, 66780 'The Cemex Express' - Era 11	DCC READY	8 PIN CONNECTION

NEW Q1

Designer: Electro-Motive Diesel	Entered Service: 1998	Length: 280mm	Motor: 5 Pole Skew Wound	Curved Track: Hornby 2nd Radius + / 438mm+

On 15 December 2017 GBRf completed the acquisition of ten surplus Class 66 locomotives from DB Cargo UK, one of which was 66008, which had originally arrived in the UK on 3 October 1998. Renumbered to 66780 on 11 September 2018, the locomotive was the last of the ten to be repainted, leaving Eastleigh Arlington in a new silver/blue Cemex livery and on 12 June 2019, 66780 was named 'The Cemex Express' at a dedicated naming ceremony held at Dove Holes Quarry near Buxton, being unveiled at the event by Pete Waterman.

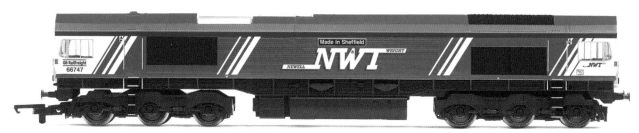

R3940	GBRf/Newell & Wright, Class 66, Co-Co, 66747 'Made in Sheffield' - Era 11	DCC READY	8 PIN CONNECTION

NEW Q2

Designer: Electro-Motive Diesel	Entered Service: 2003	Length: 280mm	Motor: 5 Pole Skew Wound	Curved Track: Hornby 2nd Radius + / 438mm+

The reduction in European freight traffic volumes prompted GBRf to purchase three unused Class 66s in late 2012 from Crossrail Benelux N.V and as a result, 66747 arrived via the Channel Tunnel in a convoy with 66748 & 66749 on 20 December 2012, all three being in European all-over plain grey livery. Adapted to UK specification at Midland Railway Centre by EMD, the work was completed by the beginning of August 2013 and after several years in traffic 66747 was named 'Made in Sheffield' at a dedicated naming ceremony that took place at DP World's Thurrock 'London Gateway' site on 9 July 2019. The ceremony marked the collaboration between GBRf and Newell & Wright in providing freight services into Newell & Wright's Rotherham Terminal, the NWT livery having been applied a few days earlier on the 5th July.

R3950	GBRf/Belmond Royal Scotsman, Class 66, Co-Co, 66743 - Era 11	DCC READY	8 PIN CONNECTION

NEW Q1

Designer: Electro-Motive Diesel	Entered Service: 2003	Length: 280mm	Motor: 5 Pole Skew Wound	Curved Track: Hornby 2nd Radius + / 438mm+

Introduced in 1985 by the operating company, Great Scottish & Western Railway Co. (GS&WR), since 2005 the overnight luxury train has been run by Belmond Ltd. Initially hauled by West Coast Railways using Class 37, 47 or 57 locomotives, since 2016 GBRf have held the haulage contract; two Class 66 locomotives being dedicated to the train: 66743 and 66746. Both locomotives carry the Belmond Royal Scotsman maroon livery, featuring the GS&WR crest, which was applied during April/May 2016 at Arlington Fleet Services' Eastleigh works. 66746 entered traffic on 11th April and 66743 followed shortly after, on 30th May.

R3950A	GBRf/Belmond Royal Scotsman, Class 66, Co-Co, 66746 - Era 11	DCC READY	8 PIN CONNECTION

NEW Q1

Designer: Electro-Motive Diesel	Entered Service: 2003	Length: 280mm	Motor: 5 Pole Skew Wound	Curved Track: Hornby 2nd Radius + / 438mm+

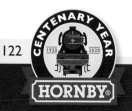

| R3922 | G&W/Freightliner, Class 66, Co-Co, 66623 - Era 11 | | | | Permission granted | DCC READY | 8 PIN CONNECTION |

NEW Q1

Designer: Electro-Motive Diesel | **Entered Service:** 2007 | **Length:** 280mm | **Motor:** 5 Pole Skew Wound | **Curved Track:** Hornby 2nd Radius + / 438mm+

Arriving into the United Kingdom on 6 February 2007, 66623 entered traffic in the unusual Bardon Aggregates livery of green, blue and yellow, being named 'Bill Bolsover' on 16 November 2007 to honour the chairman of Aggregate Industries. With the loss of the Bardon traffic, 66623 reverted to Freightliner branding, but kept the old Bardon base livery, a situation that remained until 29 March 2019 when the locomotive was de-named and repainted into the new Genesee & Wyoming/Freightliner livery of orange with black stripes.

| R3921 | Freightliner, Class 66, Co-Co, 66514 - Era 9 | | | | Permission granted | DCC READY | 8 PIN CONNECTION |

NEW Q2

Designer: Electro-Motive Diesel | **Entered Service:** 2000 | **Length:** 280mm | **Motor:** 5 Pole Skew Wound | **Curved Track:** Hornby 2nd Radius + / 438mm+

Delivered into Newport Docks on board the MV Stellaprima on 15 August 2000, 66514 was part of the second batch of fifteen Class 66/5 locomotives ordered by the Freightliner Group to replace their Class 47 and Class 57 fleet on intermodal freight services, as well as fulfilling haulage for their new Railtrack infrastructure contract. Since importation, 66514 has remained unnamed and has maintained the same base Freightliner livery of green and yellow, with minor logo changes proving the only changes.

| R3919 | PD Ports, Class 66, Co-Co, 66109 'Teesport Express' - Era 11 | | | | | DCC READY | 8 PIN CONNECTION |

NEW Q1

Designer: Electro-Motive Diesel | **Entered Service:** 1999 | **Length:** 280mm | **Motor:** 5 Pole Skew Wound | **Curved Track:** Hornby 2nd Radius + / 438mm+

Arriving in the United Kingdom on 28 May 1999 as part of the original order of 250 Class 66 locomotives, 66109 entered traffic with EWS, allocated to Toton. The EWS fleet was absorbed into the DB Schenker fleet on 1 January 2009 and retained its base maroon and yellow livery right up until the end of April 2019, when it received the PD Ports dark blue livery. On 25th April, 66109 was named 'Teesport Express' to celebrate the success of PD Ports' second daily rail freight connection to Scotland, five years after the launch of the Intermodal Rail Terminal at Teesport.

| R3887 | DB Cargo UK, Class 66, Co-Co, 66047 'Maritime Intermodal Two' - Era 11 | | | | | DCC READY | 8 PIN CONNECTION |

NEW Q1

Designer: Electro-Motive Diesel | **Entered Service:** 1999 | **Length:** 280mm | **Motor:** 5 Pole Skew Wound | **Curved Track:** Hornby 2nd Radius + / 438mm+

In company with 66005, 66047 was named as 'Maritime Intermodal Two' at Maritime Transport Ltd's Wakefield Rail Terminal on 29 March 2019, in a ceremony that marked a new long term contract with DB Cargo (UK) to expand intermodal haulage services to and from Southampton and Felixstowe. Delivered to the United Kingdom on 5 January 1999, 66047 first entered service with EWS, eventually passing into DB Schenker's ownership on 1 January 2009.

R3886	Malcolm Logistics Services, Class 66, Co-Co, 66405 - Era 10				DCC READY	8 PIN CONNECTION

NEW Q2

Designer: Electro-Motive Diesel | **Entered Service:** 2003 | **Length:** 280mm | **Motor:** 5 Pole Skew Wound | **Curved Track:** Hornby 2nd Radius + / 438mm+

66405 entered service with Direct Rail Services in October 2003, retaining the DRS 'Compass' livery until December that year when it was repainted into DRS Malcolm Logistics Services' dark blue scheme. 66405 ran in this livery until 15 April 2011, when it was repainted into the revised Europorte

design of GBRf's original yellow/blue livery, having been one of five Class 66s sold to GBRf by DRS. 66405 had been renumbered to 66737 on 4 February 2011, prior to relivery and was subsequently named Lesia on 7 May 2011.

R3920	Malcolm Rail, Class 66, Co-Co, 66434 - Era 10				DCC READY	8 PIN CONNECTION

NEW Q2

Designer: Electro-Motive Diesel | **Entered Service:** 2008 | **Length:** 280mm | **Motor:** 5 Pole Skew Wound | **Curved Track:** Hornby 2nd Radius + / 438mm+

Delivered into Newport Docks on board the MV Stellanova on 7 November 2008, 66434 went into service with Direct Rail Services, retaining the DRS Compass livery until 18 February 2010, when the locomotive was hired out to Fastline for use mainly on their coal flow traffic.

When Fastline/Jarvis plc went into administration, 66434 was returned to DRS and the locomotive went back into traffic in Malcolm Rail's livery, operating on rapid rail operations between the Midlands and the central belt of Scotland between 29 December 2011 and 22 September 2014.

R3923	Ocean Network Express, Class 66, Co-Co, 66587 'As One, We Can' - Era 11			Permission granted	DCC READY	8 PIN CONNECTION

NEW Q2

Designer: Electro-Motive Diesel | **Entered Service:** 2007 | **Length:** 280mm | **Motor:** 5 Pole Skew Wound | **Curved Track:** Hornby 2nd Radius + / 438mm+

66587 arrived in the United Kingdom on 21 April 2007 and entered traffic with Freightliner in the company's original green livery with yellow cabs and Freightliner logo. The locomotive remained in this livery until 10 June 2019, when Freightliner presented 66587 at Southampton Docks in

Ocean Network Express magenta to mark Freightliner's new partnership with the global container shipping company. Named 'As One, We Can', this is the first time that Freightliner has painted one of its locomotives entirely in a customer's branding.

124

To place an order contact Hornby Customer Services on: **01843 233512** or visit your local stockist.

| R3774 | DB Cargo UK, Class 67, Bo-Bo, 67024 'Belmond British Pullman' - Era 11 | DCC READY | 8 PIN CONNECTION |

Designer: General Motors | **Entered Service:** 2000 | **Length:** 259mm | **Motor:** 5 Pole Skew Wound | **Curved Track:** Hornby 2nd Radius + / 438mm+

On 20 October, 2017, 67024, along with 67021, was rolled out in an unbranded British Pullman brown and cream livery from DB Cargo UK's Toton workshop, the locomotives making their debut on 29 October, 2017.

At the end of January 2018, the full Belmond British Pullman branding was added to both locomotives.

| R3574 | DB Schenker, Class 67, Bo-Bo, 67013 - Era 10 | DCC READY | 8 PIN CONNECTION |

Designer: General Motors | **Entered Service:** 2000 | **Length:** 259mm | **Motor:** 5 Pole Skew Wound | **Curved Track:** Hornby 2nd Radius + / 438mm+

Built in March 2000, locomotive 67013 formerly operated with Wrexham & Shropshire, carrying the name Dyfrbont Ponycysylite from 9 July, 2008 until December 2012.

In August 2015, the locomotive was repainted into the DB Cherry Red livery, with DB Schenker branding.

| R3569 | BR, Class 71, Bo-Bo, E5005 - Era 6 | DCC READY | 8 PIN CONNECTION |

Designer: British Rail | **Entered Service:** 1960 | **Length:** 203mm | **Motor:** 5 Pole Skew Wound | **Curved Track:** Hornby 2nd Radius + / 438mm+

Leaving Doncaster Works in June 1960 numbered as E5020, the first allocation was to Stewarts Lane Following transfer to Ashford Chart Leacon on 22 August, 1966, the locomotive was renumbered as E5005,

following the conversion of the previous E5005 to Class 74 in March 1967. Under TOPS, the locomotive became 71005.

| R3374 | BR, Class 71, Bo-Bo, 71012 - Era 7 | DCC READY | 8 PIN CONNECTION |

Designer: British Rail | **Entered Service:** 1959 | **Length:** 203mm | **Motor:** 5 Pole Skew Wound | **Curved Track:** Hornby 2nd Radius + / 438mm+

71012 entered service as E5012 on 27 October,1959 and from 22 August, 1966 was allocated to Shed 73F, Ashford Chart Leacon for duties.

Moved to storage from September 1976, 71012 was finally withdrawn from service on 26 November, 1977 and sent to Cashmore's in Newport where it was cut up on 31 August, 1978.

125

R3376 — BR, Class 71, Bo-Bo, E5022 - Era 6

DCC READY | **8 PIN CONNECTION**

Designer: British Rail | **Entered Service:** 1960 | **Length:** 203mm | **Motor:** 5 Pole Skew Wound | **Curved Track:** Hornby 2nd Radius + / 438mm+

E5022 was re-numbered to E5006 in September 1968, to take up the gap in numbering caused by the withdrawal of locomotives for conversion to Class 74. Under TOPS E5022 became 71006 and was finally withdrawn in November 1977, being scrapped at Cashmore's in Newport during August 1978.

R3568 — BR, Class 71, Bo-Bo, E5018 - Era 6

DCC READY | **8 PIN CONNECTION**

Designer: British Rail | **Entered Service:** 1960 | **Length:** 203mm | **Motor:** 5 Pole Skew Wound | **Curved Track:** Hornby 2nd Radius + / 438mm+

E5018 entered traffic in April 1960, allocated to Stewarts Lane. Transferred to Ashford Chart Leacon in August 1966, in December 1968 the locomotive was renumbered as E5003 following the conversion of ten of the class to Class 74 locomotives. Under TOPS, the locomotive became 71003 in December 1973.

RAILWAY MUSEUM Produced under licence for SCMG Enterprises Ltd. © SCMGE. Every purchase supports the museum.

R3373 — BR, Class 71, Bo-Bo, E5001 - Era 11

DCC READY | **8 PIN CONNECTION**

Designer: British Rail | **Entered Service:** 1960 | **Length:** 203mm | **Motor:** 5 Pole Skew Wound | **Curved Track:** Hornby 2nd Radius + / 438mm+

Once the Class 33 and 73 Electro-diesels had taken over the Class 71's duties, the class was withdrawn, but locomotive 71001 was saved for preservation as part of the National Collection. Moved to York, and restored to its original BR Green livery and number, E5001, it worked a number of mainline specials during the 1990s.

CENTENARY YEAR 1920 2020

HORNBY®

To place an order contact Hornby Customer Services on: **01843 233512** or visit your local stockist.

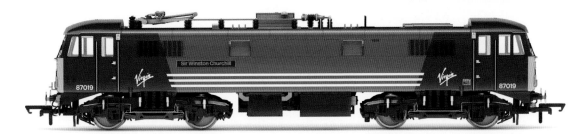

| R3656 | Virgin Trains, Class 87, Bo-Bo, 87019 'Sir Winston Churchill' - Era 9 | DCC READY | 8 PIN CONNECTION |

| Designer: British Rail | Entered Service: 1974 | Length: 243mm | Motor: 5 Pole Skew Wound | Curved Track: Hornby 2nd Radius + / 438mm+ |

87019 'Sir Winston Churchill' was built at Crewe, entering traffic in March 1974 and allocated to Willesden depot. Named as 'Sir Winston Churchill' in May 1978, the name was removed when the locomotive was repainted into L&NWR lined black livery during March 2005 and renamed as ACoRP Association of Community Rail.

| R3751 | Caledonian Sleeper, Class 87, Bo-Bo, 87002 'Royal Sovereign' - Era 10 | DCC READY | 8 PIN CONNECTION |
| Due Q2 | | | |

| Designer: British Rail | Entered Service: 1974 | Length: 243mm | Motor: 5 Pole Skew Wound | Curved Track: Hornby 2nd Radius + / 438mm+ |

87002 was built at Crewe, entering traffic on 29 June 1973, allocated to Willesden depot. Named as 'Royal Sovereign' on 4 July, 1978, the name was removed when the locomotive was repainted into Porterbrook Leasing's purple livery during 2003. Now renamed, 87002 is currently utilised by Caledonian Sleeper for empty stock workings.

| R3739 | BR, Class 87, Bo-Bo, 87001 (dual named) 'Royal Scot' and 'Stephenson' - Era 11 | DCC READY | 8 PIN CONNECTION |
| Due Q2 | | | |

| Designer: British Rail | Entered Service: 1973 | Length: 243mm | Motor: 5 Pole Skew Wound | Curved Track: Hornby 2nd Radius + / 438mm+ |

87001 was built at Crewe, entering traffic on 29 June, 1973 allocated to Willesden depot. The Stephenson Locomotive Society persuaded British Rail to name 87001 as 'Stephenson' to mark the 1975 celebrations of 150 years of railways in the United Kingdom and a naming ceremony was held on 14 January, 1976.

| R3924 | Malcolm Rail, Class 90, Bo-Bo, 90024 - Era 11 | DCC READY | 8 PIN CONNECTION |
| NEW Q4 | | | |

| Designer: BREL | Entered Service: 1989 | Length: 245mm | Motor: 5 Pole Skew Wound | Curved Track: Hornby 2nd Radius + / 438mm+ |

90024 entered service on March 10, 1989 and has appeared in a number of liveries during its lifetime but without a doubt, the current Malcolm Logistics scenic livery has to rate as the most eye-catching to feature on a Class 90. 90024 was unveiled on Saturday 2 July 2016 at Crewe IEMD wrapped in a stunning scene of Coigach in the Northwest Highlands of Scotland, an image captured by internationally renowned landscape photographer, Colin Prior. Featuring a vista that shows Ben Mo`r Coigach, Stac Pollaidh and Cu`l Beag from Loch Cu`l Dromannan, 90024 joins the Malcolm Logistics road trailer fleet in featuring photographs by Colin Prior, the scenes being used to highlight Malcolm Logistics' multimodal capability between Daventry in Northamptonshire and Grangemouth and Mossend in Scotland.

127

CLASS 91

ELECTRIC Locomotives

In 1984, with electrification well under way on the East Coast Main Line, the British Railways Board decided that a fleet of new high-power locomotives and rolling stock would be required to operate alongside the existing highly successful HST fleet.

The design, led by GEC Transportation Projects Ltd as the main contractor, owed a lot to work undertaken on the Advanced Passenger Train project and the first of the Class 91 Bo-Bo locomotives, 91001, was unveiled to the press at British Rail Engineering Limited's Crewe works on 12 February 1988.

The British Railways Board ordered thirty-one Class 91s, split between two batches, with an initial batch of ten locomotives numbered 91001-91010 for mileage accumulation and testing and a production batch of twenty-one locomotives numbered 91011-91031 At 6,300hp, the Class 91 locomotives were the most powerful on the network at that time and on September 17, 1989, 91010 'David Livingstone' set the speed record for a British locomotive hauled train, reaching 162.4mph at Stoke Bank near Peterborough. Unfortunately, the promised Government funding for upgraded track and signalling on the ECML that would allow these new trains to achieve their anticipated operating speed of 140mph was never approved, limiting the 91s to 125mph, the same as their HST predecessors.

The design of the Class 91 included two drivers' cabs, front and back, as initially it was planned to operate the loco as a high-speed passenger train during the day and to haul freight during the night. Only the leading end was streamlined, with locomotives operating 'blunt end' first being restricted to 110mph to avoid damage to the roof mounted pantograph from aerodynamic buffering. Ideas of using the Class 91 as a mixed traffic locomotive were soon scrapped and the class has only ever operated in passenger service since, although with the full retirement of the class from ECML duties during 2020 the future for the fleet is currently uncertain, with a number of plans being proposed by open access operators.

| R3890 | BR, Class 91, Bo-Bo, 91002 'Durham Cathedral' - Era 8 | DCC READY | 8 PIN CONNECTION |

NEW Q4

| Designer: GEC/BREL | Entered Service: 1988 | Length: 255mm | Motor: 5 Pole Skew Wound | Curved Track: Hornby 2nd Radius + / 438mm+ |

91002 entered traffic in April 1988 and went straight into testing on the East Coast Main Line, hauling test trains comprised of Mk.2 and Mk.3 stock, before being delivered into Bounds Green for operational use from the middle of June that year. From Autumn 1989, British Rail started naming the Class 91 fleet and on 4 May 1993 91002 received the name 'Durham Cathedral', which it carried until February 2009.

| R3891 | LNER, Class 91, Bo-Bo, 91118 'The Fusiliers' - Era 11 | DCC READY | 8 PIN CONNECTION |

NEW Q4

| Designer: GEC/BREL | Entered Service: 1990 | Length: 255mm | Motor: 5 Pole Skew Wound | Curved Track: Hornby 2nd Radius + / 438mm+ |

91118 entered traffic in August 1990 carrying the number 91018 and in November 1993 was named 'Robert Louis Stevenson', which it carried until May 1997. Between February 2000 and February 2009, the locomotive carried the name 'Bradford Film Festival', receiving the Project Delta Class 91/1 upgrade in November 2002.

On 27 March 2018, the locomotive was named 'The Fusiliers' at a ceremony commemorating the 50th anniversary of the Regiment, representatives from the First and Fifth Fusiliers providing the Guard of Honour, along with Colonel of the Regiment, General Paul Nanson, who officially named 91118.

| R3893 | GNER, Class 91, Bo-Bo, 91117 'Cancer Research UK' - Era 10 | DCC READY | 8 PIN CONNECTION |

NEW Q4

| Designer: GEC/BREL | Entered Service: 1990 | Length: 255mm | Motor: 5 Pole Skew Wound | Curved Track: Hornby 2nd Radius + / 438mm+ |

91117 entered traffic during July 1990 as 91017, carrying the name 'The Commonwealth Institute' during BR Intercity service between July 1993 and November 1996, when the locomotive became part of Great North Eastern Railway's fleet at privatisation. In an unpopular move with both staff and enthusiasts alike, GNER decided to abandon the use of cast nameplates in favour of vinyl graphics and so both names featured during the GNER period, 'City of Leeds' (October 1999 to December 2001) and 'Cancer Research UK' (February 2002 to February 2009), were never featured on cast nameplates.

| R3892 | VTEC, Class 91, Bo-Bo, 91111 'For the Fallen' - Era 10 | DCC READY | 8 PIN CONNECTION |

NEW Q4

| Designer: GEC/BREL | Entered Service: 1990 | Length: 255mm | Motor: 5 Pole Skew Wound | Curved Track: Hornby 2nd Radius + / 438mm+ |

It is estimated that the railway in Britain lost 20,000 men during the First World War, and many railway stations in Britain have a memorial to their sacrifice, listing the names of those who worked on the railway but never returned to their jobs when the guns fell silent. To mark the contribution of, and the lives lost by, regiments up and down the East Coast Mainline route during the First World War, East Coast held a ceremony at Newcastle station on 14 October 2014 to unveil 91111 in a special livery scheme created by designer Paul Gentleman, with the new name of 'For the Fallen'. The nameplate of the locomotive bears the crests of regiments local to the East Coast route and 91111's livery depicts soldiers, artefacts and tributes commemorating the contribution they made to the war effort. *Livery designed and created by Paul R Gentleman*

129

EAST MIDLANDS

| R3740 | Caledonian Sleeper, Class 92, Co-Co, 92023 - Era 10 | DCC READY | 8 PIN CONNECTION |

Designer: Brush Traction | **Entered Service:** 1995 | **Length:** 280mm | **Motor:** 5 Pole Skew Wound | **Curved Track:** Hornby 2nd Radius + / 438mm+

Built in June 1995, 92023 entered service named as Ravel; one of the nine SNCF owned locomotives. In May 2014 Serco, using traction supplied by GBRf, won the franchise to operate the Caledonian Sleeper services and along with 92010/14/18/33/38, 92023 was prepared in Caledonian Sleeper 'Midnight Teal' Stag livery.

| R3742F | DB Cargo Romania, Class 92, Co-Co, 91 53 0 472 001-3 'Mihai Eminescu' - Era 10 | DCC READY | 8 PIN CONNECTION |

Designer: Brush Traction | **Entered Service:** 1994 | **Length:** 280mm | **Motor:** 5 Pole Skew Wound | **Curved Track:** Hornby 2nd Radius + / 438mm+

92012 entered service named as Thomas Hardy, one of Railfreight Distribution's locomotives. Passing through EWS ownership to DB Schenker, 92012 was transferred to DB Cargo Romania in DB Cherry Red livery, renumbered to 91 53 0 472 001-3 'Mihai Eminescu', yet retaining the Channel Tunnel roundels and BR arrow logo.

| **R3741** | **GBRf Europorte, Class 92, Co-Co, 92043 'Debussy' - Era 11** | DCC READY | 8 PIN CONNECTION |

| **Designer:** Brush Traction | **Entered Service:** 1996 | **Length:** 280mm | **Motor:** 5 Pole Skew Wound | **Curved Track:** Hornby 2nd Radius + / 438mm+ |

Built in March 1996, 92043 entered service named as 'Debussy', being one of the nine SNCF owned locomotives. Under-utilised, the locomotive was sold to Europorte and retained its two tone grey livery until the end of 2016, when it received the new 'GB Railfreight, part of Europorte' livery of blue with mustard yellow cabs.

| **R3575** | **East Midlands Trains, Class 153, DMSL, 57379 - Era 10** | DCC READY | 8 PIN CONNECTION |

| **Designer:** Hunslet-Barclay | **Entered Service:** 1992 | **Length:** 310mm | **Motor:** 5 Pole Skew Wound | **Curved Track:** Hornby 2nd Radius + / 438mm+ |

Originally built as a two-car Class 155 'Super Sprinter' by British Leyland between 1987 and 1988, using a construction technique similar to that used in the Pacers, pre-formed panels were riveted together, creating a lightweight body on a welded floor assembly.

Introduction was rapid, but teething troubles with the door mechanisms soon emerged and consequently the fleet was taken out of use and modified, with the Class 156 units taking over the duties.

131

COACHES
& Coach Packs

The Rainhill Trials and Stephenson's Rocket introduced the public to the notion of travelling by rail and the resulting rapid expansion of the railways made the United Kingdom a less intimidating place to travel through.

Travel by rail was still intended for the wealthy though, with coaches still being built in a similar fashion to the stagecoaches that they were quickly replacing and travel for the masses, in Third Class, still involved being exposed to the elements. As passenger numbers increased, so did the revenue generated from travel and, as a consequence, more attention to passengers' comfort and safety was taken. Third class coaches became enclosed and luggage, along with the Guard, was moved to the inside. Four wheel vehicles gave way to six wheeled variants that gave a better ride. Steam from the locomotive was used to heat the coaches, oil lamps lit the interior and braking systems were continuous, being controlled by the driver from the locomotive. By the turn of the 20th century, bogies were being used to improve the ride even further and steel underframes were replacing wooden ones, with lighting being provided by gas lamps. Electricity replaced gas for lighting, following a number of catastrophic fires and all wooden bodies were superseded by wooden framing, with fitted steel panels. In turn, these were replaced by bodies built from steel and it soon became practical to combine underframe and body into a single 'monocoque' type design.

Hornby's 2020 range of coaches cover every era of coach development, from Stephenson's First Class coaches that mimicked the livery of the fastest stagecoaches and suggested speed and reliability to a new class of travelling public, to Hitachi's Class 800, Class 395 and Wabtec's Mk3SD coaches that bring the comforts of home to the travelling experience. New coach tooling for 2020 comes in the form of British Rail's tilting Class 370 coaches from the Advanced Passenger Train, the experimental design that paved the way for the Class 91/Mk.IV sets on the ECML, the Pendolino on the WCML, the never realised InterCity 250 and, indirectly through shared R&D, the Eurostar Class 373. Paired by coach type in two car coach packs, the APT coaches will allow for expansion of the APT train packs into the full fourteen car APT sets that were intended to bring speed and unsurpassed comfort to passengers on the West Coast Main Line.

To place an order contact Hornby Customer Services on: **01843 233512** or visit your local stockist.

R4829 | LNER, 61' 6" Gresley Corridor Buffet, 21611 - Era 3

Designer: Sir Nigel Gresley | **Livery:** LNER Teak | **Length:** 247mm

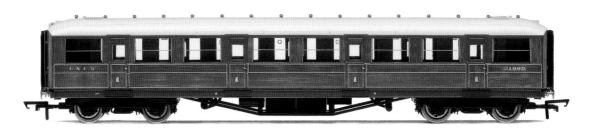

R4827 | LNER, 61' 6" Gresley Corridor First, 31885 - Era 3

Designer: Sir Nigel Gresley | **Livery:** LNER Teak | **Length:** 247mm

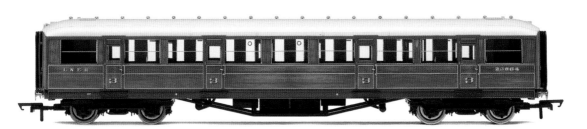

R4828 | LNER, 61' 6" Gresley Corridor Third, 23864 - Era 3

Designer: Sir Nigel Gresley | **Livery:** LNER Teak | **Length:** 247mm

R4826 | LNER, 61' 6" Gresley Corridor Composite Brake, 32557 - Era 3

Designer: Sir Nigel Gresley | **Livery:** LNER Teak | **Length:** 247mm

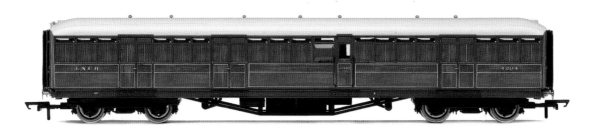

R4830 | LNER, 61' 6" Gresley Full Brake, 4234 - Era 3

Designer: Sir Nigel Gresley | **Livery:** LNER Teak | **Length:** 247mm

R4904 | Pullman, Standard 'K' Type 'New Century Bar' Car - Era 4

Designer: Pullman Car Company | **Livery:** Umber and Cream | **Length:** 263mm

R4549B/C | GWR, E140 'B' Set Brake Composite 6371/ 6372 - Era 3

NEW Q4 | **Designer:** Charles Collett | **Livery:** GWR, Chocolate & Cream | **Length:** 242mm

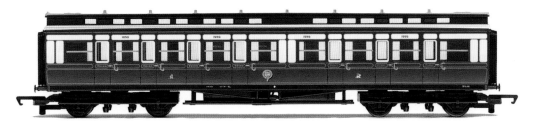

R4899 | GWR, C15 'Clerestory' Corridor Composite, 1609 - Era 2

Designer: William Dean | **Livery:** GWR Chocolate & Cream | **Length:** 236mm

R4900 | GWR, D29 'Clerestory' Corridor Brake Third, 3357 - Era 2

Designer: William Dean | **Livery:** GWR Chocolate & Cream | **Length:** 236mm

135

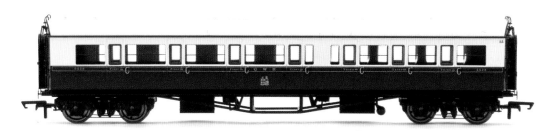

R4682A | GWR, Collett 'Bow Ended' Corridor Composite (Left Hand), 6528 - Era 3

Designer: C.B Collett | Livery: GWR Chocolate & Cream | Length: 242mm

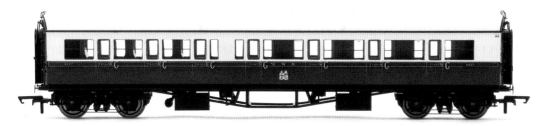

R4683A | GWR, Collett 'Bow Ended' Corridor Composite (Right Hand), 6527 - Era 3

Designer: C.B Collett | Livery: GWR Chocolate & Cream | Length: 242mm

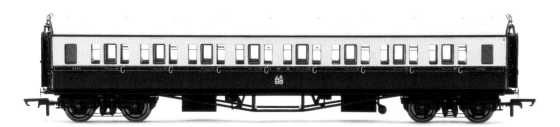

R4679A | GWR, Collett 'Bow Ended' Corridor Third, 4556 - Era 3

Designer: C.B Collett | Livery: GWR Chocolate & Cream | Length: 242mm

R4681A | GWR, Collett 'Bow Ended' Corridor Brake Third (Left Hand), 4942 - Era 3

Designer: C.B Collett | Livery: GWR Chocolate & Cream | Length: 242mm

R4680A | GWR, Collett 'Bow Ended' Corridor Brake Third (Right Hand), 4941 - Era 3

Designer: C.B Collett | Livery: GWR Chocolate & Cream | Length: 242mm

To place an order contact Hornby Customer Services on: **01843 233512** or visit your local stockist.

R4874/A | GWR, Collett 57' Bow Ended E131 Nine Compartment Composite (Left Hand), 6360/6626 - Era 3

Designer: C.B Collett | Livery: GWR Chocolate & Cream 'Shirt Button' | Length: 242mm

R4875/A | GWR, Collett 57' Bow Ended E131 Nine Compartment Composite (Right Hand), 6362/6627 - Era 3

Designer: C.B Collett | Livery: GWR Chocolate & Cream 'Shirt Button' | Length: 242mm

R4876/A | GWR, Collett 57' Bow Ended D98 Six Compartment Brake Third (Left Hand), 4971/5503 - Era 3

Designer: C.B Collett | Livery: GWR Chocolate & Cream 'Shirt Button' | Length: 242mm

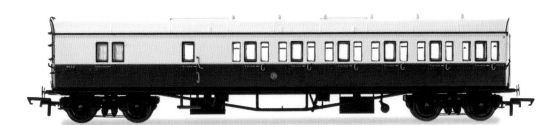

R4877/A | GWR, Collett 57' Bow Ended D98 Six Compartment Brake Third (Right Hand), 4972/5504 - Era 3

Designer: C.B Collett | Livery: GWR Chocolate & Cream 'Shirt Button' | Length: 242mm

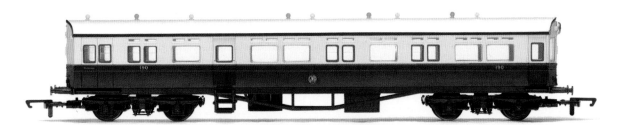

R4831 | GWR, 63' Collett A30 Autocoach, 190 - Era 3

Designer: Charles Collett | Livery: GWR Chocolate & Cream | Length: 265mm

LMS 'CORONATION SCOT' Coaches

In response to the LNER's own 'Coronation' sets, hauled by their A4 Pacific locomotives, the LMS Board announced the advent of a similar train, the 'Coronation Scot', to run between Euston and Glasgow.

Full service of the full nine car 'Coronation Scot' commenced on 5 July 1937 and consisted of nine cars, the formation (from the London end) being; Brake Corridor First (BFK), Corridor First (FK), Restaurant Open First (RFO), Kitchen (RK), Restaurant Open Third (RTO), Restaurant Open Third (RTO), Kitchen (RK), Restaurant Open Third (RTO) and Brake Corridor Third (BTK). Three sets of coaches were to be provided for the 'Coronation Scot', with any two sets operating at one time, with the other being spare. Most of the coaches for the 'Coronation Scot' were selected from the latest new batches of Stanier's Period III stock, with the exception being the FKs and BTKs, which were built new for the service. The selected coaches were sent to the LMSR's Wolverton works where they were converted for service, the interiors being completely refitted to a luxurious standard befitting the service and, apart from the RKs, pressure heating and ventilation systems being installed for the passengers' comfort, the coaches' roofs featuring boxed ventilation shrouds.

NEW Q4		
R4963/A	LMS, Stanier D1912 Coronation Scot 50' RK, 30084/ 30086 - Era 3	
Designer: Sir William Stanier	Livery: LMS, Caledonian Blue	Length: 200mm

NEW Q4		
R4965/A/B	LMS, Stanier D1981 Coronation Scot 57' RTO, 8961/8993/ 8996 - Era 3	
Designer: Sir William Stanier	Livery: LMS, Caledonian Blue	Length: 228mm

NEW Q4		
R4964	LMS, Stanier D1902 Coronation Scot 65' RFO, 7507 - Era 3	
Designer: Sir William Stanier	Livery: LMS, Caledonian Blue	Length: 260mm

NEW Q4		
R4961	LMS, Stanier D1961 Coronation Scot 57' BFK, 5052 - Era 3	
Designer: Sir William Stanier	Livery: LMS, Caledonian Blue	Length: 228mm

NEW Q4		
R4962	LMS, Stanier D1960 Coronation Scot 57' FK, 1069 - Era 3	
Designer: Sir William Stanier	Livery: LMS, Caledonian Blue	Length: 228mm

NEW Q4		
R4960	LMS, Stanier D1905 Coronation Scot 57' BTK, 5812 - Era 3	
Designer: Sir William Stanier	Livery: LMS, Caledonian Blue	Length: 228mm

R4802 | LMS, Period II 68' Dining/Restaurant Car, 238 - Era 3

Designer: Sir Ernest Lemon | Livery: LMS Crimson Lake | Length: 285mm

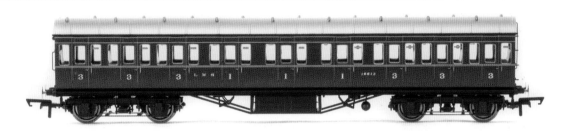

R4656A | LMS, Period III Non-Corridor 57' Composite, 16612 - Era 3

Designer: Sir William Stanier | Livery: LMS Crimson Lake | Length: 242mm

R4657A | LMS, Period III Non-Corridor 57' Third Class, 11718 - Era 3

Designer: Sir William Stanier | Livery: LMS Crimson Lake | Length: 242mm

R4677B/C | LMS, Period III Non-Corridor 57' Third Class Brake, 20754/20755 - Era 3

Designer: Sir William Stanier | Livery: LMS Crimson Lake | Length: 242mm

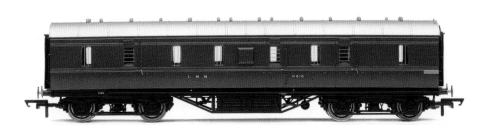

R4843 | LMS, Period III 50' Gangwayed Passenger Brake, 31010 - Era 3

Designer: Sir William Stanier | Livery: LMS Crimson Lake | Length: 215mm

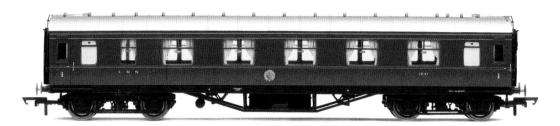

R4803	LMS, Period III Corridor First, 1041 - Era 3

Designer: Sir William Stanier   **Livery:** LMS Crimson Lake   **Length:** 242mm

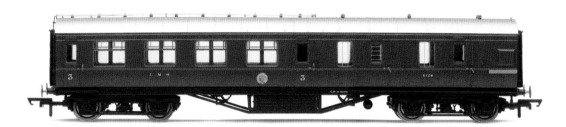

R4805	LMS, Period III Corridor Brake Third, 5726 - Era 3

Designer: Sir William Stanier   **Livery:** LMS Crimson Lake   **Length:** 242mm

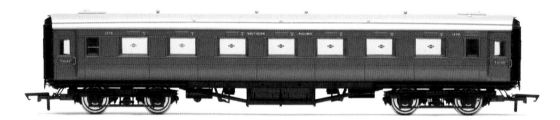

R4833	SR, Maunsell Open Third, 1375 - Era 3

Designer: Richard Maunsell   **Livery:** SR Olive   **Length:** 243mm

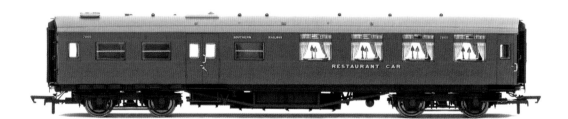

R4816A	SR, Maunsell Kitchen/Dining First, 7865 - Era 3

Designer: Richard Maunsell   **Livery:** SR Olive   **Length:** 243mm

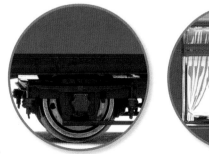  

To place an order contact Hornby Customer Services on: **01843 233512** or visit your local stockist.

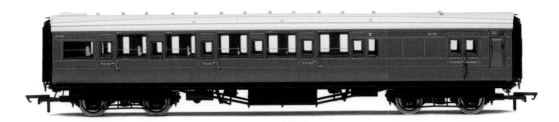

R4768A   SR, Maunsell Corridor Brake Third Class, 3778 'Set 243' - Era 3

Designer: Richard Maunsell | Livery: SR Olive | Length: 243mm

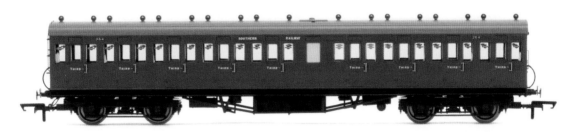

R4720A   SR, 58' Maunsell Rebuilt (Ex-LSWR 48'), Nine Compartment Third, 364 - Era 3

Designer: Richard Maunsell | Livery: SR Olive | Length: 246mm

R4719A   SR, 58' Maunsell Rebuilt (Ex-LSWR 48'), Six Compartment Brake Composite, 6401 'Set 42' - Era 3

Designer: Richard Maunsell | Livery: SR Olive | Length: 246mm

R4718A   SR, 58' Maunsell Rebuilt (Ex-LSWR 48'), Six Compartment Brake Third, 2625 - Era 3

Designer: Richard Maunsell | Livery: SR Olive | Length: 246mm

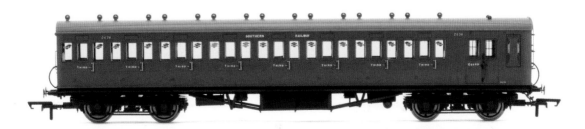

R4717A   SR, 58' Maunsell Rebuilt (Ex-LSWR 48'), Eight Compartment Brake Third, 2636 'Set 42' - Era 3

Designer: Richard Maunsell | Livery: SR Olive | Length: 246mm

R4795 — SR, 58' Maunsell Rebuilt (Ex-LSWR 48'), Nine Compartment Third, 320 - Era 3

Designer: Richard Maunsell | Livery: SR Green | Length: 246mm

R4794 — SR, 58' Maunsell Rebuilt (Ex-LSWR 48'), Six Compartment Brake Composite, 6403 'Set 44' - Era 3

Designer: Richard Maunsell | Livery: SR Green | Length: 246mm

R4793 — SR, 58' Maunsell Rebuilt (Ex-LSWR 48'), Six Compartment Brake Third, 2628 - Era 3

Designer: Richard Maunsell | Livery: SR Green | Length: 246mm

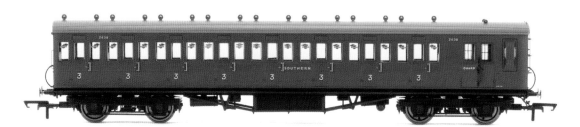

R4792 — SR, 58' Maunsell Rebuilt (Ex-LSWR 48'), Eight Compartment Brake Third, 2638 'Set 44' - Era 3

Designer: Richard Maunsell | Livery: SR Green | Length: 246mm

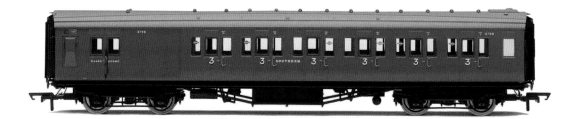

R4737 — SR, Maunsell Corridor Brake Third Class, 3798 'Set 328' - Era 3

Designer: Richard Maunsell | Livery: SR Green | Length: 243mm

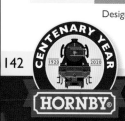

CENTENARY YEAR 1920 2020

HORNBY®

To place an order contact Hornby Customer Services on: **01843 233512** or visit your local stockist.

R4882/A | SR, Bulleid 59' Corridor Composite, 5711/5719 - Era 3

Designer: Oliver Bulleid | Livery: SR Green | Length: 243mm

R4884/A/B/C | SR, Bulleid 59' Corridor Brake Third, 2845/2846/2861/2862 - Era 3

Designer: Oliver Bulleid | Livery: SR Green | Length: 243mm

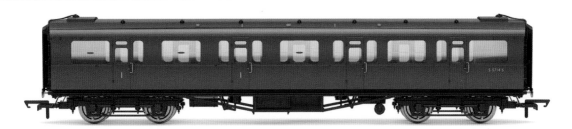

R4886/A | BR, Bulleid 59' Corridor Composite, S5714S/S5718S - Era 4

Designer: Oliver Bulleid | Livery: BR Green | Length: 243mm

R4888/A/B/C | BR, Bulleid 59' Corridor Brake Third, S2851S/S2852S/S2859S/S2860S - Era 4

Designer: Oliver Bulleid | Livery: BR Green | Length: 243mm

143

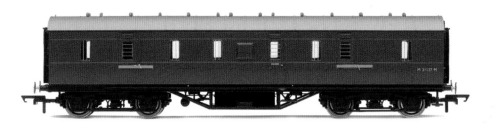

R4844 | BR, Stanier Period III Parcels Van, M31137 - Era 4

Designer: Sir William Stanier | Livery: BR Maroon | Length: 215mm

R4131C | BR, Period II 68' Dining/Restaurant Car, M232M - Era 5

Designer: Sir Ernest Lemon | Livery: BR Maroon | Length: 285mm

R4689/A | BR, 57' Stanier Non-Corridor Composite, M16574M/M16587M - Era 5

Designer: Sir William Stanier | Livery: BR Maroon | Length: 242mm

R4690/A | BR, 57' Stanier Non-Corridor Third, M11912M/M11886M - Era 5

Designer: Sir William Stanier | Livery: BR Maroon | Length: 242mm

R4691/A/B | BR, 57' Stanier Non-Corridor Brake Third, M20787M/M20788M/M20752M - Era 5

Designer: Sir William Stanier | Livery: BR Maroon | Length: 242mm

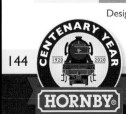

R4521C	BR, 51' Gresley Non-Vestibuled Suburban Composite, E88067E - Era 5		
Designer: Sir Nigel Gresley		**Livery:** BR Maroon	**Length:** 217mm

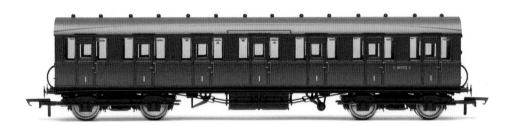

R4519B	BR, 51' Gresley Non-Vestibuled Suburban First, E81032E - Era 5		
Designer: Sir Nigel Gresley		**Livery:** BR Maroon	**Length:** 217mm

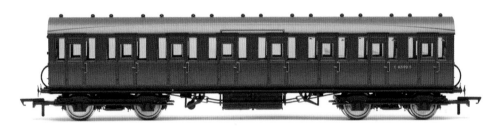

R4520B	BR, 51' Gresley Non-Vestibuled Suburban Third, E82190E - Era 5		
Designer: Sir Nigel Gresley		**Livery:** BR Maroon	**Length:** 217mm

R4522C	BR, 51' Gresley Non-Vestibuled Suburban Brake Third, E86109E - Era 5		
Designer: Sir Nigel Gresley		**Livery:** BR Maroon	**Length:** 217mm

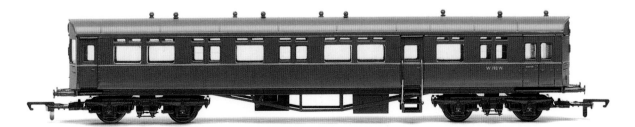

R4832	BR, 63' Collett A30 Autocoach, W193W - Era 5		
Designer: Charles Collett		**Livery:** BR Maroon	**Length:** 265mm

145

R4799 BR, 57' Stanier Non-Corridor Composite, M16635M - Era 4

Designer: Sir William Stanier | Livery: BR Crimson | Length: 242mm

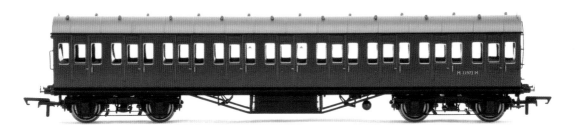

R4800 BR, 57' Stanier Non-Corridor Third, M11973M - Era 4

Designer: Sir William Stanier | Livery: BR Crimson | Length: 242mm

R4801/A BR, 57' Stanier Non-Corridor Brake Third, M20736M/M20737M - Era 4

Designer: Sir William Stanier | Livery: BR Crimson | Length: 242mm

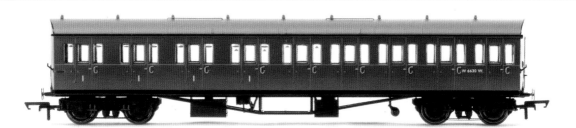

R4878/A BR, Collett 57' Bow Ended E131 Nine Compartment Composite (Left Hand), W6630W/W6237W - Era 4

Designer: C.B Collett | Livery: BR Crimson | Length: 242mm

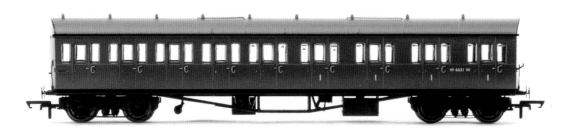

R4879/A BR, Collett 57' Bow Ended E131 Nine Compartment Composite (Right Hand), W6631W/W6242W - Era 4

Designer: C.B Collett | Livery: BR Crimson | Length: 242mm

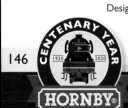

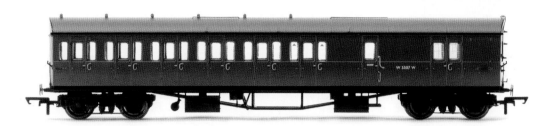

R4880/A | BR, Collett 57' Bow Ended D98 Six Compartment Brake Third (Left Hand), W5507W/W4949W - Era 4

Designer: C.B Collett | Livery: BR Crimson | Length: 242mm

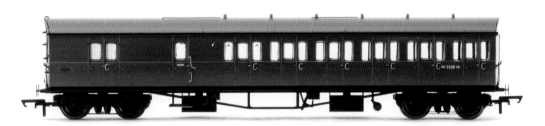

R4881/A | BR, Collett 57' Bow Ended D98 Six Compartment Brake Third (Right Hand), W5508W/W4951W - Era 4

Designer: C.B Collett | Livery: BR Crimson | Length: 242mm

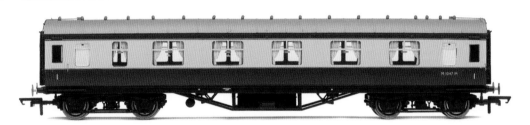

R4447B | BR, Period III Corridor First, M1047M - Era 4

Designer: Sir William Stanier | Livery: BR Crimson & Cream | Length: 242mm

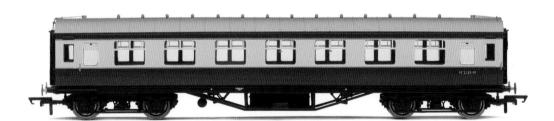

R4448B | BR, Period III Corridor First, M2139M - Era 4

Designer: Sir William Stanier | Livery: BR Crimson & Cream | Length: 242mm

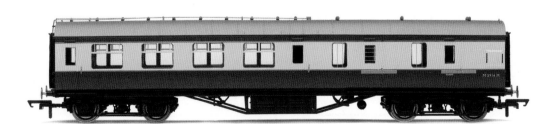

R4449B | BR, Period III Corridor Brake Third, M5914M - Era 4

Designer: Sir William Stanier | Livery: BR Crimson & Cream | Length: 242mm

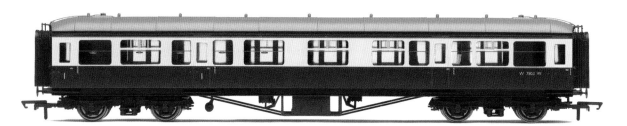

R4407B | BR, 63' Hawksworth Corridor Composite, W7803W - Era 4

Designer: Frederick Hawksworth | Livery: BR Crimson & Cream | Length: 267mm

R4493B | BR, 63' Hawksworth Corridor First, W8119W - Era 4

Designer: Frederick Hawksworth | Livery: BR Crimson & Cream | Length: 267mm

R4405B | BR, 63' Hawksworth Corridor Third, W2267W - Era 4

Designer: Frederick Hawksworth | Livery: BR Crimson & Cream | Length: 267mm

R4408B | BR, 63' Hawksworth Brake Composite, W7858W - Era 4

Designer: Frederick Hawksworth | Livery: BR Crimson & Cream | Length: 267mm

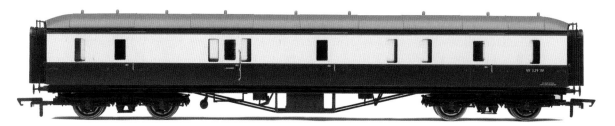

R4404B | BR, 63' Hawksworth Passenger Brake, W329W - Era 4

Designer: Frederick Hawksworth | Livery: BR Crimson & Cream | Length: 267mm

R4406B | BR, 63' Hawksworth Corridor Brake Third, W2251W - Era 4

Designer: Frederick Hawksworth | Livery: BR Crimson & Cream | Length: 267mm

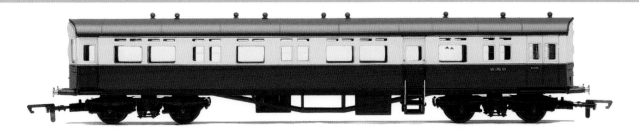

R4791 | BR, 63' Collett A30 Autocoach, W190W - Era 4

Designer: Charles Collett | Livery: BR Crimson & Cream | Length: 265mm

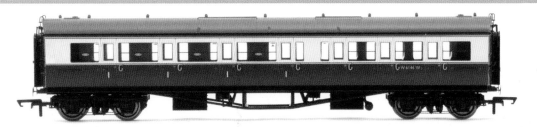

R4687A | BR, Collett 'Bow-Ended' Corridor Composite (Left Hand), W6146W - Era 4

Designer: Charles Collett | Livery: BR Crimson & Cream | Length: 242mm

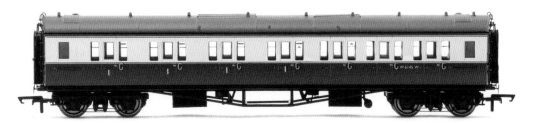

R4688A | BR, Collett 'Bow-Ended' Corridor Composite (Right Hand), W6145W - Era 4

Designer: Charles Collett | Livery: BR Crimson & Cream | Length: 242mm

R4684A | BR, Collett 'Bow-Ended' Corridor Third, W4910W - Era 4

Designer: Charles Collett | Livery: BR Crimson & Cream | Length: 242mm

149

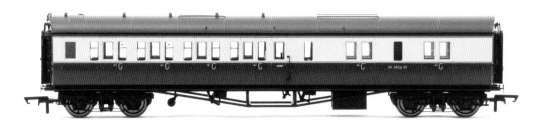

R4686A | BR, Collett 'Bow-Ended' Corridor Brake Third (Left Hand), W4926W - Era 4

Designer: Charles Collett | Livery: BR Crimson & Cream | Length: 242mm

R4685A | BR, Collett 'Bow-Ended' Corridor Brake Third (Right Hand), W4925W - Era 4

Designer: Charles Collett | Livery: BR Crimson & Cream | Length: 242mm

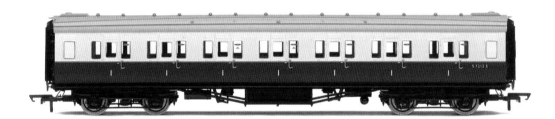

R4797 | BR, Maunsell Corridor First, S7212S - Era 4

Designer: Richard Maunsell | Livery: BR Crimson & Cream | Length: 243mm

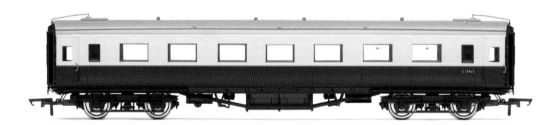

R4835 | BR, Maunsell Open Second, S1346S - Era 4

Designer: Richard Maunsell | Livery: BR Crimson & Cream | Length: 243mm

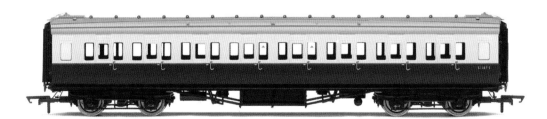

R4798 | BR, Maunsell Corridor Third, S1187S - Era 4

Designer: Richard Maunsell | Livery: BR Crimson & Cream | Length: 243mm

Coaches & Coach Packs

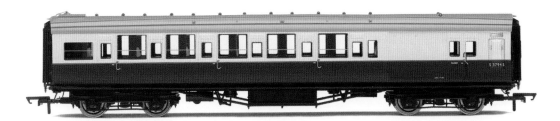

R4796/A — BR, Maunsell Corridor Brake Third, S3777S/S3794S - Era 4
Designer: Richard Maunsell | Livery: BR Crimson & Cream | Length: 243mm

R4188D — BR, Period II 68' Dining/Restaurant Car, M236M - Era 4
Designer: Sir Ernest Lemon | Livery: BR Crimson & Cream | Length: 285mm

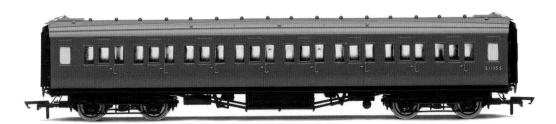

R4834 — BR, Maunsell Corridor Second, S1135S - Era 5
Designer: Richard Maunsell | Livery: BR Green | Length: 243mm

R4842 — BR, Maunsell Corridor Composite, S5145S 'Set 399' - Era 5
Designer: Richard Maunsell | Livery: BR Green | Length: 243mm

R4839 — BR, Maunsell Corridor Composite, S5673S 'Set 230' - Era 5
Designer: Richard Maunsell | Livery: BR Green | Length: 243mm

R4840	BR, Maunsell Corridor Four Compartment Brake Second, S3232S 'Set 399' - Era 5		
	Designer: Richard Maunsell	**Livery:** BR Green	**Length:** 243mm

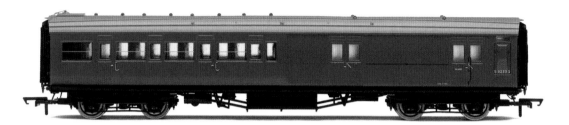

R4841	BR, Maunsell Corridor Four Compartment Brake Second, S3233S 'Set 399' - Era 5		
	Designer: Richard Maunsell	**Livery:** BR Green	**Length:** 243mm

R4836	BR, Maunsell Corridor Six Compartment Brake Second, S2763S 'Set 230' - Era 5		
	Designer: Richard Maunsell	**Livery:** BR Green	**Length:** 243mm

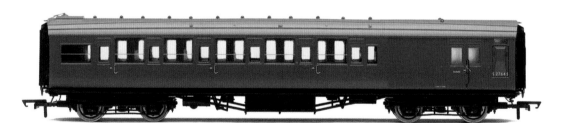

R4838	BR, Maunsell Corridor Six Compartment Brake Second, S2764S 'Set 230' - Era 5		
	Designer: Richard Maunsell	**Livery:** BR Green	**Length:** 243mm

R4817A	BR, Maunsell Kitchen/Dining First, S7858S - Era 5		
	Designer: Richard Maunsell	**Livery:** BR Green	**Length:** 244mm

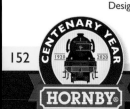

R4981	BR(S), Mk1 FO, S3065 - Era 5		
NEW Q4	Designer: BREL	Livery: BR Green	Length: 265mm

R4976	BR(S), Mk1 CK, S15574 - Era 5		
NEW Q4	Designer: BREL	Livery: BR Green	Length: 265mm

R4975	BR(S), Mk1 SK, S34310 - Era 5		
NEW Q4	Designer: BREL	Livery: BR Green	Length: 265mm

R4979	BR(S), Mk1 TSO, S4009 - Era 5		
NEW Q4	Designer: BREL	Livery: BR Green	Length: 265mm

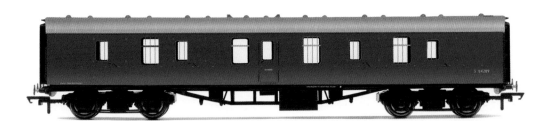

R4982	BR(S), Mk1 BG, S84289 - Era 5		
NEW Q4	Designer: BREL	Livery: BR Green	Length: 238mm

R4977	BR(S), Mk1 BSK, S34967 - Era 5		

NEW Q4

Designer: BREL | Livery: BR Green | Length: 265mm

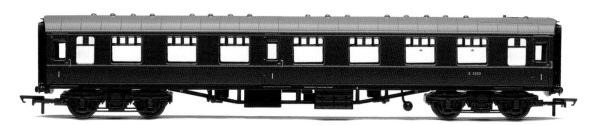

R4789	BR, Mk1 First Open, E3050 - Era 5		

Designer: British Railways | Livery: BR Maroon | Length: 265mm

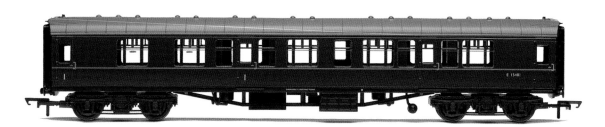

R4784	BR, Mk1 Corridor Composite, E15481 - Era 5		

Designer: British Railways | Livery: BR Maroon | Length: 265mm

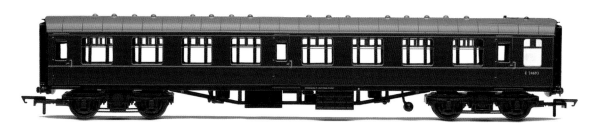

R4783	BR, Mk1 Corridor Second, E24693 - Era 5		

Designer: British Railways | Livery: BR Maroon | Length: 265mm

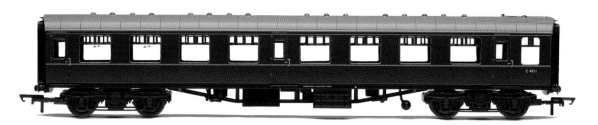

R4786	BR, Mk1 Second Open, E4811 - Era 5		

Designer: British Railways | Livery: BR Maroon | Length: 265mm

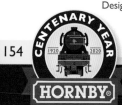

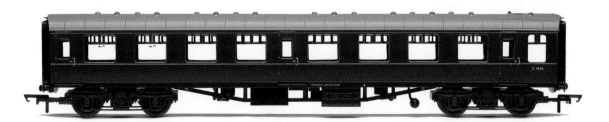

R4787 BR, MkI Tourist Second Open, E4656 - Era 5

Designer: British Railways | Livery: BR Maroon | Length: 265mm

R4782 BR, MkI Parcels, E80627 - Era 5

Designer: British Railways | Livery: BR Maroon | Length: 238mm

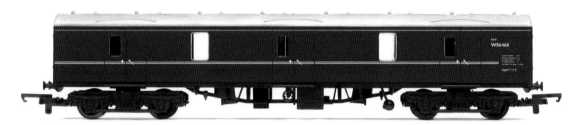

R4936 BR, GUV, W86468 - Era 5

Designer: British Railways | Livery: BR Maroon | Length: 238mm

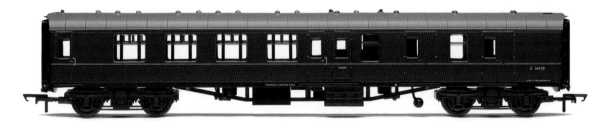

R4785 BR, MkI Corridor Brake Second, E34729 - Era 5

Designer: British Railways | Livery: BR Maroon | Length: 265mm

155

BR Mk1 RB Dining Cars

The first phase of building British Railways' Mk 1 catering vehicles followed the traditional pattern of dining that had been catered for since Edwardian times, with large Kitchen Cars preparing multiple course dining for consumption in both First and Third Class Dining Cars.

However during the early 1950s it became apparent that social patterns regarding rail travel catering were changing, a direct consequence of WWII attitudes towards dining. The catering department of British Railways was experiencing a demand from travellers for cheaper and lighter meals and was seeing an increase in social drinking that was not related to dining. This change in dining patterns meant that the use of a Buffet vehicle, rather than a full Kitchen Car/Dining Car combination, was sometimes a better option and the third phase 1957-62 Mk.1 building programme provided many of BR's vehicles with buffet facilities, not just in addition to full meal provision, but also replacing it.

Three prototype catering vehicles were built by Eastleigh to basic requirements set out by the Hotels and Catering Services Department of British Railways, with each stage of construction incorporating feedback from restaurant car staff, these being M1546 Kitchen-Buffet (RKB), W1900 Unclassed Restaurant (RU) and E1700 Buffet-Restaurant (RB). The RB kept the same kitchen, staff area and seating type as the other two vehicles, but by sacrificing ten seats, the pantry was extended, and a new service counter was introduced for the serving of light refreshments. Propane gas units were introduced for gas cooking, reducing the reliance on electric power which, in turn, allowed for a smaller dynamo and battery. Access to the water tanks was also improved, along with door access for the catering staff; the single 24" doors being replaced with a 'door and a third' arrangement that offered a second 9" wide door alongside the main door. The prototypes were a success and 128 vehicles were ordered, built in four lots between 1960 and 1962 by Pressed Steel and Birmingham RC&W, but in a change from the prototype, some of the window sizes were altered and the serving area was rotated through 90 degrees to become longitudinal.

By 1977, British Rail had come to realise that existing Mk.1 catering stock would

have to be retained for a longer period on long haul services than originally anticipated, especially as the APT and HST programmes were behind schedule. The catering fleet was suffering as vehicle availability decreased and services increased, leading to a lack of morale among catering staff and an increase in public dissatisfaction with on-train catering; in 1960, 850 catering vehicles covered 794 daily booked services but by 1977 this had dropped to 460 vehicles covering over a thousand daily services. Following a high profile public opinion survey, BR realised that catering needed to become part of the corporate InterCity image and an accelerated programme of refurbishment ensued.

The onboard equipment needed to be standardised to ensure that spares were readily available to keep the vehicles in service, while at the same time interior layouts needed to become standardised so that serving patterns were consistent across the fleet to improve working conditions for staff. The resulting fleet refurbishment of all catering vehicles was based on alterations to the diagram 24 vehicles and was grouped under diagram 33 RB(R). Doors were installed between bars, pantries and kitchens which allowed for manning by fewer staff and interiors were improved by raising illumination levels through fluorescent lighting and removing bulkheads, using brighter colours and having 'wipe-clean' surfaces and seating.

With no Mk.2 catering cars being built from new, Mk.1 restaurants and buffet vehicles were included in Mk.3 rakes on the major main lines until the Mk.3 catering coaches became available. Certain services continued to use them into the early 1990s; The Clansman and the Holyhead trains had RBRs in 1990/1991 and Norwich services still had them in 1993 according to the coaching stock book. Once the Mk.2f RFBs were fully in service, especially on Intercity cross country services, there was no further need for Mk.1 stock and the vehicles were relegated to charter stock.

R4971/A	BR(W), Mk1 RB, W1739/W1743 - Era 5		
NEW Q4	Designer: British Railways	Livery: BR Maroon	Length: 265mm

R4973/A	BR(M), Mk1 RB(R), M1712/M1627 - Era 7		
NEW Q4	Designer: British Railways	Livery: BR Blue & Grey	Length: 265mm

R4972/A	BR(S), Mk1 RB, S1720/S1757 - Era 5		
NEW Q4	Designer: BREL	Livery: BR Green	Length: 265mm

R4974/A	BR Intercity, Mk1 RB(R), IC1667/1981 - Era 8		
NEW Q4	Designer: British Railways	Livery: BR Intercity, Intercity Executive	Length: 265mm

To place an order contact Hornby Customer Services on: **01843 233512** or visit your local stockist.

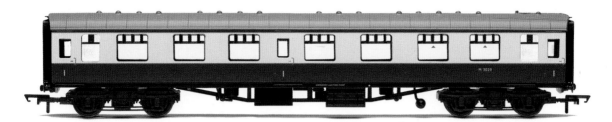

R4825	BR, Mk1 First Open, M3029 - Era 4		
	Designer: British Railways	**Livery:** BR Crimson & Cream	**Length:** 265mm

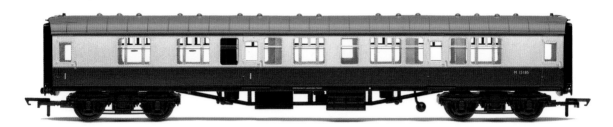

R4847	BR, Mk1 Corridor Composite, M15185 - Era 4		
	Designer: British Railways	**Livery:** BR Crimson & Cream	**Length:** 265mm

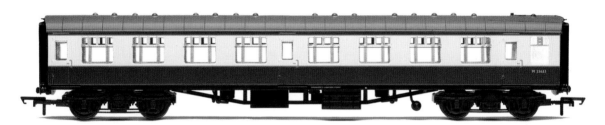

R4846	BR, Mk1 Corridor Second, M25633 - Era 4		
	Designer: British Railways	**Livery:** BR Crimson & Cream	**Length:** 265mm

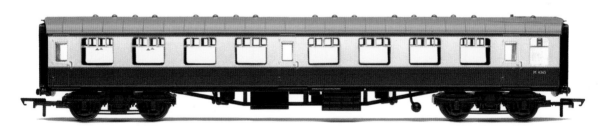

R4849	BR, Mk1 Second Open, M4365 - Era 4		
	Designer: British Railways	**Livery:** BR Crimson & Cream	**Length:** 265mm

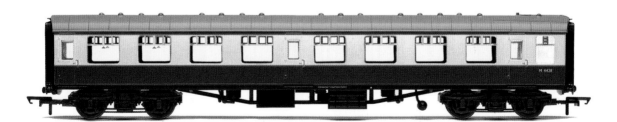

R4850	BR, Mk1 Tourist Second Open, M4428 - Era 4		
	Designer: British Railways	**Livery:** BR Crimson & Cream	**Length:** 265mm

157

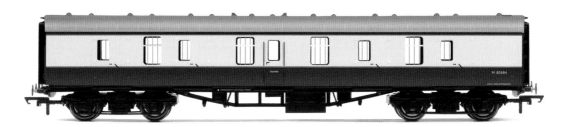

R4845 | BR, Mk1 Parcels, M80584 - Era 4

Designer: British Railways | Livery: BR Crimson & Cream | Length: 238mm

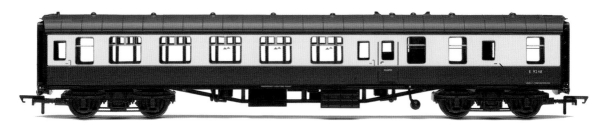

R4823 | BR, Mk1 Brake Second Open, E9248 - Era 4

Designer: British Railways | Livery: BR Crimson & Cream | Length: 265mm

R4848 | BR, Mk1 Corridor Brake Second, M34466 - Era 4

Designer: British Railways | Livery: BR Crimson & Cream | Length: 265mm

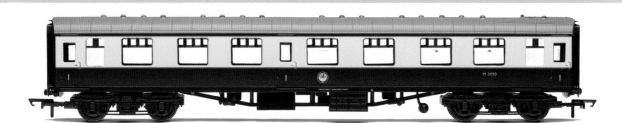

R4824 | BR, Mk1 First Open, W3090 - Era 5

Designer: British Railways | Livery: BR Chocolate & Cream | Length: 265mm

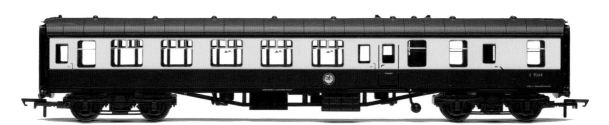

R4822 | BR, Mk1 Brake Second Open, E9264 - Era 5

Designer: British Railways | Livery: BR Chocolate & Cream | Length: 265mm

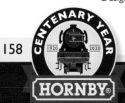
To place an order contact Hornby Customer Services on: **01843 233512** or visit your local stockist.

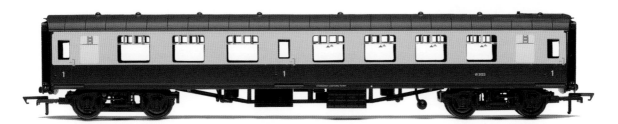

R4778 | BR, Mk1 First Open, W3123 - Era 7

Designer: British Railways | Livery: BR Blue & Grey | Length: 265mm

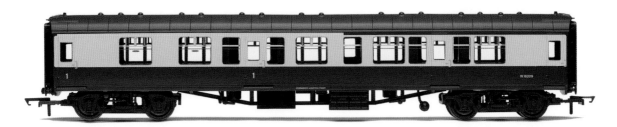

R4773 | BR, Mk1 Corridor Composite, W16209 - Era 7

Designer: British Railways | Livery: BR Blue & Grey | Length: 265mm

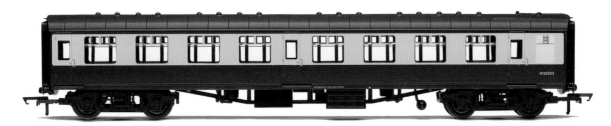

R4772 | BR, Mk1 Corridor Second, W25923 - Era 7

Designer: British Railways | Livery: BR Blue & Grey | Length: 265mm

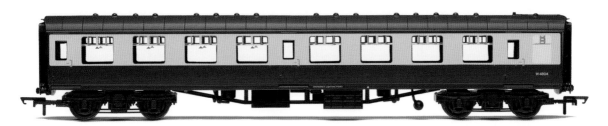

R4775 | BR, Mk1 Second Open, W4804 - Era 7

Designer: British Railways | Livery: BR Blue & Grey | Length: 265mm

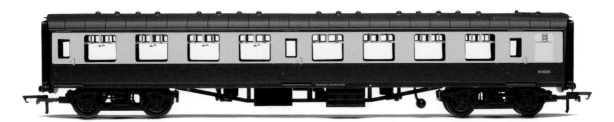

R4776 | BR, Mk1 Tourist Second Open, W5025 - Era 7

Designer: British Railways | Livery: BR Blue & Grey | Length: 265mm

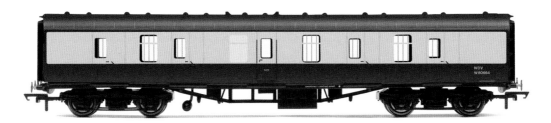

R4771 | BR, Mk1 Parcels, W80664 - Era 7

Designer: British Railways | **Livery:** BR Blue & Grey | **Length:** 238mm

R4774 | BR, Mk1 Corridor Brake Second, W34845 - Era 7

Designer: British Railways | **Livery:** BR Blue & Grey | **Length:** 265mm

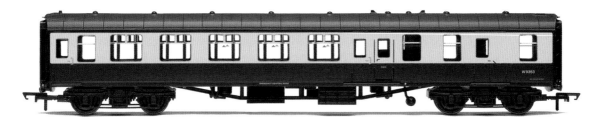

R4777 | BR, Mk1 Brake Second Open, W9353 - Era 7

Designer: British Railways | **Livery:** BR Blue & Grey | **Length:** 265mm

Limited Availability

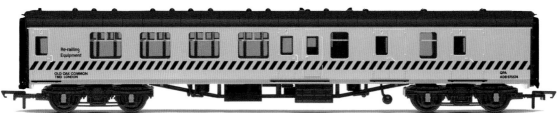

R4902 | BR, Mk1 BTU Staff & Dormitory Coach, QPX ADB 975574 - Era 9

Designer: British Railways | **Livery:** Departmental Yellow | **Length:** 265mm

Limited Availability

R4903 | BR, Mk1 BTU Tool Van, QQX ADB 975613 - Era 9

Designer: British Railways | **Livery:** Departmental Yellow | **Length:** 238mm

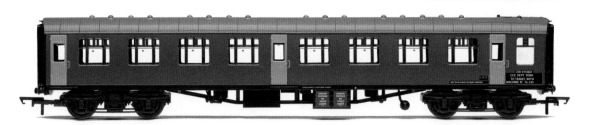

R40007 | BR Departmental, ex-Mk1 SK Ballast Cleaner Train Staff Coach, DB 975802 - Era 7

NEW Q4 | **Designer:** BREL | **Livery:** BR Departmental, Olive | **Length:** 265mm

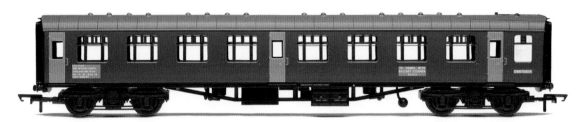

R40008 | BR Departmental, ex-Mk1 SK Ballast Cleaner Train Staff Coach, DB 975804 - Era 7

NEW Q4 | **Designer:** BREL | **Livery:** BR Departmental, Olive | **Length:** 265mm

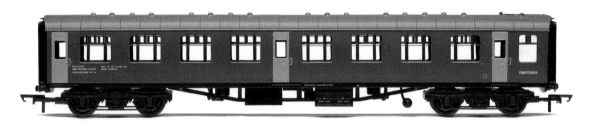

R40006 | BR Departmental, ex-Mk1 SK Ballast Cleaner Train Staff Coach, DB 975805 - Era 7

NEW Q4 | **Designer:** BREL | **Livery:** BR Departmental, Olive | **Length:** 265mm

R40010 | BR Departmental, ex-Mk1 BSO Landore Breakdown Unit, ADB 975082 - Era 7

NEW Q4 | **Designer:** BREL | **Livery:** BR Departmental, Red/Blue | **Length:** 265mm

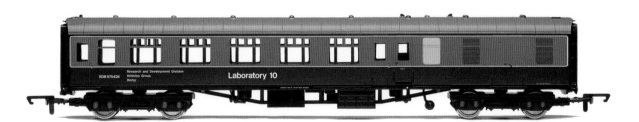

R40009 | BR R&D Division, ex-Mk1 BSO Laboratory 10, RDB 975428 - Era 7

NEW Q4 | **Designer:** BREL | **Livery:** BR R&D, Red/Blue | **Length:** 265mm

161

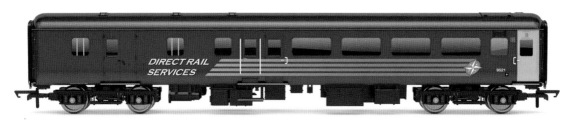

R4967/A	DRS, Mk2F Brake Standard Open, 9521/9525 - Era 11		
NEW Q4	Designer: BREL	Livery: DRS, Compass Blue	Length: 268mm

R4966	DRS, Mk2F Standard Open, 5937 - Era 11		
NEW Q4	Designer: BREL	Livery: DRS, Compass Blue	Length: 268mm

R4807	BR, Mk2D First Open, E3180 - Era 7		
	Designer: British Railways	Livery: BR Blue & Grey	Length: 273mm

R4806	BR, Mk2D Tourist Second Open, E5714 - Era 7		
	Designer: British Railways	Livery: BR Blue & Grey	Length: 273mm

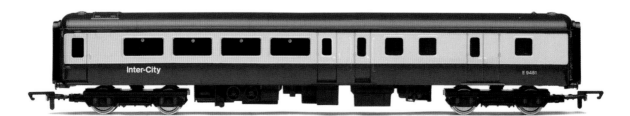

R4808	BR, Mk2D Brake Second Open, E9481- Era 7		
	Designer: British Railways	Livery: BR Blue & Grey	Length: 273mm

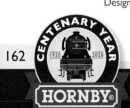

R4916/A | BR, Mk2F Tourist Second Open, M6011/M6015 - Era 7

Designer: BREL | Livery: BR Blue & Grey | Length: 268mm

R4917/A | BR, Mk2F First Open, M3345/M3374 - Era 7

Designer: BREL | Livery: BR Blue & Grey | Length: 268mm

R4918/A | BR, Mk2F Brake Second Open, M9534/M9519 - Era 7

Designer: BREL | Livery: BR Intercity Executive | Length: 268mm

R4810 | BR, Mk2E First Open, 3237 - Era 8

Designer: British Railways | Livery: BR Intercity Executive | Length: 273mm

R4809 | BR, Mk2E Tourist Second Open, 5889 - Era 8

Designer: British Railways | Livery: BR Intercity Executive | Length: 273mm

163

R4920/A | BR Intercity, Mk2F First Open, 3387/3295 - Era 8

Designer: BREL | Length: BR Intercity Executive | Length: 268mm

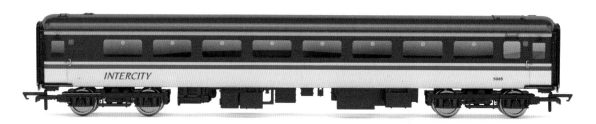

R4919/A | BR Intercity, Mk2F Tourist Second Open, 5985/5988 - Era 8

Designer: BREL | Livery: BR Intercity Executive | Length: 268mm

R4811 | BR, Mk2E Brake Second Open, 9502 - Era 8

Designer: British Railways | Livery: BR Intercity Executive | Length: 273mm

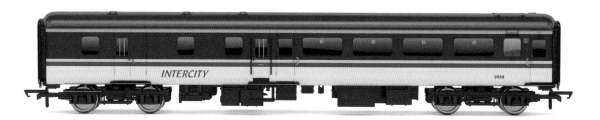

R4921/A | BR Intercity, Mk2F Brake Second Open, 9533/9525 - Era 8

Designer: BREL | Livery: BR Intercity Executive | Length: 268mm

CENTENARY YEAR 1920 2020

HORNBY

To place an order contact Hornby Customer Services on: **01843 233512** or visit your local stockist.

R40002/A   BR, Mk3 Trailer First Open, Coach H, 41085/41086 - Era 8

NEW Q4   Designer: BREL | Livery: BR Intercity, Intercity Executive | Length: 303mm

R40003/A/B/C   BR, Mk3 Trailer Standard Open, Coach E, 42169/42168/42167/42103 - Era 8

NEW Q4   Designer: BREL | Livery: BR Intercity, Intercity Executive | Length: 303mm

R40004   BR, Mk3 Trailer Buffet, Coach F, 40703 - Era 8

NEW Q4   Designer: BREL | Livery: BR Intercity, Intercity Executive | Length: 303mm

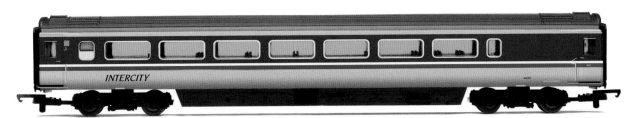

R40005   BR, Mk3 Trailer Guard Standard, Coach A, 44055 - Era 8

NEW Q4   Designer: BREL | Livery: BR Intercity, Intercity Executive | Length: 303mm

R4996   BR, Mk3 DVT, 82116 - Era 8

NEW Q4   Designer: BREL | Livery: BR Intercity, Intercity Swallow | Length: 246mm

165

R4896A	GWR, Mk3 Sliding Door TGS, 49104 - Era 11		
	Designer: Wabtec Doncaster	Livery: GWR Green	Length: 303mm

Limited Availability

R4915B/C	GWR, Mk3 Sliding Door TS, 48110/48131 - Era 11		
	Designer: Wabtec Doncaster	Livery: GWR Green	Length: 303mm

R4895A	GWR, Mk3 Sliding Door TSD, 48111 - Era 11		
	Designer: Wabtec Doncaster	Livery: GWR Green	Length: 303mm

R4912	GWR Mk3 TSD Class Coach, 42015 Coach C - Era 11		
NEW Q2	Designer: BREL	Livery: GWR, Green	Length: 303mm

R4780B	GWR Mk3 Trailer Guard Standard (TGS), 44005 Coach A - Era 11		
NEW Q2	Designer: BREL	Livery: GWR, Green	Length: 303mm

R4779B — GWR Mk3 Buffet TRFB, 40755 Coach K - Era 11

NEW Q2

Designer: BREL | Livery: GWR, Green | Length: 303mm

R4815B — GWR Mk3 First Class TFO, 41160 Coach L - Era 11

NEW Q2

Designer: BREL | Livery: GWR, Green | Length: 303mm

R4781G/H/J/L — GWR Mk3 Standard Open TSO, 42361/42005/42554/42016 - Era 11

NEW Q2

Designer: BREL | Livery: GWR, Green | Length: 303mm

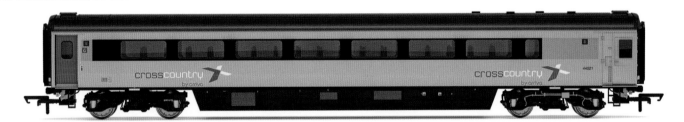

R4938/A — Cross Country Trains, Mk3 Sliding Door TGS, 44021/44052 - Era 11

Due Q2

Designer: Wabtec Doncaster | Livery: XC Grey & Magenta | Length: 303mm

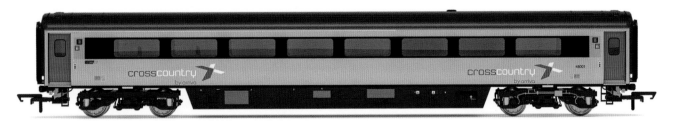

R4941/A — Cross Country Trains, Mk3 Sliding Door TCC, 45001/45003 - Era 11

Due Q2

Designer: Wabtec Doncaster | Livery: XC Grey & Magenta | Length: 303mm

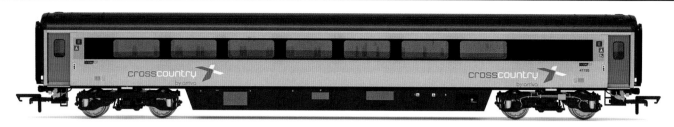

R4942/A | Cross Country Trains, Mk3 Sliding Door TFD, 41193/41195 - Era 11

Due Q2

Designer: Wabtec Doncaster | Livery: XC Grey & Magenta | Length: 303mm

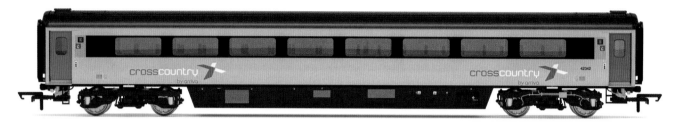

R4940/A/B/C/D/E/G/H | Cross Country Trains, Mk3 Sliding Door TS, 42342/42097/42377/42370/42378/42036/42051/42369 - Era 11

Due Q2

Designer: Wabtec Doncaster | Livery: XC Grey & Magenta | Length: 303mm

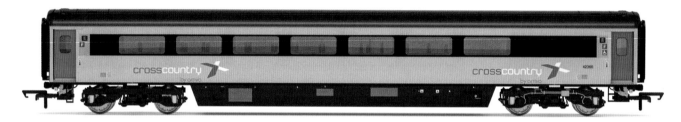

R4939/A/B/C | Cross Country Trains, Mk3 Sliding Door TSD, 42366/42376/42380/42371 - Era 11

Due Q2

Designer: Wabtec Doncaster | Livery: XC Grey & Magenta | Length: 303mm

R4892A | ScotRail, Mk2F Brake Second Open, 9527 - Era 10 | Trade marks used with permission of the Scottish Ministers.

NEW Q4

Designer: BREL | Livery: ScotRail, Saltire | Length: 268mm

R4893B/C | ScotRail, Mk2F Standard Open, 6176/6183 - Era 10 | Trade marks used with permission of the Scottish Ministers.

NEW Q4

Designer: BREL | Livery: ScotRail, Saltire | Length: 268mm

R4937/A ScotRail, Mk3 Sliding Door TS, 42561/42562 - Era 11

Due Q1 | **Designer:** Wabtec Doncaster | **Livery:** ScotRail Inter7City | **Length:** 303mm

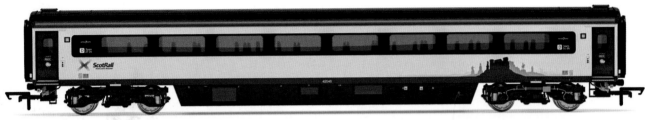

R4890/A/B/C ScotRail, Mk3 Sliding Door TSL, 42046/42045/42343/42184 - Era 11

Due Q1 | **Designer:** Wabtec Doncaster | **Livery:** ScotRail Inter7City | **Length:** 303mm

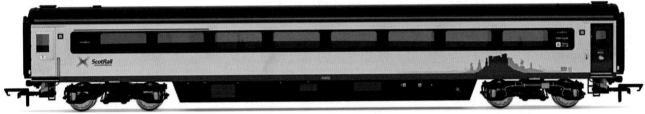

R4907/A ScotRail, Mk3 Sliding Door TGFB, 40601/40602 - Era 11

Due Q2 | **Designer:** Wabtec Doncaster | **Livery:** ScotRail Inter7City | **Length:** 303mm

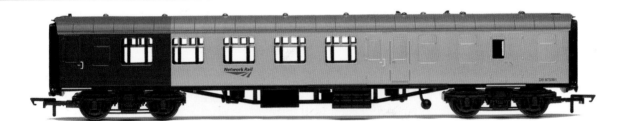

R4994 Network Rail, Ex-BR Mk1 Structure Gauging Train Driving & Instrumentation Vehicle, 975081 - Era 11

NEW Q4 | **Designer:** BREL | **Livery:** Network Rail, Yellow | **Length:** 265mm

R4995 Network Rail ex-Mk1 BG Generator Van, 6264 - Era 11

NEW Q4 | **Designer:** BREL | **Livery:** Network Rail, Yellow | **Length:** 238mm

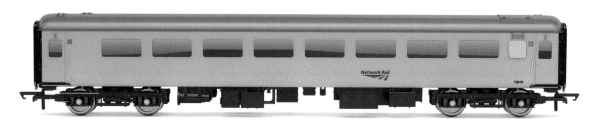

R4946 Network Rail, ex-BR Mk2F TSO, Test Train Brake Force Runner, 72616 - Era 11

NEW Q3 | Designer: BREL | Livery: Network Rail, Yellow | Length: 268mm

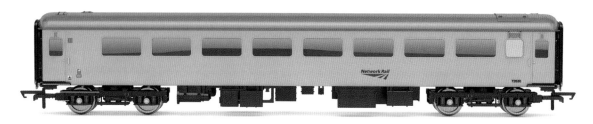

R4991 Network Rail, ex-BR Mk2F TSO Structure Gauging Train Support Coach, 72630 - Era 10

NEW Q4 | Designer: BREL | Livery: Network Rail, Yellow | Length: 268mm

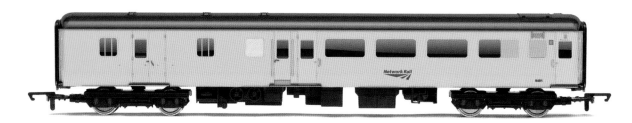

R4992 Network Rail, Mk2D Support Coach, 9481 - Era 11

NEW Q4 | Designer: BREL | Livery: Network Rail, Yellow | Length: 268mm

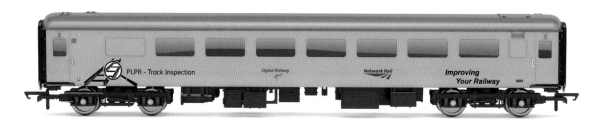

R4993 Network Rail, ex-BR Mk2F TSO Brake Plain Line Pattern Recognition Vehicle PLPR2, 5981 - Era 11

NEW Q4 | Designer: BREL | Livery: Network Rail, Yellow | Length: 268mm

R4997 Network Rail, Ex-BR Super GUV, ADB 971003 QQA - Era 11

NEW Q4 | Designer: BREL | Livery: Network Rail, Yellow | Length: 265mm

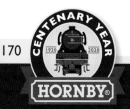

Limited Availability

R4911	Network Rail, Mk3 New Measurement Train OHPL Test Coach, 977993 - Era 10		
	Designer: BREL	Livery: Network Rail, Yellow	Length: 303mm

R4988	Network Rail, Mk3 Lecture Coach, New Measurement Train, 975984 - Era 11		
NEW Q4	Designer: BREL	Livery: Network Rail, Yellow	Length: 303mm

R4989	Network Rail, Mk3 Standby Generator Coach, New Measurement Train, 977995 - Era 11		
NEW Q4	Designer: BREL	Livery: Network Rail, Yellow	Length: 303mm

R4990	Network Rail, Mk3 DVT, 82129 - Era 11		
NEW Q4	Designer: BREL	Livery: Network Rail, Yellow	Length: 246mm

171

R4704 | **Virgin Trains, Mk2E Brake Second Open, 9507 - Era 9**

Designer: British Railways | Livery: Virgin Trains Red/Blue | Length: 273mm

R4944/A | **Virgin Trains, Mk2F First Open, 3340/5946 - Era 9**

NEW Q3

Designer: BREL | Livery: Virgin Trains, Red/Grey | Length: 268mm

R4943/A | **Virgin Trains, Mk2F Standard Open, 5945/5946 - Era 9**

NEW Q3

Designer: BREL | Livery: Virgin Trains, Red/Grey | Length: 268mm

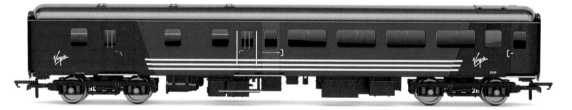

R4945/A | **Virgin Trains, Mk2F Brake Standard Open, 9539/9523 - Era 9**

NEW Q3

Designer: BREL | Livery: Virgin Trains, Red/Grey | Length: 268mm

R4855 — Virgin Trains, Mk3 Buffet (TRFB), 10235 - Era 9

Designer: British Railways | Livery: Virgin West Coast | Length: 303mm

R4857/A — Virgin Trains, Mk3 First Open (FO), 11097/11074 - Era 9

Designer: British Railways | Livery: Virgin West Coast | Length: 303mm

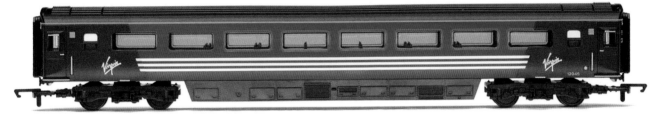

R4858/A/B — Virgin Trains, Mk3 Trailer Standard Open (TSO), 12132/12045/12087 - Era 9

Designer: British Railways | Livery: Virgin West Coast | Length: 303mm

R4859 — Virgin Trains, Mk3 Driving Van Trailer (DVT), 82141 - Era 9

Designer: British Railways | Livery: Virgin West Coast | Length: 246mm

Avanti West Coast
PENDOLINO

R40015	Avanti West Coast, Pendolino Pantograph Standard Buffet (PTSRMB) - Era 11

NEW Q4

Designer: Alstom | Livery: Avanti West Coast, Black/Blue | Length: 335mm

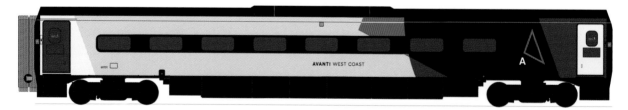

R40016	Avanti West Coast, Pendolino Trailer Standard (TS) - Era 11

NEW Q4

Designer: Alstom | Livery: Avanti West Coast, Black/Blue | Length: 335mm

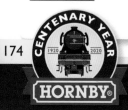

To place an order contact Hornby Customer Services on: **01843 233512** or visit your local stockist.

During the 1970s, British Railways had pursued the concept of tilting train technology for the West Coast Main Line through the Class 370 Advanced Passenger Train concept, allowing for higher speeds to be taken through curves. By minimising lateral forces on the passengers, the tendency to slide sideways was reduced, which in turn allowed passenger comfort levels to be maintained at higher speeds.

Even with the cancellation of the APT project, the idea of train tilt was still being considered in the 1980s for the InterCity 225 project, and again during the 1990s for the aborted InterCity 250 concept. In 1997, the franchise to operate the West Coast Main Line following the privatisation of British Rail, was awarded with the proviso that new rolling stock was to be introduced, replacing the ageing Class

86/87/90 locomotives and Mark 2/3 coaches. Consequently a £500 million order was placed with Alstom/Fiat Ferroviaria to construct fifty-four, eight-car tilting train sets, later increasing to nine, then eleven car sets.

The current Pendolino fleet of 56 sets comprises 35 eleven-car sets and 21 nine-car sets and all have been transferred to Avanti West Coast, the operating name for the new West Coast Partnership between FirstGroup plc and Trenitalia UK that took over the operation of the existing West Coast Main Line services on 8 December 2019, from Virgin Trains.

Our models show the new Avanti West Coast livery and branding which will be rolled out across the Pendolino fleet during 2020.

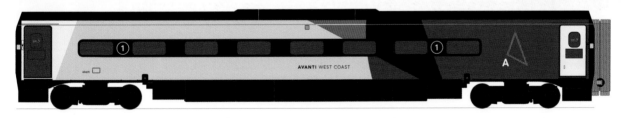

R40017	Avanti West Coast, Pendolino Motor First (MF) - Era 11		
NEW Q4	Designer: Alstom	Livery: Avanti West Coast, Black/Blue	Length: 335mm

R40018/A	Avanti West Coast, Pendolino Motor Standard (MS) - Era 11		
NEW Q4	Designer: Alstom	Livery: Avanti West Coast, Black/Blue	Length: 335mm

R4932A	LNER, Mk3 Trailer Buffet, Coach J, 40750 - Era 11		
NEW Q3	Designer: BREL	Livery: LNER, Red/Silver	Length: 303mm

R4929B	LNER, Mk3 Trailer First Open, Coach L, 41098 - Era 11		
NEW Q3	Designer: BREL	Livery: LNER, Red/Silver	Length: 303mm

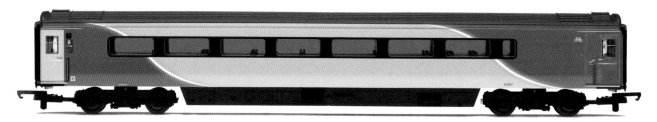

R4933A	LNER, Mk3 Trailer Guard Standard, Coach B, 44061 - Era 11		
NEW Q3	Designer: BREL	Livery: LNER, Red/Silver	Length: 303mm

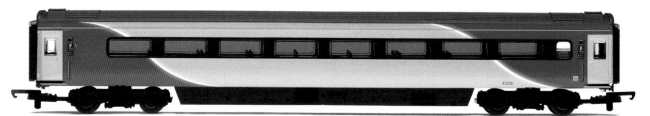

R4930A	LNER, Mk3 Trailer Standard Disabled, Coach F, 42238 - Era 11		
NEW Q3	Designer: BREL	Livery: LNER, Red/Silver	Length: 303mm

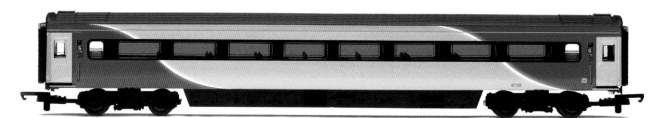

R4931D/E/G	LNER, Mk3 Trailer Standard Open, Coach G, 42158/42191/42192 - Era 11		
NEW Q3	Designer: BREL	Livery: LNER, Red/Silver	Length: 303mm

To place an order contact Hornby Customer Services on: **01843 233512** or visit your local stockist.

COACH PACKS

R4580	Eurostar, Class 373/1 e300 Divisible Centre Saloons Coach Pack - Era 10

Designer: GEC-Alstom | **Livery:** Eurotunnel e300 Blue/Yellow/Grey | **Length:** 290mm Each

Side 1 and Side 2 are shown below

R40001	Eurostar, Class 373/1 'Yellow Submarine' Divisible Centre Saloons Coach Pack - Era 9

NEW Q2

Designer: GEC-Alstom | **Livery:** Eurostar, Beatles imagery | **Length:** 288mm Each

R4999	South Eastern, Class 395 Highspeed Train 2-car Coach Pack, MSO 39134 and MSO 39135 - Era 11

NEW Q1

Designer: Hitachi Rail | **Livery:** South Eastern, Blue | **Length:** 263mm

Almost ten years to the day after Class 395 001 preview services commenced, a ceremony at South Eastern's Ramsgate Engineering Depot Open Day on Saturday 8 June officially named Set 395 013 as 'Hornby Visitor Centre', recognising the value to tourism in Thanet that the attraction provides, as well as marking the return to Margate by the manufacturer after an absence of four years. These two MSO vehicles complement the R3813 train pack, completing the full six car set 395 013.

R4534E	BR, (Ex-Maunsell) Pull/Push Coach Pack, Set 601 - Era 5

Designer: Richard Maunsell | **Livery:** BR Green | **Length:** 243mm

R4534D	BR, (Ex-Maunsell) Pull/Push Coach Pack, Set 619 - Era 5

Designer: Richard Maunsell | **Livery:** BR Green | **Length:** 243mm

WAGONS
& Wagon Packs

It was the movement of bulk mineral loads by wagons that was to drive the development of the railway system in the United Kingdom, with mining engineers at the end of the 16th century creating a number of wagonways for the purpose of moving wagon loads.

Rails were made from wood, then stone, after that granite and iron with man power giving way to horse power for the haulage. All this was before a Cornish mining engineer, Richard Trevithick, created a steam powered locomotive engine to haul wagon loads in 1804. Consequently, out of the industrial areas of Britain, the web of railway lines began to expand across the country. At first, wagons were simple wooden bodied types, used for the conveyance of minerals but as the rail network expanded, more and more goods were moved by rail, necessitating different wagon types for different goods traffic. Tankers were constructed for the conveyance of liquids, while livestock vehicles were constructed to move stock around, either to market or the abattoir. In 1838, the Royal Mail began to transport mail by rail, rather than by coach and the distribution of newspapers by rail led to a change in the public consumption of current affairs. Goods traffic increased year on year and became the backbone of goods transportation during the First World War, which continued during the subsequent two decades. The railways also bore the brunt of goods transportation during the Second World War but from the late 1940s to the mid 1980s, rail freight traffic declined, losing out to road haulage on Britain's ever improving road network. This trend has now been reversed, as since Privatisation, rail freight has gradually increased by tonne per kilometre (30% growth between 2006 and 2016) and by 2030 it is expected that levels will hit 50.4 billion tonne per kilometre.

This year's range of wagons, inspired by the range of Class 66 locomotives offered, has an emphasis on intermodal freight, with five KFA wagon options and a number of mixed 20' and 40' container packs being available for the first time. The new plank wagon chassis design has been further expanded this year, with even more Private Owner liveried examples being available. There are also number of reintroductions to the range, such as the HAA and CDA wagons, as well as additional liveries for our range of highly detailed brake vans.

178

CENTENARY YEAR
1920 2020
HORNBY®

www.hornby.com

R6804 3 Plank Wagon, Field & Mackay - Era 3

Livery: Private Owner | Length: 71mm

NEW Q3

NEM

R6943 3 Plank Wagon, GWR - Era 2/3

Livery: GWR, Brown | Length: 71mm

NEW Q3

NEM

R6944 3 Plank Wagon, LSWR Engineer's Dept - Era 2

Livery: LSWR, Brown | Length: 71mm

NEM

R6863 4 Plank Wagon, Elders - Era 3

Livery: Private Owner | Length: 71mm

NEM

R6864 4 Plank Wagon, Stonehouse Brick & Tile Co. - Era 3

Livery: Private Owner | Length: 71mm

NEM

R6899 4 Plank Wagon, Walter Harper - Era 2

Livery: Private Owner | Length: 71mm

NEM

R6900 4 Plank Wagon, C&F Gaen - Era 2

Livery: Private Owner | Length: 71mm

R6746 4 Plank Wagon, Stephens & Co. - Era 3

Livery: Private Owner | Length: 71mm

NEW Q3

NEM

R6946 4 Plank Wagon, Bestwood - Era 2/3

Livery: Private Owner | Length: 71mm

NEW Q3

R6945	4 Plank Wagon, C. Addicott & Son - Era 2/3

NEM | Livery: Private Owner | Length: 71mm

R6869	5 Plank Wagon, John Lovering & Co. - Era 2

NEM | Livery: Private Owner | Length: 71mm

R6748	5 Plank Wagon, Foster Wilson - Era 3

Livery: Private Owner | Length: 71mm

R6749	5 Plank Wagon, Farndon - Era 3

Livery: Private Owner | Length: 71mm

R6750	5 Plank Wagon, Shap Tarred Granite - Era 3

Livery: Private Owner | Length: 71mm

R6866	5 Plank Wagon, Lilleshall - Era 2

NEM | Livery: Private Owner | Length: 71mm

R6868	5 Plank Wagon, C&F Gaen - Era 3

NEM | Livery: Private Owner | Length: 71mm

R6901	5 Plank Wagon, Hereford Coal Co. - Era 2

NEM | Livery: Private Owner | Length: 71mm

NEW Q4

R6947	5 Plank Wagon, Dowlow Lime & Stone Co. - Era 2/3

NEM | Livery: Private Owner | Length: 71mm

NEW Q4

R6948	5 Plank Wagon, Herbert Rigler - Era 2/3

NEM | Livery: Private Owner | Length: 71mm

181

R6754 6 Plank Wagon, London Brick Company - Era 3

Livery: Private Owner | Length: 76mm

R6815 6 Plank Wagon, Jeayes Kasner & Co. - Era 3

Livery: Private Owner | Length: 76mm

R6816 6 Plank Wagon, Crynant Colliery Company - Era 3

Livery: Private Owner | Length: 76mm

R6817 6 Plank Wagon, J W Gadsden & Co. - Era 3

Livery: Private Owner | Length: 76mm

R6870 6 Plank Wagon, Pilkington Brothers Ltd. - Era 3

NEM

Livery: Private Owner | Length: 76mm

R6871 6 Plank Wagon, J.B.Scholes & Sons Ltd. - Era 3

NEM

Livery: Private Owner | Length: 76mm

R6872 6 Plank Wagon, John Lancaster & Co. - Era 3

NEM

Livery: Private Owner | Length: 76mm

R6902 6 Plank Wagon, Cadbury Bournville - Era 2

NEM

Livery: Private Owner | Length: 76mm

NEW Q4

R6949 6 Plank Wagon, Crigglestone Collieries - Era 2/3

NEM

Livery: Private Owner | Length: 76mm

NEW Q4

R6950 6 Plank Wagon, T. Harrison & Sons - Era 2/3

NEM

Livery: Private Owner | Length: 76mm

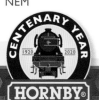

R6873 | 6 Plank Wagon, J.O Murgatroyd & Co. - Era 2

NEM

Livery: Private Owner | Length: 76mm

R6757 | 7 Plank Wagon, Richard White and Sons - Era 3

Livery: Private Owner | Length: 76mm

R6758 | 7 Plank Wagon, Arthur Wharton Ltd - Era 3

Livery: Private Owner | Length: 76mm

R6755 | 7 Plank Wagon, Gregory - Era 3

Livery: Private Owner | Length: 76mm

R6810 | 7 Plank Wagon, Crystalate - Era 3

Livery: Private Owner | Length: 76mm

R6811 | 7 Plank Wagon, Staveley - Era 3

Livery: Private Owner | Length: 76mm

R6812 | 7 Plank Wagon, John Vipond & Co. - Era 3

Livery: Private Owner | Length: 76mm

R6813 | 7 Plank Wagon, Phillips, George & Co. - Era 3

Livery: Private Owner | Length: 76mm

R6874 | 7 Plank Wagon, Hale Fuels - Era 2

NEM

Livery: Private Owner | Length: 76mm

R6875 | 7 Plank Wagon, Hawkins & Sons - Era 2

NEM

Livery: Private Owner | Length: 76mm

R6876 7 Plank Wagon, George & Matthews - Era 2

NEM

Livery: Private Owner | Length: 76mm

R6904 7 Plank Wagon, North's Navigation - Era 2

NEM

Livery: Private Owner | Length: 76mm

NEW Q4

R6952 7 Plank Wagon, Madge - Era 2/3

NEM

Livery: Private Owner | Length: 76mm

NEW Q3

R6976 8T Lime Wagon, Crawshay Brothers - Era 2/3

Livery: Private Owner | Length: 71mm

R6903 7 Plank Wagon, Sherwood - Era 2

NEM

Livery: Private Owner | Length: 76mm

NEW Q4

R6951 7 Plank Wagon, Gardner - Era 2/3

NEM

Livery: Private Owner | Length: 76mm

NEW Q3

R6977 8T Lime Wagon, John Delaney - Era 2/3

Livery: Private Owner | Length: 71mm

R6818   21T Mineral Wagon, P.J. & J.P. - Era 3

Livery: Private Owner | Length: 88mm

R6819   21T Mineral Wagon, Avon Tyres - Era 3

Livery: Private Owner | Length: 88mm

R6905   21T Mineral Wagon, BR - Era 6

Livery: Freight Grey | Length: 88mm

R6841   21T Mineral Wagon, Stevens - Era 6

Livery: Private Owner | Length: 88mm

R6842   21T Mineral Wagon, Blaenavon - Era 6

Livery: Private Owner | Length: 88mm

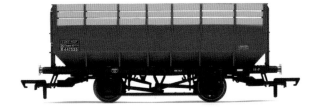

R6837   20T Coke Wagon, British Rail - Era 6

 NEM

Livery: British Railways | Length: 112mm

R6838/A   20T Coke Wagon, British Rail - Era 6

NEM

Livery: British Railways | Length: 112mm

R6821/A   20T Coke Wagon, Appleby Iron Co. - Era 3

NEM

Livery: Private Owner | Length: 112mm

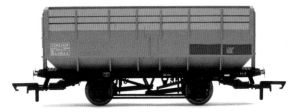

R6822/A   20T Coke Wagon, British Rail - Era 6

NEM

Livery: British Rail | Length: 112mm

185

NEW Q2

R6966	27T MSV Iron Ore Tippler, BR - Era 7

NEM

Livery: BR, Brown | Length: 90mm

R6929	MHA 'Coalfish' Ballast Wagon, EWS - Era 9

NEM

Livery: EWS | Length: 119mm

R6894	ZBA 'Rudd' Wagon, Departmental - Era 8

NEM

Livery: British Rail Departmental | Length: 100mm

R6895	ZGV 'Clam' Wagon, Departmental - Era 8

NEM

Livery: British Rail Departmental | Length: 100mm

R6808	21T Hopper Wagon, Coalite Fuels - Era 7

NEM

Livery: Private Owner | Length: 100mm

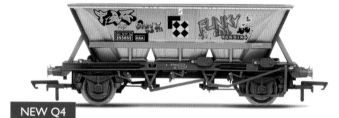

NEW Q4

R6961	HAA Wagon with graffiti, BR - Era 8

NEM

Livery: BR, Graffiti | Length: 120mm

NEW Q3

R6960	HAA Top Skip, BR - Era 8

NEM

Livery: BR, Metallic | Length: 120mm

NEW Q4

R6962	CDA Hopper, DB Cargo (UK) - Era 11

NEM

Livery: DB Cargo, Metallic | Length: 118mm

R6845	YGB 'Seacow' Bogie Ballast Hopper Wagon, Mainline - Era 9

NEM

Livery: Mainline Blue | Length: 147mm

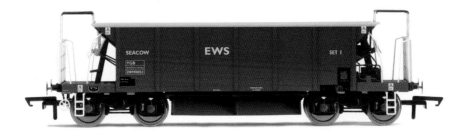

R6846	YGB 'Seacow' Bogie Ballast Hopper Wagon, EWS - Era 9

NEM

Livery: EWS Red & Gold | Length: 147mm

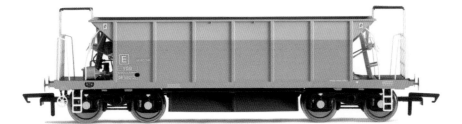

NEW Q4

R6953	YGB 'Seacow' Bogie Ballast Hopper, BR - Era 8

NEM

Livery: BR, 'Dutch' Grey/Yellow | Length: 147mm

Limited Availability

Limited Availability

R6827A	Dia.1529 Cattle Wagon, Southern Railway - Era 3

NEM

Livery: British Railways | Length: 90mm

R6826/A	Dia.1530 Cattle Wagon, British Railways - Era 4

NEM

Livery: Southern Railway | Length: 90mm

R6839/A	Dia.1529 Cattle Wagon, British Railways - Era 4

NEM

Livery: British Railways | Length: 90mm

R6840/A	Dia.1530 Cattle Wagon, BR - Era 4

NEM

Livery: British Railways | Length: 90mm

R6917 — 12T Fish Van, BR - Era 6

NEM

Livery: BR White | Length: 90mm

R6799 — Horse Box, LMS - Era 3

NEM

Livery: LMS Crimson | Length: 90mm

R6800 — Horse Box, British Railways - Era 4

NEM

Livery: British Railways | Length: 90mm

NEW Q2

R6972 — N13 Horse Box, GWR - Era 3

NEM

Livery: GWR Brown | Length: 90mm

NEW Q2

R6973 — N13 Horse Box, BR - Era 4

NEM

Livery: BR Crimson | Length: 90mm

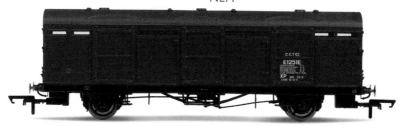

R6918 — Extra-Long CCT, BR - Era 6

NEM

Livery: BR Blue | Length: 151mm

NEW Q4

R60005 — BR R&D Division, ex-LMS CCT Track Research Laboratory - Era 7

NEM

Livery: BR R&D, Red/Blue | Length: 150mm

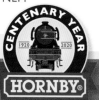

NEW Q3

R6968   BR, ZYX ex-Ferry Van Electrification Engineer Construction - Era 8

Livery: BR Departmental, Olive | Length: 180mm

NEW Q3

R6984   ZRA Civil Link Van, BR - Era 8

Livery: BR Civil Link, Grey/Yellow | Length: 146mm

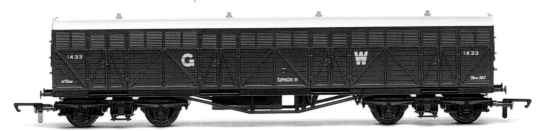

NEW Q4

R6980   Siphon H, GWR - Era 3

Livery: GWR Brown | Length: 213mm

NEW Q4

R6981   Siphon H, BR - Era 4

Livery: BR Crimson | Length: 213mm

189

R6934   LWB Box Van, Coca-Cola® (Suitable for adult collectors)

Livery: Coca Cola® Red   Length: 115mm

R6933   Tank Wagon, Coca-Cola® (Suitable for adult collectors)

Livery: Coca Cola® Red   Length: 115mm

NEW Q4

R6954   14T Tank Wagon, Burmah - Era 3/4

Livery: Private Owner   Length: 90mm

NEW Q4

R6955   20T Tank Wagon, United Molasses - Era 3/4

Livery: Private Owner   Length: 108mm

NEW Q3

R6978   6-wheel Milk Tanker, St. Ivel - Era 3/4

Livery: Private Owner   Length: 95mm

R6854   14 Ton Tank Wagon, Sinclair Oils - Era 3

Livery: Private Owner   Length: 90mm

R6856   PCA Vee Tank Wagon, Rockware Glass - Era 8

Livery: Private Owner   Length: 108mm

R6771   PCA Vee Tank Wagon, Mineral Industries Ltd - Era 8

Livery: Private Owner   Length: 108mm

NEW Q3

R6979   APCM, 102T PDA Bogie Presflo Cement Tank - Era 7

Livery: APCM, Grey   Length: 232mm

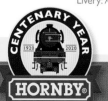

NEW Q3

R6967	VTC, 100T TEA Bogie Tank - Era 9

Livery: Heavily weathered/Graffiti | Length: 232mm

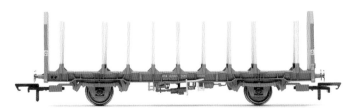

R6791	OTA Timber Wagon (Parallel Stanchions), Transrail - Era 8

Livery: Transrail Blue | Length: 151mm

NEM

R6792	OTA Timber Wagon (Tapered Stanchions), EWS - Era 9

Livery: EWS Red | Length: 151mm

NEM

R6847	OTA Timber Wagon (Parallel Stanchions), EWS - Era 9

Livery: EWS Red | Length: 151mm

NEM

R6848	OTA Timber Wagon (Tapered Stanchions), EWS - Era 9

Livery: EWS Red | Length: 151mm

NEM

NEW Q3

R6982	Macaw H Bogie Bolster, GWR - Era 3

Livery: GWR, Dark Grey | Length: 105mm

NEW Q3

R6983	Bogie Bolster A, BR - Era 4/5

Livery: BR, Freight Grey | Length: 105mm

191

R6927 Tiphook, KFA Container wagon, with 20' Maritime and 40' Hyundai containers - Era 11

NEM

Livery: Tiphook Blue | Length: 281mm

NEW Q2

R6956 Tiphook, KFA Container wagon, with 20' and 40' ONE containers - Era 11

NEM

Livery: Tiphook, Blue | Length: 281mm

NEW Q2

R6957 Tiphook, KFA Container wagon, with 3 x 20' tanktainers; RMI/Tate & Lyle/Contank - Era 11

NEM

Livery: Tiphook, Blue | Length: 281mm

NEW Q3

R6958 Tiphook, KFA Container wagon, with 3 x 20' containers; Delmas/Hatsu Marine/"K" Line - Era 11

NEM

Livery: Tiphook, Blue | Length: 281mm

R6926   Tihook, KFA Intermodal Wagon (No Containers) - Era 10

NEM

Livery: Tiphook Blue   Length: 281mm

NEW Q2

R60001   Freightliner, Container Pack,
1 x 40' and 1 x 20' Containers - Era 11

NEW Q2

R60002   Pentalver, Container Pack,
1 x 40' and 1 x 20' Containers - Era 11

NEW Q2

R60003   ONE, Container Pack,
1 x 40' and 1 x 20' Containers - Era 11

NEW Q2

R6998   PD Ports, Container Pack,
1 x 40' and 1 x 20' Containers - Era 11

NEW Q2

R6999   Malcolm Logistics, Container Pack,
1 x 40' and 1 x 20' Containers - Era 11

R6897   75T Breakdown Crane, BR - Era 6

Livery: Departmental Yellow   Length: 356mm

NEW Q3

R6974   Shunters Truck, Bordesley Junc., GWR - Era 3

NEM

Livery: GWR, Dark Grey   Length: 68mm

NEW Q3

R6975   Shunters Truck, Taunton, BR - Era 4

NEM

Livery: BR, Dark Grey   Length: 68mm

R6833A — Dia.034 'Toad B' 20T Brake Van, LNER - Era 3
 NEM
Livery: Bauxite | Length: 90mm

R6923 — Dia.064 'Toad E' Brake Van, LNER - Era 3
 NEM
Livery: Bauxite | Length: 90mm

R6834/A — Dia.064 'Toad E' 20T Brake Van, BR - Era 4
 NEM
Livery: Freight Grey | Length: 90mm

R6924 — Dia.034 'Toad B' Brake Van, BR - Era 4
 NEM
Livery: Freight Grey | Length: 90mm

NEW Q2

R6835 — AA15 20T 'Toad' Goods Brake Van, British Railways - Era 4
 NEM
Livery: British Railways | Length: 107mm

R6941 — AA15 20T 'Toad' Brake Van, BR - Era 4
 NEM
Livery: BR, Freight Grey | Length: 108mm

NEW Q2

R6922 — AA15 20T 'Toad' Goods Brake Van, BR - Era 4
 NEM
Livery: Freight Grey | Length: 107mm

R6940 — AA15 20T 'Toad' Brake Van, GWR - Era 3
 NEM
Livery: GWR, Dark Grey | Length: 108mm

R6921 — AA15 20T 'Toad' Goods Brake Van, GWR - Era 3
 NEM
Livery: Dark Grey | Length: 107mm

NEW Q3

R6985	Dia.1/507 20T Brake Van, BR - Era 7

NEM

Livery: BR, Brown/Yellow | Length: 90mm

R6920	20T Brake Van, Weathered, BR - Era 6

NEM

Livery: Freight Grey | Length: 90mm

NEW Q3

R6942	Dia.1/507 20T Brake Van, BR - Era 8

NEM

Livery: BR Departmental, Olive | Length: 90mm

R6851	ZUA 'Shark' Ballast Plough Brake Van, EWS - Era 8

NEM

Livery: EWS Red | Length: 106mm

NEW Q3

R6935 — 20T D1919 Brake Van, LMS - Era 3

NEM

Livery: LMS, Bauxite | Length: 108mm

R6907/A — 20T D1919 Brake Van, LMS - Era 3

NEM

Livery: Freight Grey | Length: 108mm

NEW Q3

R6936 — 20T D2068 Brake Van, BR - Era 7

NEM

Livery: BR Departmental, Olive | Length: 108mm

R6801 — 20T Goods Brake Van, British Railways - Era 4

Livery: British Railways | Length: 108mm

R6909/A — 20T D2068 Brake Van, BR - Era 4

NEM

Livery: Bauxite | Length: 108mm

R6802 — 20T Goods Brake Van, Southern Railway - Era 3

NEM

Livery: Southern Railway | Length: 106mm

Due Q4

R6911/A — 20T 'New Van' Goods Brake Van, LSWR - Era 2

NEM

Livery: Bauxite, with Venetian Red Ends | Length: 92mm

NEW Q3

R6911B — 20T 'New Van' Goods Brake Van, LSWR - Era 2

NEM

Livery: LSWR, Bauxite | Length: 92mm

NEW Q3

R6938 — 24T Diag.1543 Goods Brake Van, SR - Era 3

NEM

Livery: SR, Bauxite | Length: 92mm

R6913/A — 24T Diag. 1543 Goods Brake Van, SR - Era 3

NEM

Livery: Bauxite, with Venetian Red Ends | Length: 92mm

CENTENARY YEAR
1920 2020
HORNBY®

To place an order contact Hornby Customer Services on: **01843 233512** or visit your local stockist.

NEW Q3

R6915/A	24T Diag.1543 Goods Brake Van, BR - Era 4

NEM — Livery: Freight Grey — Length: 92mm

R6915B	24T Diag.1543 Goods Brake Van, BR - Era 4

NEM — Livery: BR, Freight Grey — Length: 92mm

R6803	Father's Day Plank Wagon

Length: 76mm

R6878	Father's Day Plank Wagon

Length: 76mm

NEW Q2

R6986	Hornby Wagon - 2020 Centenary Year

Length: 116mm

NEW Q3

R6988	Hornby Christmas Wagon - 2020

Length: 76mm

R6779	Hornby Visitor Centre 2016, 7 Plank Open Wagon

Livery: Hornby Visitor Centre — Length: 76mm

R6882 — Plank Wagons, Three Pack, Various Private Owner - Era 3

NEM

Livery: Private Owner | Length: 3 x 76mm

R6783 — 20T Coke Hoppers Wagons, Three Pack, British Railways - Era 5/6

NEM

Livery: British Railways | Length: 3 x 112mm

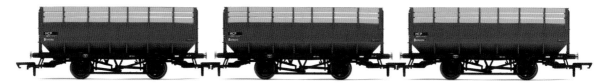

R6830 — 20T Coke Hopper Wagons, Three Pack, British Railways - Era 5/6

NEM

Livery: British Railways | Length: 3 x 112mm

NEW Q3

R6965 — 27T MSV Iron Ore Tipplers, Three Pack, BR - Era 7

NEM

Livery: BR, Brown | Length: 3 x 90mm

R6928 — MHA 'Coalfish' Ballast Wagons, Weathered, Three Pack, EWS - Era 9

NEM

Livery: EWS | Length: 3 x 119 mm

R6893 — Rudd/Clam/Tope Departmental Wagons, Three Pack, British Rail - Era 8/9

NEM

Livery: British Rail Departmental | Length: 3 x 118mm

R6885 — HEA Hopper Wagons, Three Pack, EWS - Era 9

Livery: EWS Red and Gold | Length: 3 x 118mm

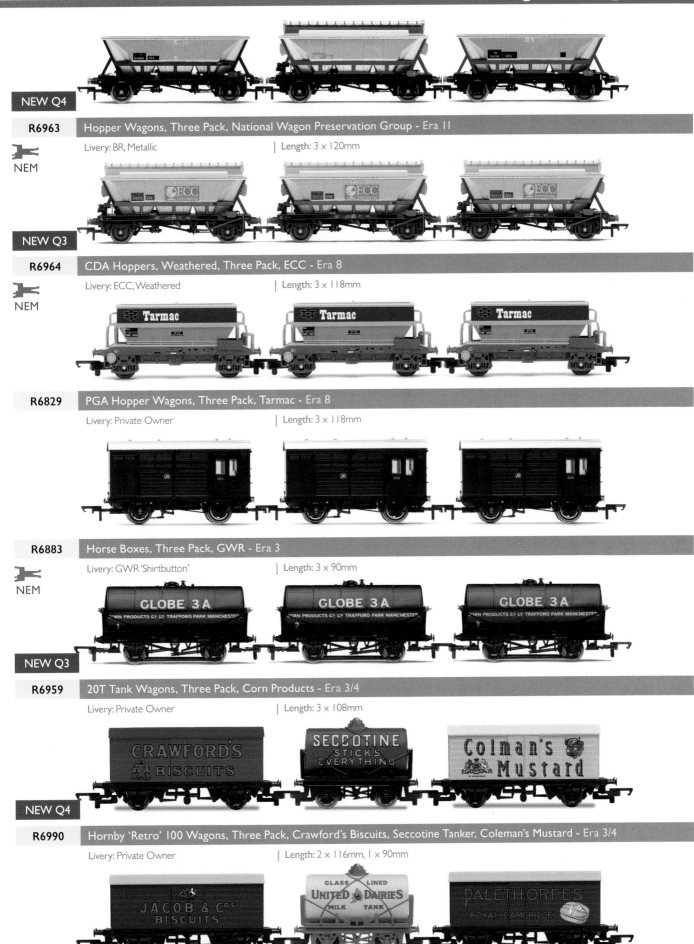

NEW Q4

R6963 Hopper Wagons, Three Pack, National Wagon Preservation Group - Era 11

NEM
Livery: BR, Metallic | Length: 3 × 120mm

NEW Q3

R6964 CDA Hoppers, Weathered, Three Pack, ECC - Era 8

NEM
Livery: ECC, Weathered | Length: 3 × 118mm

R6829 PGA Hopper Wagons, Three Pack, Tarmac - Era 8

Livery: Private Owner | Length: 3 × 118mm

R6883 Horse Boxes, Three Pack, GWR - Era 3

NEM
Livery: GWR 'Shirtbutton' | Length: 3 × 90mm

NEW Q3

R6959 20T Tank Wagons, Three Pack, Corn Products - Era 3/4

Livery: Private Owner | Length: 3 × 108mm

NEW Q4

R6990 Hornby 'Retro' 100 Wagons, Three Pack, Crawford's Biscuits, Seccotine Tanker, Coleman's Mustard - Era 3/4

Livery: Private Owner | Length: 2 × 116mm, 1 × 90mm

NEW Q4

R6991 Hornby 'Retro' 100 Wagons, Three Pack, Jacob & Co's Biscuits, United Dairies Tanker, Palethorpes - Era 3/4

Livery: Private Owner | Length: 2 × 116mm, 1 × 90mm

TRACK, POWER & ACCESSORIES

Analogue or digital control of your locomotives? Tactile or remote layout operation? The options available to the enthusiast, at any level of experience, can be bewildering at times and so Hornby have sought to provide a seamless path through the maze of Power and Control items.

Hornby have long taken the view to support both analogue and digital platforms and new developments have been made to support the upgrade path of both formats. A basic analogue set, the starting point of many a railway modelling adventure, would have contained a standard train controller (R8250), with the dual controller HM2000 (R8012) being the only upgrade choice, consequently a new train and accessory controller, R7229, has been introduced that sits perfectly between R8250 and R8012.

For those who have embarked upon the digital control pathway, where typically the R8213 Hornby 'Select' controller has been the introduction to digital operation, the firmware has been upgraded to version 1.6, to give added functionality; including support for individual CV programming, a new 'Emergency Off' feature and disabling of the 'Loco Zero' function by default.

The introduction of the Terrier and Peckett B2 locomotive models in 2019 prompted the development of the Hornby 6-pin decoder and this roll out has been extended by the decoder's use in the new Stephenson's Rocket. Featuring direct plug in pins, the 6-pin decoder complements the existing 8-pin and 21-pin decoders in the range and is joined by the 4-pin decoder as a stock item, rather than as a spare. New locomotives, whether DCC ready or fitted, can benefit from being run in well to provide optimum performance and with this in mind, the reintroduction of the Rolling Road, along with spare roller packs, will prove to be a popular choice for the enthusiast.

Scale, Gauge & Hornby Set Track

The scale of a 00 gauge model train is 1:76, or 4mm to every 12 inches, which gives rise to the common saying of 'modelling in 4mm'. The model railway track that Hornby's locomotives and rolling stock run on has a gauge of 16.5mm, this being the distance between the inside faces of the running rails and it is this combination of scale and gauge that is commonly referred to as '00 Gauge'.

With nearly thirty different elements, the comprehensive Hornby Code 100 set track can be used to create an almost infinite number of layout combinations. Produced with nickel silver rail to enhance conductivity, aid track maintenance and improve the running characteristics of your locomotives, Hornby track is an ideal companion when using the latest DCC equipment, as well as providing a solid base for those enthusiasts that choose to run their layouts in analogue.

An important, yet often overlooked, feature of Hornby track is the pair of slots between the underside of the rails and the sleeper base. These slots can be used to accommodate power connecting clips, or as anchor points for signals, together with many of Hornby's trackside accessories and help to maintain the correct distance from the track, or the loading gauge as it is known on the national rail network. Four radii of track curves are available, as well as a number of standard and curved radius points, 'Y' points, specialist diamond crossings, a variety of straight sections and flexible track sections. This vast selection of track sections can be used to produce a myriad of layout combinations.

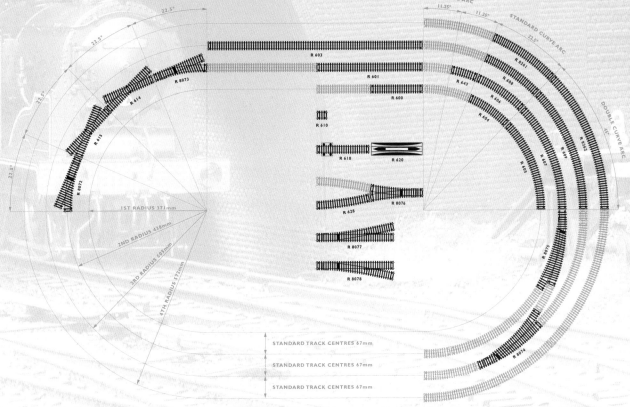

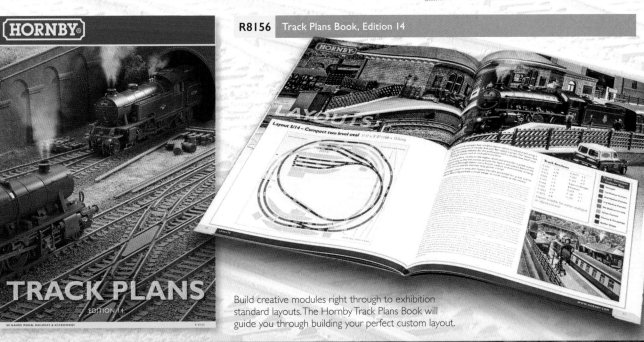

R8156 Track Plans Book, Edition 14

TRACK PLANS
EDITION 14

Build creative modules right through to exhibition standard layouts. The Hornby Track Plans Book will guide you through building your perfect custom layout.

Straight Track

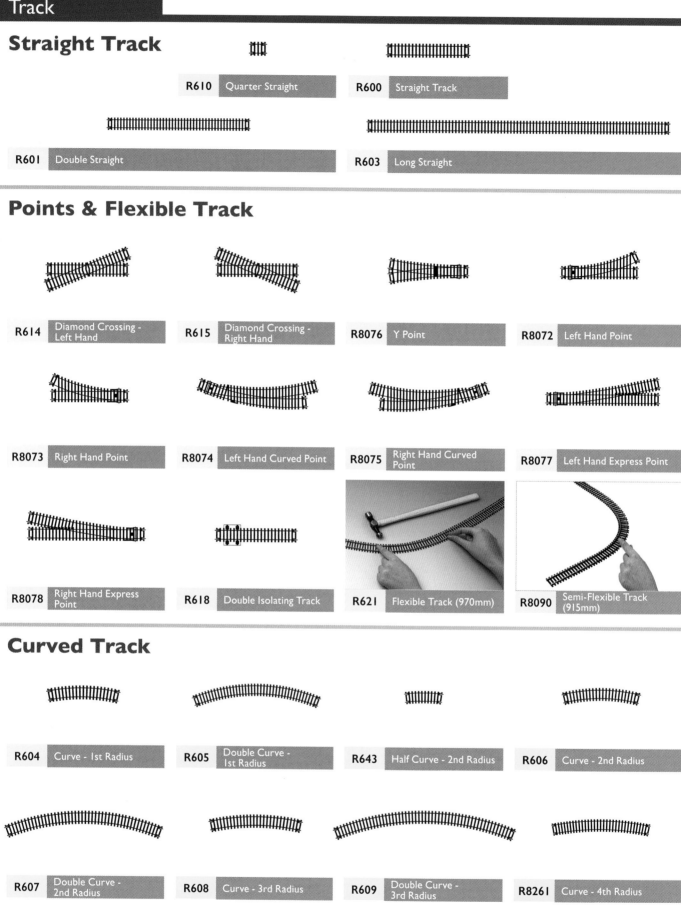

R610 Quarter Straight	R600 Straight Track
R601 Double Straight	R603 Long Straight

Points & Flexible Track

R614 Diamond Crossing - Left Hand	R615 Diamond Crossing - Right Hand	R8076 Y Point	R8072 Left Hand Point
R8073 Right Hand Point	R8074 Left Hand Curved Point	R8075 Right Hand Curved Point	R8077 Left Hand Express Point
R8078 Right Hand Express Point	R618 Double Isolating Track	R621 Flexible Track (970mm)	R8090 Semi-Flexible Track (915mm)

Curved Track

R604 Curve - 1st Radius	R605 Double Curve - 1st Radius	R643 Half Curve - 2nd Radius	R606 Curve - 2nd Radius
R607 Double Curve - 2nd Radius	R608 Curve - 3rd Radius	R609 Double Curve - 3rd Radius	R8261 Curve - 4th Radius
R8262 Double Curve - 4th Radius	R628 Half Curve (33") Large Radius	R8087 Track Rubber	

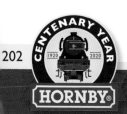

Track Accessories

R617 Uncoupling Ramp

R620 Railer/Uncoupler

R8244 Uncoupler Unit

R910 Fishplates (x 12)

R920 Insulated Fishplates (x 12)

R207 Track Pins

R626 Underlay Sheets (x 4)

R638 Roll of Underlay

Wheels & Coupling Hooks

R8098 12.6mm Spoked Wheels (x 10)

R8097 12.6mm Disc Wheels - 3 hole (x 10)

R8096 12.6mm Disc Wheels (x 10)

R8218 14.1mm Disc Wheels (x 10)

R8264 14.1mm Disc Wheels - 2 hole (x 10)

R8234 14.1mm Disc Wheels - 4 hole (x 10)

R8100 12.6mm Split Spoked Wheels (x 10)

R913 Con Rod Nut Spanner - Double Ended

R8268 Large Width Couplings (x 10)

R8267 Medium Width Couplings (x 10)

R8099 Coupling Assemblies (x 10)

R8220 Pocket Coupling (x 10)

R8219 NEM Couplings (x 10)

R7200 Small Coupling Assembly (Pack 4)

Rolling Road

Locomotive not included

Spare Rollers available in packs of two as **R8212**

R8211 Rolling Road

203

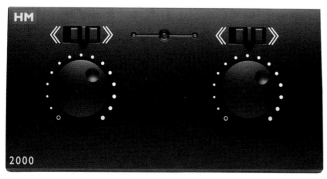

R8012 — HM 2000 Analogue Controller

A complete transformer with built-in control for two seperate trains. Power output is 2 Amps, with compensation to regularise speed under varying conditions of load. Positive 'off' rotary speed control cuts all power when the control knob is turned to zero. Features include forward and reverse switch, plus LED indicators for mains supply and output power. Outputs include non-variable AC and DC power for point motors and other powered accessories.

P9000 — Standard Wall Plug Mains Transformer

Replacement transformer for R8250 Standard Train Controller.

R7229 — Analogue Train and Accessory Controller

Note: Do not connect directly to the mains electricity supply. For use with P9000 Mains Transformer ONLY

220-240V 50-60Hz Transformer, supplying 16V AC current to R8250 and R7229 Analogue Train Controllers. Comes fitted with a 3m output lead.

This Analogue Train and Accessory Controller features a sturdy casing, as well as an additional uncontrolled DC output, with integral capacitor discharge unit (CDU) to support solenoid point motors. The Auxiliary output can also be used to power lighting on the layout up to a current of 150mA. A recessed reduction switch also limits the output to reduce loco speed.

R8213 — 'Select' Digital Controller

Note: This controller can only access Functions F0 to F8

R8214 — 'Elite' Digital Controller

The Select is capable of controlling up to 60 locomotives and, providing power is available, of running up to 10 locomotives at once. The Select can also operate 40 solenoid operated accessories, including points.

- Commands up to 10 locomotives simultaneously (providing power is available).
- The possibility of up to 3 locomotives running at any one time using the 1 amp transformer supplied.
- A 4 amp transformer is available for added power, allowing command of up to 10 locomotives simultaneously.
- Incorporates 128 speed steps for smooth locomotive control. Can be programmed to accommodate 14 and 28 speed steps.
- Able to programme 59 locomotives and 38 accessories. (The 60th locomotive would be coded as '0' and does not require a decoder).
- Supports XpressNet protocol.
- The 'Select' can also be used as a 'Walkabout' unit when connected to another Hornby 'Select' or the Hornby 'Elite' unit.
- Up to 8 locomotive functions. Can switch on and off locomotive lights and sounds including whistles, horns, etc. when used with locomotives fitted with sound decoders.

The Elite has twin, press switch controls, 17 button keyboard, wide LCD screen display, a 4 amp transformer and is capable of registering 254 locomotive addresses, as well as 255 accessory addresses, including point control.

- The 'Elite' can programme in all 4 modes: Direct, Register, Paged and Operate.
- 3 speed steps - 14, 28, 128.
- NMRA Certificated. Complies with EMC requirements.
- Supports Short and Extended Addressing.
- Allows 64 consists (Double Heading).
- Controls up to 64 locomotives at any one time providing the power is available.
- The facility to operate up to 29 functions.
- Single button press for fast selection of last 10 locomotive or accessory addresses under control.
- USB for downloading system updates and for connection to third party software.
- Separate Programming and Mainline Connections.
- Locomotive search function.
- A Programmable 'scale' clock. Ratios from 1:1 (real time) up to 1:10.

204

To place an order contact Hornby Customer Services on: **01843 233512** or visit your local stockist.

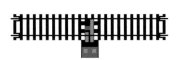

R8206 Power Track

R602 Power Connecting Clip

R8201 Track Link Wire Pack

R8015 Point Motor Housing (Adaptor Base)

R044 Point Motor Passing Contact Switch - Black

R046 Two Way Lever Switch On/On - Yellow

R047 Two Way Lever Switch On/Off - Green

R171 Single Home Signal

R8014 Point Motor

R8243 Surface Mounted Point Motor

R406 Coloured Light Signal *(Remote Control)*

R172 Single Distant Signal

R169 Junction Home Signal

R170 Junction Distant Signal

R8241 Digital Power Track

DIGITAL

R8232 Digital Electric Point Clips (x 20)

DIGITAL

R8242 Digital Power Connecting Clip

DIGITAL

NEW Q2

R7274 4 Pin Decoder

DIGITAL

R7150 Standard 6 pin Decoder

DIGITAL

R8249 Standard 8 pin Decoder

DIGITAL

Includes 21 pin/8 pin adapter

R8247 Digital Accessory & Point Decoder

DIGITAL

HORNBY rail MASTER

DIGITAL

Powerful digital layout design and intuitive digital operation.

Launched in 2011, Hornby's RailMaster computer software is designed for easy operation, via either conventional computer click mode, or touch screen control. All three of Hornby's digital controllers, the 'Select', the 'eLink' and the 'Elite' can now be linked to RailMaster via the computer, bringing track layout design and digital control together.smartphones and tablets by simply downloading the dedicated app and linking your device to your computer network, enabling true remote operation of your layout.

Track planning becomes simplified, as the Hornby operating accessories such as signalling, points and turntables can be controlled from the screen and track plans can be created by dragging Hornby track items into place on screen. An up to date database provides profiles of over 2,500 Hornby locomotives, with scale speeds and driving characteristics already pre-loaded and cover releases from the last forty years. Creating new custom entries is straightforward, with the ability to add photographs aiding the process significantly.

RailMaster enables up to 9,999 individual locomotive addresses to be assigned and can also operate up to 2,048 points and electrical accessories. Up to twenty-five DCC sound and light functions can be accessed on each locomotive with route setting being also possible by setting multiple points to change at the same time, creating a single route for your train. It is also possible to connect a second Elite or eLink as a seperate dedicated power supply for the points and accessories on their own.

The ability to create automated sequences has long been seen as a particular plus point of RailMaster, particularly useful in running shuttle services outside of normal train operations.

This automated sequence is time based and enables the train to be moved, the points changed, sound and light functions to be selected and pauses implemented between movements.

RailMaster is always evolving, with new updates being added automatically over the internet and extra features are also available by purchasing of the Pro-Pack add on. Offering extra functionality, including a second large on-screen power controller, voice control of all movements via a microphone-enabled headset and the option to control multiple aspect signalling with automatic switching of other signals in sequence, it aslo caters for more specialised turnouts such as double slips and three way points.

The ability to add new 45 degree point elements in design mode enables more complex track plans to be drawn and the printing of CVs, track plans and automated programme schedules gives extra functionality to the programme.

It is also possible to operate RailMaster via smartphones and tablets by simply downloading the dedicated app and linking your device to your computer network, enabling true remote operation of your layout.

CENTENARY YEAR 1920 2020

HORNBY®

The Most Straightforward PC Model Railway Control System

R8312	eLink, with Railmaster Software
R8312P	E-LINK + RAILMASTER + 1 Amp PSU

The eLink box has been designed to work hand in hand with Hornby's RailMaster software, being an electronic box that has all the same functionality as the Elite but withouth keypad or buttons, as these controls are replicated on the computer's screen from within the RailMaster software.

Hornby RailMaster is the simplest way to control a DCC model railway as the software, designed for Windows operating systems (XP, Vista, Windows 7, 8, 8.1 and 10), harnesses the power of either the Hornby eLink or Elite DCC controllers to provide an exceptional level of control over a model railway layout. The eLink and RailMaster combination is arguably the most cost effective DCC control system available on the market today.

- Set up a database of up to 9999 locomotives and control them from your PC screen.
- Depending on screen size, use up to ten locomotive controllers on screen at once.
- Allows the control of up to 25 sound and light functions for each locomotive, without typing in numbers.
- Operate up to 2048 points and signals from your PC, just by clicking them on screen.
- Operate locomotives at their correct scale speeds for added layout authenticity.
- Railmaster contains profiled characteristics of almost all Hornby locomotives from 1975 to the present day.

Top Tips For Enjoying DCC Operation

1. Keep things simple and move one step at a time.
2. The Select, eLink and Elite have different abilities. Check their specifications before making your choice.
3. Always use a programming track or a Rolling Road when adjusting locomotive CVs.
4. Keep a record of locomotive addresses and CV adjustments.
5. Choose a basic locomotive as your first DCC installation project.
6. Keep fleet DCC upgrading projects to a sensible scale and timeframe.
7. Keep your addressing system to the same format for simplicity.
8. When adding accessory decoders, select number ranges for certain operations, such as 1-10 for points and 20-29 for signalling.
9. Consider keeping an isolated oval for analogue operation.
10. Enjoy the feeling that digital control gives you!

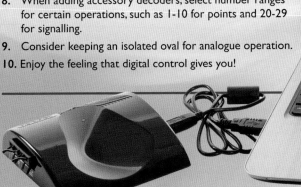
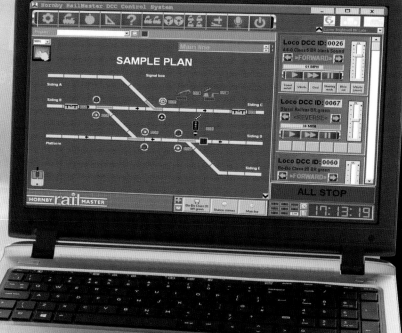

Email support@rail-master.com to give suggestions for any future topics about computer control for model railways and in particular Hornby's RailMaster system.

The power is at your fingertips!

HM6000

App based analogue Control _____

HM6000

NEW Q2

| R7292 | HM6000 App Based Analogue Control |

NEW Q2

| R7293 | HM6010 App Based Analogue Control |

Features include...

- **Controls up to 8 separate circuits**

- **Operates locomotive, points and accessories**

- **Features locomotive sounds including horns, whistles, steam sounds and many more**

- **Individual Acceleration and Deceleration controls per circuit**

- **Intuitive layout design feature**

- **Works with all major IOS or Android smart 'phones and tablets**

The 21st Century control system for today's 12vDC model railway. Control literally at your fingertips.

HM ANALOGUE CONTROL HORNBY

CENTENARY YEAR 1920 2020

HORNBY®

To place an order contact Hornby Customer Services on: **01843 233512** or visit your local stockist.

Technology has moved on when it comes to controlling a 12vDC layout. There is no need for the controller to be tethered to the track as by utilising Bluetooth low energy (BLE) technology Hornby's latest control system can now control a model railway layout with simplistic ease.

Circuit Controller
(Loco Controller)

Setup Page
Inertia/Min Max Speed

Circuit Controller
(Once layout is complete)

The HM6000 12vDC Control App. and supporting HM6010 Points & Accessory Control Unit (PAC) allows the control of a 12vDC analogue layout using Bluetooth technology via either a smart 'phone or tablet. Connection to the device is simple and follows the usual pairing protocol associated with Bluetooth equipment. (1)

The HM6000 App will allow the user to select up to 8 locomotives (2) and control their speed (3), inertia (4) and braking (5), as well as being able to implement an Emergency Stop. Also included is the added function of sound (6) as the system incorporates the ability to switch on and off generic steam(6), diesel (6) and electric (6) locomotive sounds activated by the smart device – mobile 'phone or tablet.

An added feature invaluable to those building their model railway layout is the comprehensive and simple to use 'Track Builder' (7) function that allows the operator to construct their own layout and operate accessories directly via the track matrix (8). The HM6010 Points & Accessory Control Unit (PAC) can independently operate either via pulse (point control) or constant (lighting etc.) 4 accessories. Up to 3 PACs can be operated via the HM6000 App.

In total the HM6000 and utilising the HM6010 PAC units can, with ease support 8 independently controlled locomotives running on 8 independent circuits (2), plus 12 accessories.

Locomotive Control

Each HM6000 unit has the capabilities of powering up to two circuits, however a total of 4 units (9) (1/2, 3/4, 5/6 etc. 1/2 being one HM6000) may be added to a layout, which will allow for a total of 8 circuits (2). This in turn provides the selected control via a handheld smart device of 8 locomotives controlled independently on their individual circuits. The direction, inertia, braking and Emergency Stop (10) controls are clearly marked on the App's screen. Also, up to 12 accessories, be they points (11), lighting (12) or other auxiliary (13) items that require power can be operated via the App's screen once they are connected to the HM6010 PAC.

Holding the 'phone or tablet in the horizontal or landscape position will provide a full screen image showing all the control features for a maximum of four locomotive, while if held in the portrait or vertical position the screen will just show two.

Individual slide controls (3) operate the speed of the locomotives while a diagram (14) of the layout is visible so that accessories are easily operated with a tap the tap of a digital button.

The system allows for each circuit to be programmed with its own individual inertia settings (4) (automatic acceleration and deceleration) so that they correspond with the locomotive running on that circuit.

Adding selected sounds, which are emitted from the handheld device, is also a strong feature of the HM6000 App. control. There are three groups of sounds with six generic sounds per group (6). Included are 'steam beat' or 'chuffing', 2 whistles, 2 x diesel/electric horns and the sound of braking, plus a selection of other railway based sounds, with each appropriate sound capable of being allocated to the chosen circuit and corresponding locomotive.

Settings

The usual App settings are incorporated into the system allowing for the assignment of Language, plus device and theme settings. There is also a 'Help' setting which will direct users to the Hornby website where they will be able to access frequently asked questions, support links and helpful forums.

HM6010 Accessories & Point Control (PAC)

The HM6000 App is able to operate up to 12 accessories – pulsed for point control and constant current for lighting and other accessories using 3 x HM6010 PAC units. Simple to use, the screen of the chosen mobile device will show each of the accessories under control and whether they are pulsed for point motor control or constant current for lighting, colour light signals, turntables etc.

HM6000 Track Builder

Without question one of the strongest features of the HM6000 App is the Track Builder (7).

Built into the software are several track diagrams including those featured on the Hornby MidiMat which is included in the majority of Hornby train sets. The larger TrakMat is also included along with an assortment of layout diagrams.

The Track Builder will also allow the user to build their own track diagram by the simple use of 'pick, drag and drop' (15) with the track sections snapping into place. Should a track piece not be required it can be easily pulled away from the circuit and deposited into a 'Bin' function (16).

Once the diagram has been completed the auxiliary operating components can be added and with the ability to 'pinch and zoom' (17) even the smallest of track pieces can be easily positioned.

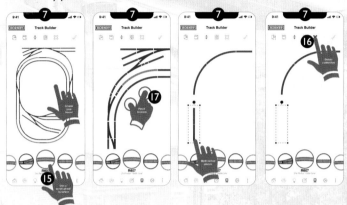

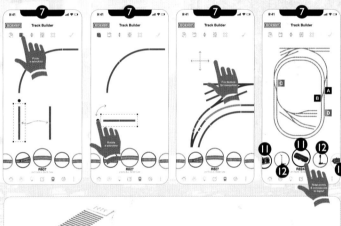

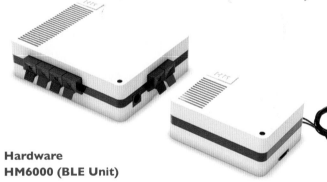

Hardware
HM6000 (BLE Unit)

The HM6000 has the capabilities to operate up to 8 locomotives independently on a layout providing they are on individual circuits. Each circuit requires to be linked to a Bluetooth low energy (BLE) unit. Each BLE unit has two outlets enabling it to be connected to two individual circuits. Therefore, 4 BLE units would be required for 8 individual circuits. It is possible, however to still operate 8 locomotives using just one BLE unit via the HM6000 App but it would mean removing or adding to either one of the two circuits on the railway layout, individual locomotives so that there would only be one locomotive on each of the two circuits at any given time. The BLE unit is connected to the circuit using an R8206 Power Track (recommended) or an R602 Power Connecting clip. Each BLE unit will require its own transformer.

HM6010 (PAC Unit)

Four operating accessories or point motors maybe connected to each PAC unit with the power being supplied by a separate wall mounted transformer. It is possible to connect up to three PAC units to one transformer but this does depend on how much power is being taken by the accessories, consequently it may be necessary to add a further power unit.

Track & Building Extension Packs

The set track layout as shown on the MidiMats provided in most train sets can be extended in easy steps by adding Track Packs, all the way up to the full layout and beyond.

R8217	TrakMat 1800mm x 1200mm

R8227	Building Extension Pack 1

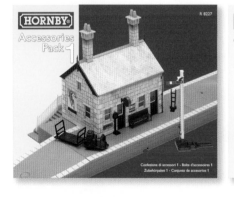

R8228	Building Extension Pack 2

R8229	Building Extension Pack 3

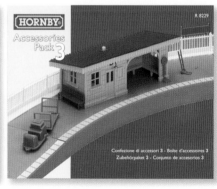

R8230	Building Extension Pack 4

R8231	Building Extension Pack 5

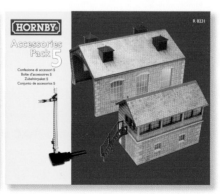

R574	Trackside Accessories

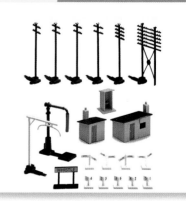

To place an order contact Hornby Customer Services on: **01843 233512** or visit your local stockist.

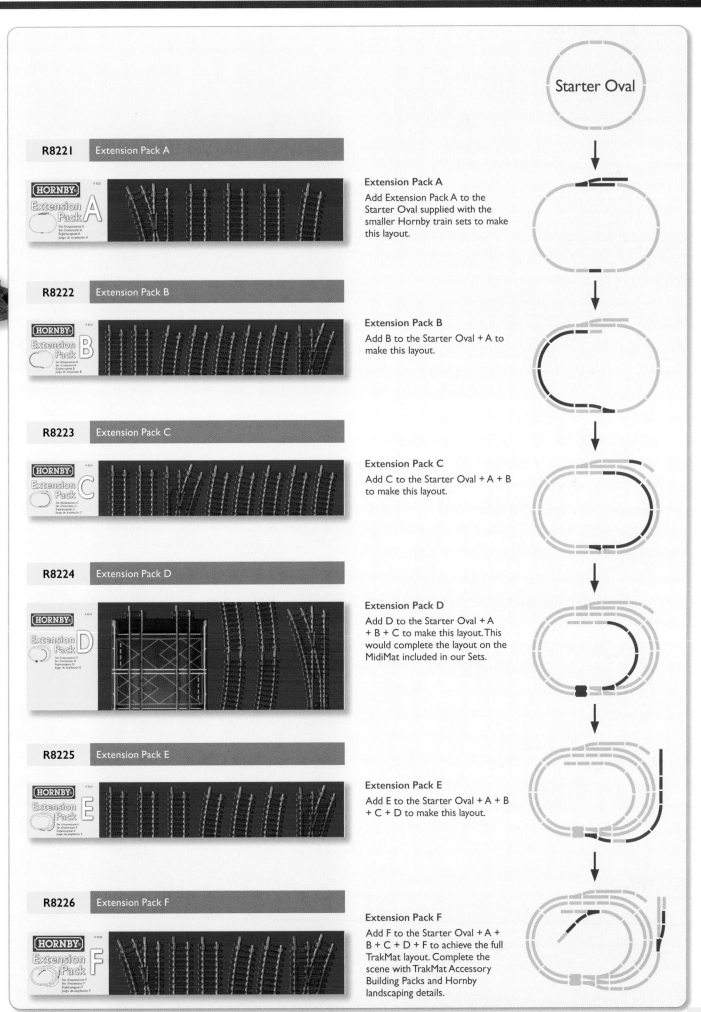

Starter Oval

R8221 — Extension Pack A

Extension Pack A

Add Extension Pack A to the Starter Oval supplied with the smaller Hornby train sets to make this layout.

R8222 — Extension Pack B

Extension Pack B

Add B to the Starter Oval + A to make this layout.

R8223 — Extension Pack C

Extension Pack C

Add C to the Starter Oval + A + B to make this layout.

R8224 — Extension Pack D

Extension Pack D

Add D to the Starter Oval + A + B + C to make this layout. This would complete the layout on the MidiMat included in our Sets.

R8225 — Extension Pack E

Extension Pack E

Add E to the Starter Oval + A + B + C + D to make this layout.

R8226 — Extension Pack F

Extension Pack F

Add F to the Starter Oval + A + B + C + D + F to achieve the full TrakMat layout. Complete the scene with TrakMat Accessory Building Packs and Hornby landscaping details.

YOUR WORLD
Buildings & Accessories

Just like every other aspect of railway modelling, adding scenic elements can be as easy or as demanding as the enthusiast requires. From themed packs of clip together plastic buildings, to trees and scatter, Hornby has the product to meet the demands of most modellers.

Building extension packs allow a layout to be populated quickly with the typical type of buildings normally encountered in and around the railway network. A layout can then be customised by adding individual elements, such as bridges, fences and pylons from the standard Hornby clip together range of plastic buildings. As confidence and budgets increase, plastic buildings can be replaced with hand painted resin buildings from the Skaledale range, offering the modeller an extensive range of building styles from which to choose from. This year a number of new buildings are available, both from Hornby's own Skaledale range and from Oxford Structures. The Skaledale range includes new cottages, shops and even a 19th century Tin Tabernacle, while the Oxford range offers a trackside range based on GWR buildings, as well as sympathetically themed domestic buildings.

Once buildings are in place, the addition of vehicles, people and livestock will bring some 'animation' to the layout by incorporating the range of SkaleAutos collectible vehicles as well as scenic elements, such as trees, ground cover, grass and trackways from the SkaleScenics range of detailing products that bring depth and life to a growing layout. With a wide range of deciduous and evergreen trees, plus bushes, together with long and short grass types, a typical landscape can be constructed, even down to stone tracks, scree slopes and, by using the new SkaleRoc material, even rocky terrain can be easily modelled.

For many modellers, the ability to 'weather' locomotives, rolling stock, buildings and landscapes is the final step of their modelling education and Hornby, through Humbrol, provides a number of weathering products and washes to help towards that final goal of 'Your World' being complete.

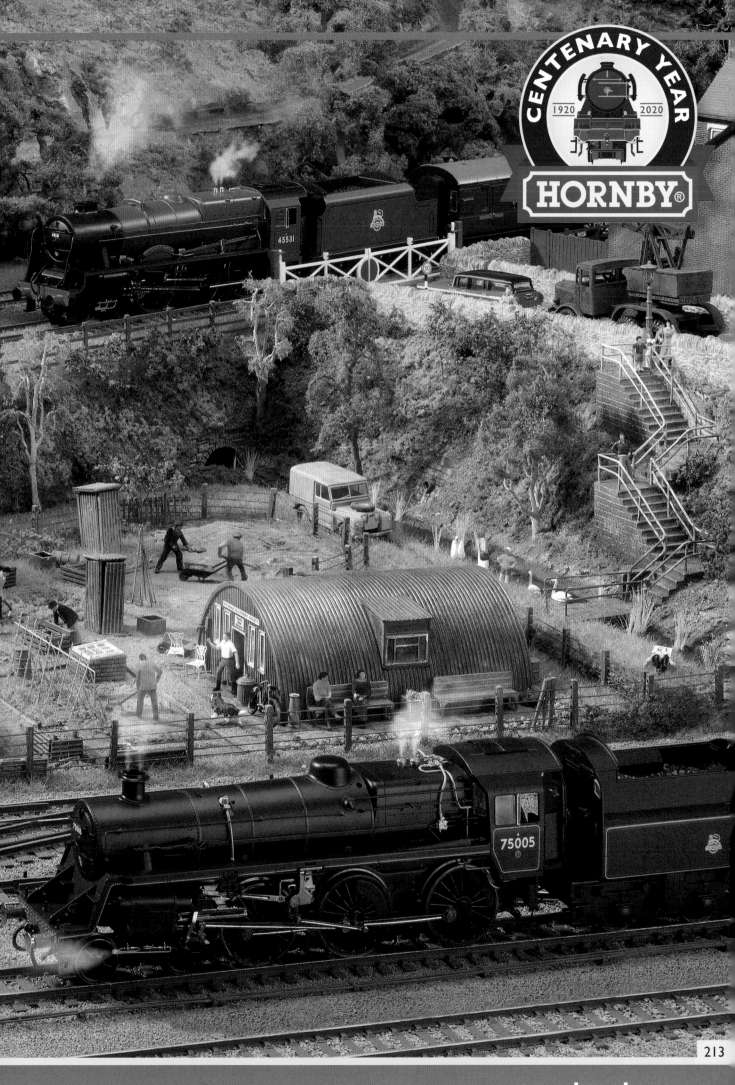

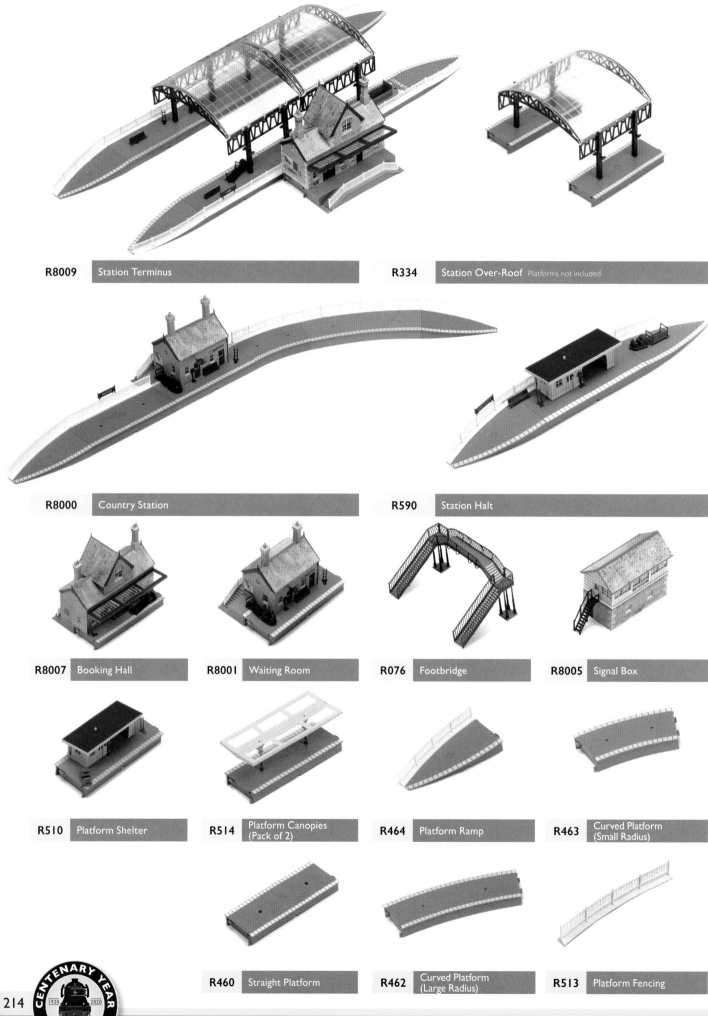

R8009 Station Terminus

R334 Station Over-Roof Platforms not included

R8000 Country Station

R590 Station Halt

R8007 Booking Hall

R8001 Waiting Room

R076 Footbridge

R8005 Signal Box

R510 Platform Shelter

R514 Platform Canopies (Pack of 2)

R464 Platform Ramp

R463 Curved Platform (Small Radius)

R460 Straight Platform

R462 Curved Platform (Large Radius)

R513 Platform Fencing

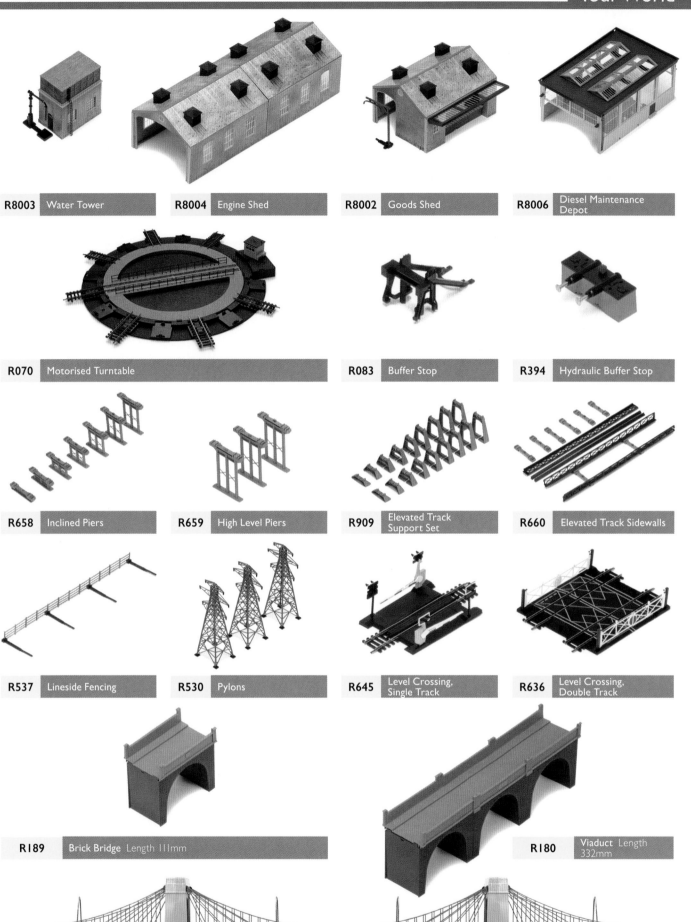

R8003 Water Tower

R8004 Engine Shed

R8002 Goods Shed

R8006 Diesel Maintenance Depot

R070 Motorised Turntable

R083 Buffer Stop

R394 Hydraulic Buffer Stop

R658 Inclined Piers

R659 High Level Piers

R909 Elevated Track Support Set

R660 Elevated Track Sidewalls

R537 Lineside Fencing

R530 Pylons

R645 Level Crossing, Single Track

R636 Level Crossing, Double Track

R189 Brick Bridge Length 111mm

R180 Viaduct Length 332mm

R8008 Grand Suspension Bridge Length 1372mm

215

SKALEDALE
Buildings & Accessories

Model features include:

- Scale 1:76
- Highly defined resin structures
- Detail features with hand finished embellishments
- Etched metal window frames
  (where appropriate)

R9836	Granite Station Building

R9837	Granite Station Waiting Room

Limited Availability

R9840	Granite Station Engine Shed

R9841	Granite Station Goods Shed

HORNBY®
SKALEDALE

R8614 Straight Platforms x 2

R8615 Platform Ramps x 2

R8674 Bench x 2

R8673 Platform Lamps x 4

NEW Q3

R7285 Platform Straight x 2

NEW Q3

R7287 Platform Island x 2

NEW Q3

R7286 Platform Ramp x 2

217

R9838 Granite Station Signal Box

R9839 Granite Station Water Tower

R9817 Raised Water Tank

R8641 Platform Footbridge

R9815 Covered Loading Bay

R9821 Wayside Halt Building

R9824 The Station Office

NEW Q3

R7282 GWR Goods Shed

NEW Q3

R7284 GWR Water Tower

NEW Q3

R7283 GWR Engine Shed

Limited Availability

R9825 The Railway Stores

R8797 Newspaper Kiosk

R8587 Coaling Stage

R8603 Coal Staithes

R8605 Loading Stage & Crane

R9512 Concrete Plate Layers Hut

R9782 Utility Lamp Huts x 2

R9783 Lamp Huts x 2

218

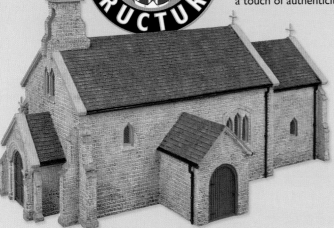

This range of stunning buildings from Oxford Rail offers the modeller a selection of finely detailed resin moulded structures which are produced to a truly exacting standard. The range comprises of both domestic and trackside based buildings. The domestic buildings feature amongst others a superbly detailed church and a particularly inviting Pub!

The trackside range, inspired by the Great Western Railway includes a fine example of a characteristic Station and new for this year is the introduction of Oxford Lighting, adding a touch of authenticity to each building when fitted.

OXOS76T001 St. Catherine's Church

OXOS76T002 The Bush Inn

OXOS76R001 GWR Station Building

OXOS76R002 GWR Signal Box

Tunnel Portals & Side Walling

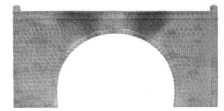

R8509 Single Stone Tunnel Portal x 2

R8511 Double Stone Tunnel Portal x 2

R8544 Stone Portal Side Walling

R8510 Single Brick Tunnel Portal x 2

R8512 Double Brick Tunnel Portal x 2

R8545 Brick Portal Side Walling

219

Domestic & Commercial Buildings

R8622 Right Hand Terraced House

R9856 Left Hand Mid-Terrace House

R9857 Right Hand Mid-Terrace House

R9801 Modern Terraced House

NEW Q3

R7291 Hazel Cottage

NEW Q3

R7290 Bungalow - 'Avalon'

R9802 Modern Prefab

R9854 The Country Cottage

R9804 Modern Detached House

R9807 Modern Bungalow

R9826 Detached Brick Garage

R9812 Triple Garage

NEW Q3

R7288 T. Davies & Grandson - Butchers

NEW Q3

R7289 E.L.Sole - Newsagent

R9829 Scott's Toy Emporium

R9830 A.C Cobbler Shoe Repairs

R9831 The Wild Bunch Florist

R9835 Batchelor's Hardware

R9845 Isles and Son Family Butchers

R9844 Bottoms Up! Off Licence

R9846 P. Morley Ironmongers

R9847 Buchanan's Fruit and Veg

R9832 La Trattoria Italian Restaurant

R9861 The Frying Scotsman

R9855 Merry Auto Repairs

R9859 Pelling's General Store

R9860 The 'Crown'

R9858 The Village Post Office

R8580 Telephone Kiosk

R8613 Refuse Skips x 2

R8579 Pillar Box

AA Wings logo and word mark are trade marks of the Automobile Association and are used under licence

RAC is a Registered Trade Mark used under licence from RAC Brand Enterprises LLP

R9827 The Memorial

R9867 AA Telephone Box

R9878 RAC Telephone Box

R8696 Police Box

SKALEDALE
New Buildings for 2020

For 2020, the Skaledale range comprises a number of new buildings, typical of those found in many villages and small market towns throughout rural England. Each model is based on an existing building, adding a sense of authenticity and atmosphere to your model railway layouts and dioramas.

NEW Q3	R7264	The Old Smithy

NEW Q3	R7265	Terraced Cottages

NEW Q3	R7266	Fisherman's Cottage

NEW Q3	R7267	Jewellers Shop

NEW Q3	R7268	Photographic Shop: M. Wilks

NEW Q3	R7269	The Offie (Corner Shop)

NEW Q3	R7270	Tin Tabanacle

NEW Q3	R7271	Single Garage

NEW Q3	R7272	Wooden Bus Stop

HORNBY®
SKALEDALE

Farm & Rural Buildings

| R9848 | Country Farm House |

| R9849 | Country Farm Outhouse |

| R9850 | Country Farm Dutch Barn |

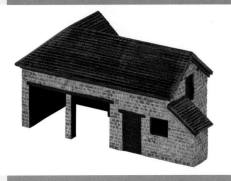

| R9851 | Country Farm Tractor Shed |

| R9808 | Timber Store & Workshop |

| R9809 | Garage Outbuilding |

| R9810 | Corrugated Iron Workshop |

| R9813 | Ex-Barrack Rooms |

| R9853 | The Cricket Club |

| R9803 | The Tin House |

| R9811 | Shiplap Lean-to |

| R8788 | Corrugated Nissen Hut |

| R8787 | Pillbox |

Brick & Stone Walling

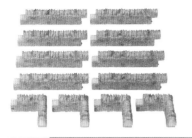

| R8526 | Granite Wall Pack No. 1 | R8527 | Granite Wall Pack No. 2 | R8538 | Granite Wall Pack No. 3 |

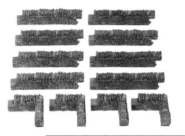

| R8539 | Cotswold Stone Pack No. 1 | R8540 | Cotswold Stone Pack No. 2 | R8541 | Cotswold Stone Pack No. 3 |

| R8977 | Brick Walling - Straight | R8978 | Brick Walling - Corners | R8979 | Brick Walling - Gates & Piers |

People & Animals

Note: These images are for illustration only, colours may differ from those illustrated.

| R7115 | City People Pack of seven different people (male & female) | R7116 | Town People Pack of eight different people (male & female, adults & children) |

| R7117 | Working People Pack of six different people and three work items (male) | R7119 | Sitting People Pack of six different people and two benches (male & female) |

| R7118 | Farm People Pack of six different people (male & female) | R7120 | Farm Animals Pack of seven different animals and four sections of fencing |

| R7121 | Cows Pack of ten cows (two breeds) | R7122 | Sheep Pack of ten sheep |

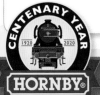

SkaleAutos...A superb range of highly detailed Diecast vehicles.

R7152 Ford Transit

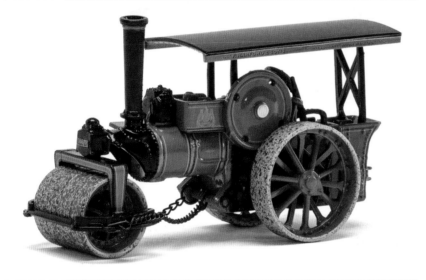

R7153 Fowler Steam Roller

R7154 Fowler Ploughing Engine

R7124 BMC Mini Saloon

R7237 Ford Anglia 105E

R7151 Land Rover 109

R7125 BMC Mini Van

R7123 FX4 Taxi

R7155 Ferguson TEA Tractor

225

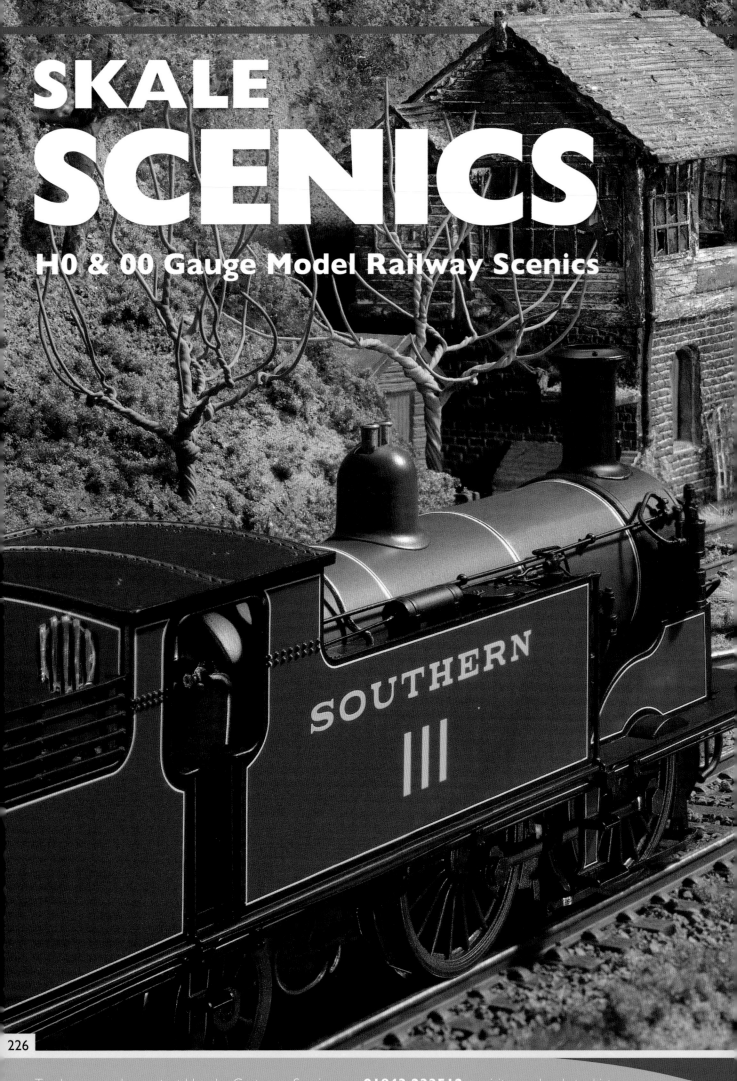

SKALE
SCENICS

H0 & 00 Gauge Model Railway Scenics

SOUTHERN
III

Classic Trees

Handmade for finer quality, the SkaleScenics Profi Tree range will bring added scenic detail to any model railway or diorama.

The trunks of the trees are painted by hand so that no shining plastic surfaces are left visible and to give more volume. All of the branches are covered with fine wool before they are flocked. This mimics the leaf shapes and colours of a real tree and, as in nature, only the fine branches of the PROFI trees have leaves, so this is replicated in our range.

R7202	Fruit Trees
80mm	Three per pack

R7203	Maple Trees
90mm	Three per pack

R7204	Beech Trees
130mm	Two per pack

R7205	Birch Trees
45mm	Three per pack

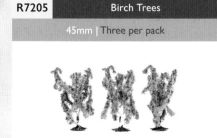

R7206	Large Fir Trees
80-120mm	Four per pack

R7207	Small Fir Trees
40-80mm	Four per pack

R7208	Bushes
30-40mm	Five per pack

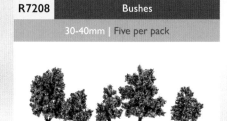

R7209	Oak Tree
150mm	Single item

R7210	Lime Tree
185mm	Single item

R7211	Horse Chestnut Tree
190mm	Single item

Hobby Trees

R7198	'Hobby' Deciduous Trees
50-90mm	Twenty per pack

R7199	'Hobby' Fir Trees
50-140mm	Twenty per pack

R7201	'Hobby' Mixed Trees
50-140mm	Twenty per pack

(Pack includes a mixture of deciduous and Fir)

CENTENARY YEAR 1920 2020 HORNBY®

To place an order contact Hornby Customer Services on: **01843 233512** or visit your local stockist.

Professional Trees

R7212	Fruit Tree
75mm	Single item

R7213	Apple Tree (with Fruit)
75mm	Single item

R7214	Pear Tree
75mm	Single item

R7215	Birch Tree
115mm	Single item

R7216	Rowan Tree (with Berries)
115mm	Single item

R7217	Acacia Tree
150mm	Single item

R7218	Tree (with Circular Bench)
115mm	Single item

R7219	Beech Tree
130mm	Single item

R7220	Oak Tree
160mm	Single item

R7221	Lime Tree
185mm	Single item

R7222	Horse-Chestnut Tree
195mm	Single item

R7223	Lime Tree
185mm	Single item

R7224	Tree (with Tree House)
150mm	Single item

R7225	Medium Nordic Fir Tree
120mm	Single item

R7226	Large Nordic Fir Tree
145mm	Single item

R7227	Medium Pine Tree
120mm	Single item

R7228	Large Pine Tree
150mm	Single item

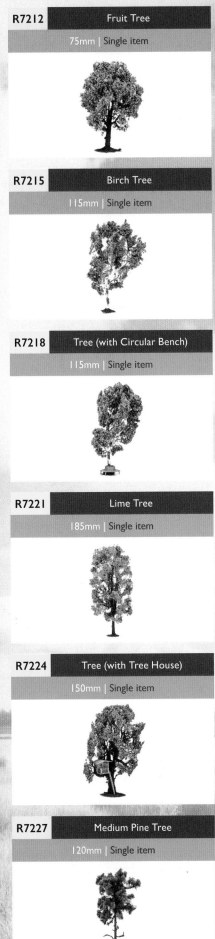

HORNBY SKALE SCENICS

00 Gauge Model Railway Scenics

Humbrol™

229

Ballast

R7164 Brown	R7165 Grey	R7166 Limestone
Weight 250g	Weight 250g	Weight 250g

  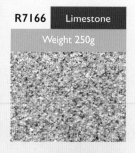

R7167 Granite	R7168 Basaltic Rock	R7169 Gneiss
Weight 250g	Weight 250g	Weight 250g

R7170 Coal
Weight 250g

HORNBY SKALE SCENICS

00 Gauge Model Railway Scenics

Scatter

R7171 Flower Meadow	R7172 Light Green
Weight 42g	Weight 42g

R7173 Medium Green	R7174 Brown
Weight 42g	Weight 42g

R7175 Grey	R7176 Dark Green
Weight 42g	Weight 42g

Note:
To cover an area of 1m² you will need approximately 100 g scatter material and 500g of Grass Glue.

Static Grass

R7177 Spring Meadow, 2.5mm	R7178 Grass Meadow, 2.5mm	R7179 Ornamental Lawn, 2.5mm	R7180 Mixed Summer, 2.5mm	R7181 Alpine Meadow, 2.5mm
Weight 20g	Weight 20g	Weight 20g	Weight 20g	Weight 20g

R7181 contains bolders

Lichen

R7193 Stone Grey	R7194 Green Mix	R7195 Large Green Mix	R7196 Autumn Mix	R7197 Large Autumn Mix
Weight 35g	Weight 35g	Weight 75g	Weight 35g	Weight 75g

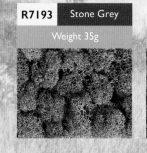    

Humbrol™

HORNBY®

To place an order contact Hornby Customer Services on: **01843 233512** or visit your local stockist.

Flockage & Flock

R7156	Bright Green Flockage
	Weight 20g

R7157	Medium Green Flockage
	Weight 20g

R7158	Dark Green Flockage
	Weight 20g

R7159	Medium Brown Flockage
	Weight 20g

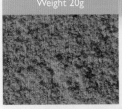

R7160	Dark Brown Flockage
	Weight 20g

R7161	Bright Green Flock
	Weight 20g

R7162	Medium Green Flock
	Weight 20g

R7163	Dark Green Flock
	Weight 20g

Accessories

R7182	Static Grass Puffer Bottle
	Use with R7183 to apply Static Grasses

R7183	Grass Glue
	Weight 250g

Foliage

R7184	Light Green
	Covering 20x23cm

R7185	Dark Green
	Covering 20x23cm

R7186	Olive Green
	Covering 20x23cm

R7187	Wild Grass (Light Green)
	Covering 20x23cm

R7188	Wild Grass (Dark Green)
	Covering 20x23cm

R7189	Yellow Green Meadow
	Covering 20x23cm

R7190	Middle Green Meadow
	Covering 20x23cm

R7191	Leafy - Middle Green
	Covering 20x23cm

R7192	Leafy - Dark Green
	Covering 20x23cm

R7273	SkaleRoc
	Pack contains: 2 x 10cm x 3m Rolls

NEW Q2

Humbrol™ Rail Paints

The Humbrol acrylic range of popular railway colours have been developed to suit many variations on the UK rail network of multiple eras. These paints are also ideally suited for weathering, dry brushing and re-touching, taking your model railways hobby to a new level.

Matt Colours 14ml

RC401 AB2401 Dirty Black	**RC403** AB2403 Crimson Lake	**RC404** AB2404 Garter Blue	**RC405** AB2405 GWR/BR Green	**RC406** AB2406 Buffer Beam Red
RC409 AB2409 Malachite Green	**RC410** AB2410 Maunsell Green	**RC411** AB2411 Diesel Blue	**RC412** AB2412 BR Coach Roof Grey	**RC413** AB2413 Engineers Grey
RC414 AB2414 Executive Dark Grey	**RC415** AB2415 Pullman Umber Brown	**RC416** AB2416 Pullman Cream	**RC418** AB2418 EWS Red	**RC419** AB2419 EWS Yellow
RC420 AB2420 Orange Lining	**RC421** AB2421 Virgin Red	**RC422** AB2422 InterCity Grey	**RC423** AB2423 Carmine	**RC424** AB2424 BR Cream

Humbrol™ Brushes

Detail Brushes

These ultra fine sable hair brushes are ideal for painting small detailed areas on your models/figures. The easy grip ergonomic handles make them a pleasure to use for short or long periods of time.

Suitable for Enamel and Acrylic paints.

Detail pack.
Size 00, 0, 1, 2 – **AG4304**

Flat Brushes

Made from high quality soft synthetic hair, the Flat Brush pack is perfect for creating a smooth professional finish. Ideal for painting large surface areas, weathering, adding washes and helping to apply decals.

Suitable for Enamel and Acrylic paints.

Flat pack.
Size 3, 5, 7, 10 – **AG4305**

Stipple Brushes

The Stipple Brushes have been designed with heavy dry brushing and weathering in mind. Made from a tough natural hair, which is perfect when adding those finishing touches when bringing your models to life.

Suitable for Enamel and Acrylic paints, as well as Weathering Powder.

Stipple pack.
Size 3, 5, 7, 10 – **AG4306**

Top tips on how best to use Humbrol products are available at: **www.Humbrol.com**. You can also see the products in action on the Official Humbrol YouTube Channel, **www.youtube.com/Humbrol**

NEW **Weathering** Powders 45ml

Humbrol Weathering Powders are a versatile means of adding realistic weathering effects to your models, figures and dioramas. They can be mixed to create different shades, enabling a full range of finishes including dust, mud, soot, rust and many more.

AV0011 Black	AV0012 White	AV0013 Sand	AV0014 Smoke	AV0015 Chrome Oxide Green	AV0016 Iron Oxide	AV0017 Dark Earth	AV0018 Rust	AV0019 Dark Rust

Enamel Washes 28ml

Enhance your models with the Humbrol Enamel Washes range, designed for a wide range of uses they are easy to use and very durable.

AV0201 Black	AV0202 White	AV0203 Dark Green	AV0204 Dark Grey	AV0205 Dark Brown
AV0206 Blue Grey	AV0207 Sand	AV0208 Dust	AV0209 Oil Stain	AV0210 Rust

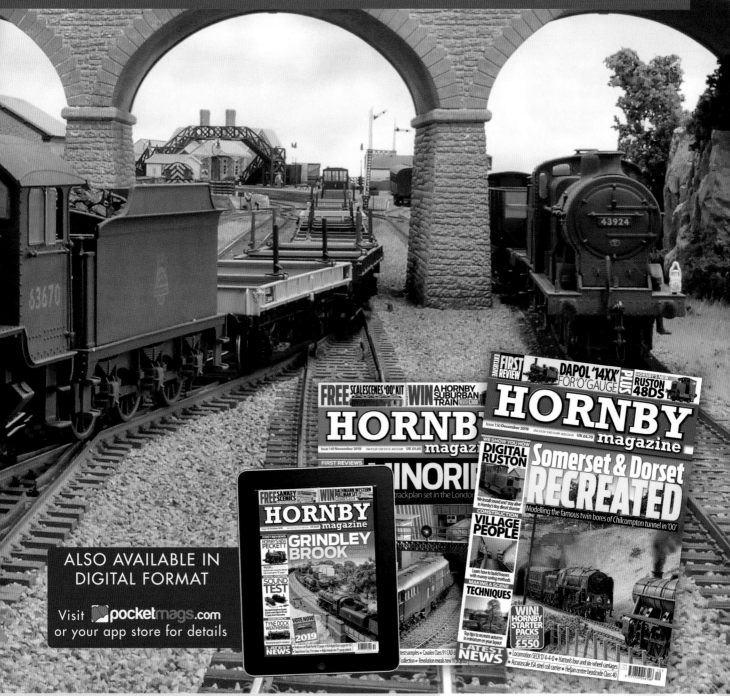

2020 INDEX

To place an order contact Hornby Customer Services on: **01843 233512** or visit your local stockist.